K.B. CO

Dealers in English
Coins and Medals.
Excellent prices paid for
single items, collections
or accumulations
(especially proof sets).

**Are you on our Mailing List?
We issue regular lists of
our extensive and rapidly
changing stock.**

*We will also service
your 'Wants' lists.*

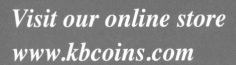

*Visit our online store
www.kbcoins.com*

**K.B. COINS
PO Box 499
Stevenage
Herts SG1 9JT**
*Tel: 01438 312661
Fax: 01438 311990*

BNTA

PAUL DAVIES

—BUYING AND SELLING—

WE SPECIALISE IN
MODERN BRITISH GOLD & SILVER PROOF COINS
ALSO BUYING ALL BRITISH & WORLD GOLD COINS

PAUL DAVIES

PO BOX 17, ILKLEY, WEST YORKSHIRE
LS29 8TZ, ENGLAND
PHONE: 01943 603116
EMAIL: paul@pauldaviesltd.co.uk

SPINK

COINS OF ENGLAND 2021

E-book available on Amazon, iBookstore,
Google, Kobo, OverDrive and across
most other platforms

For more information or enquiries please contact
Tel: +44 (0)20 7563 4119 | Email: books@spink.com
69 Southampton Row, Bloomsbury, London WC1B 4ET

WWW.SPINKBOOKS.COM

Standard Catalogue of British Coins

COINS OF ENGLAND

& THE UNITED KINGDOM
Decimal Issues

7th Edition

LONDON

A Catalogue of the Decimal Coins of
Great Britain and Ireland

Standard Catalogue of British Coins
Coins of England and the United Kingdom
7th edition, 2021

© Spink & Son Ltd, 2020
69 Southampton Row, Bloomsbury
London WC1B 4ET
www.spinkbooks.com

www.spink.com

Typeset by Design to Print UK Ltd,
9 & 10 Riverview Business Park, Forest Row, East Sussex RH18 5FS
www.designtoprintuk.com
Printed and bound in Malta by
Gutenberg Press Ltd.

Cover design: Russell Whittle
Email: uk47@me.com

The contents of this catalogue, including the numbering system and illustrations,
are protected by copyright.

All rights are reserved. No part of this publication may be
reproduced, stored in a retrieval system, or transmitted, in any form
or by any means, electronic, mechanical, photocopying, recording
or otherwise, without the prior permission of Spink & Son Ltd.

ISBN 978-1-912667-52-9

CONTENTS

ACKNOWLEDGEMENTS

We wish to acknowledge the valuable contribution of the following who have submitted information and provided photographs which have greatly enhanced this edition.

David Bayford
Kevin Clancy, Royal Mint
Paul Davies
Geoff Kitchen
London Coin Auctions
Jenny Manders, Royal Mint
Mark Ray

Also the collectors who have written in to point out errors or omissions.

SPINK

WHERE HISTORY IS VALUED

COINS OF SCOTLAND, IRELAND AND THE ISLANDS
AVAILABLE AS AN E-BOOK VIA GOOGLE PLAY
BY VISITING WWW.SPINKBOOKS.COM

COINS OF SCOTLAND,
IRELAND AND THE ISLANDS
(JERSEY, GUERNSEY, MAN & LUNDY) INCLUDING
ANGLO-GALLIC COINS

4th EDITION
SPINK
2020

FOR MORE INFORMATION OR ENQUIRIES PLEASE CONTACT
TEL: +44 (0)20 7563 4119 | EMAIL: BOOKS@SPINK.COM
69 SOUTHAMPTON ROW, BLOOMSBURY, LONDON WC1B 4ET

Welcome to the seventh edition of the *Coins of England & the United Kingdom Decimal Issues*.

Britannia has been a feature on British coins for over 1,000 years and when she no longer appeared on ordinary coins in 2008 there was quite a public outcry. She re-appeared on the £2 circulation coin in 2015, although owing to the banks still having adequate stocks of the previous types, Britannia will not yet feature very much in pockets or purses. She graces our front cover for this edition, celebrating 50 years of decimal currency in the UK.

There are quite a number of major changes in this edition and we hope these will be welcomed. The Maundy coins have been moved from their previous rather hidden place amongst the sets and they are included in the Contents index so very easy to find. The sets section has been split so that the sets now appear immediately after the relevant listings of the coins contained therein. Where previously listed sets comprise coins of the same denomination, these can now be found immediately below the individual coin listings and we hope this provides better clarity.

There has been a sharp increase in the number of new coins this year with ambitious programmes featuring the James Bond film series and leading British modern musicians. For convenience these issues have been grouped individually so may be found quite easily by referring to the Contents index.

Prices quoted are not the publisher's retail prices but prices at which we expect you might have to pay for coins in perfect condition and, where relevant, coins still in their original presentation case with certificate (where issued). Many coins, especially silver proofs, are available in the secondary market just in capsules and therefore are often available at a discount from the catalogue. Prices for coins issued within the last few years will often show the Royal Mint's issue price until such time as either sales figures are announced or a secondary market has been established. Minimum price shown for any coin is £1 but for some minors this represents a dealer's handling charge.

We are aware that there may still be coins unlisted where the Royal Mint has sold the entire mintage to an overseas company with no accompanying public announcement, which then prevents catalogue editors from being aware of such issues. We continue to encourage the Royal Mint to publish detailed sales figures of all the coins that are issued.

I was first involved with this publication in the 1980s when it had a different publisher. After Spink took it over, Geoff Kitchen became the main editor and I, with others, assisted. Geoff now wishes to reduce his responsibilities and we must thank him for all the work he has done over the last 20 plus years, especially faced with such an increase in the number of new coins.

Editing a catalogue is very much a continual work in progress especially with so many new issues, and we hope to make further improvements to the listings and add more information in the years ahead. Please feel free to send in any comments or point out any errors.

Happy collecting.

David Fletcher
Editor, Decimal Issues

INTRODUCTION

The decision to adopt a decimal currency in place of the £sd system was announced in March 1966 and the first of the new designs entered circulation in 1968, being five and ten pence pieces with the same specification as the old shilling and florin whose pedigree dates back to 1816 and 1849 respectively. In 1969 the fifty pence coin was introduced to replace the ten shilling banknote, thus presenting a gentle introduction to the decimal system prior to Decimal Day in February 1971.

Since that time other denominations have followed – the twenty pence in 1982, the one pound in 1983 and finally the two pound in 1997 though delayed until 1998. In the 1990s owing to higher metal costs and inflation the size of the 5p, 10p and 50p coins was reduced.

One fairly recent policy development either by the mint or the government is that some versions of 50p and £2 commemorative currency coins are not placed into circulation and therefore only available to collectors in brilliant uncirculated condition at a premium. This will surely discourage younger collectors especially those who have collectors' card packs with spaces for such coins. A more recent announcement indicates that the Royal Mint has sufficient stocks of 2p and £2 coins to fulfil demand well into the 2020s so it is unlikely that circulation strikes of these two denominations will be made for some years. One has to question how the continued issue of commemorative £2 coins can be justified if there is no possibility of any of them entering circulation.

Arrangement

Each part of this catalogue has the uniformity of commencing the listing with the lowest denomination and concluding with the highest. The first section lists the currency coins commencing with the lowest 1/2p up to the £2. This is followed by the crowns (which used to be currency pieces) – 25p and £5 – and then (new in this edition) the uncirculated and proof sets which contain currency type coins. This first section concludes with higher face value coins commencing with the £10 five ounce coins first introduced in 2012 and going up in denomination order to the £1000 gold kilo.

The gold sovereign range, with specifications dating back to 1816, then follows with the relevant gold sets now listed at the end of that section. Sales figures of the gold proofs are tabulated thus presenting a more accurate report of how many coins were sold singly and how many in sets.

The introduction of Britannia bullion coins in 1987 brought a totally different range of coin specifications to the UK market mainly based on the ounce and its fractions. The sections that follow the Britannia listings mainly comprise coins with Britannia based specifications with many of them issued as bullion pieces for investors as well as proof and BU pieces for collectors, but some sections also include coins with traditional currency specifications. It is not always straightforward to decide exactly where in the catalogue a new coin should be listed and we are prepared to reconsider listing decisions.

Coin numbering

Initially the catalogue numbers for the decimal coins started where the £sd coins in the pre-decimal volume ended which was 4159. The increase in the range of coins in subsequent years made it impractical to continue with this numbering sequence so a new numbering sequence commencing with A1 for the lowest denomination of 1/2p was commenced. The 2012 Olympic, 2014 WWI and Chinese New Year issues still retain their old numbers but this may be changed in later editions.

Multi-country Sets

Occasionally two or more national mints will market a multi nation commemorative set containing a UK coin, and occasionally a new coin may only be located in such set. Consideration will be given to listing these in a future edition.

Philatelic Numismatic Covers (PNCs)

The Royal Mint and the British Post Office have been issuing first day covers containing coins for much of the decimal period. Initially these covers contained only base metal coins and the numbers issued did not affect the availability of the basic coin. In more recent years part of the mintage of some gold and silver commemoratives has been allocated for PNCs and this is not currently recorded in this catalogue. There appears to be very little secondary market interest in these PNCs which is one reason why they have not been listed – but given our attempt to include accurate and detailed information about sales figures of precious metal coins, we may need to extend the listings to include PNCs.

Definitions

Edition: The number quoted refers to the authorised mintage.

Issued: The number quoted refers to the published sales figure.

Uncirculated, Unc: Coins struck to normal standard for circulation but removed from circulation at an early stage without any wear thus preserving them in mint condition. There is a range of lower grades but there are very few coins in this catalogue with prices quoted for lower grades as the vast majority which are not unc are only worth face value.

Brilliant uncirculated, BU: Coins struck to a higher standard than those minted for release into general circulation.

Proof: Carefully struck coin from special dies with a mirror-like or matt surface, thus creating the highest minting standard.

Piedfort: The word comes from the French and can be translated as 'heavy measure'. Piedfort coins are double the weight of their proof counterparts.

FDC: From the French Fleur de Coin to reflect the highest standard of production.

O, Obv, Obverse: That side of the coin which normally shows the monarch's head.

R, Rev, Reverse: The side opposite to the obverse, the 'Tails'.

Exergue: That part of the coin below the reverse design, usually separated by a horizontal line, and normally occupied by the date.

Mule: A coin with a current design on one side and an incorrect design on the other side.

Bullion prices

The prices of some coins reflect the market price of precious metals, and at the time of preparing this edition Gold was £1400 and Platinum £700 per ounce.

x   INTRODUCTION

Royal Mint Experience

In 2016 the Royal Mint opened the Royal Mint Experience at the Mint which not only offers exhibitions and tours to visitors but also has a range of fun events on offer including the opportunity for visitors to strike their own coin. We believe that some of these coins may differ from those in circulation or available for purchase. So far the Mint has not made any information available regarding such coins so check your change to see what might turn up. We may consider that catalogue status for any 'odd-ball' coins is not appropriate.

Comments from readers will be welcomed about any aspect of this catalogue to books @spink.com

Specifications of currency coins

Denomination	Diameter	Metal	Weight	Metal	Weight	Metal	Weight
½p	17.14 mm	bronze	1.78 g				
1p	20.32 mm	bronze	3.56 g	.925 silver	3.56 g	.916 gold	6.98 g
1p	20.32 mm	Copper-plated steel	3.56 g				
2p	25.91 mm	bronze	7.12 g	.925 silver	7.12 g	.916 gold	13.96 g
2p	25.91 mm	Copper-plated steel	7.12 g				
5p	23.59 mm	cupro-nickel	5.65 g	.925 silver	5.65 g		
5p from 1990	18.00 mm	cupro-nickel	3.25 g	.925 silver	3.25 g	.916 gold	6.32 g
6p	19.41 mm			.925 silver	3.35 g		
10p	28.50 mm	cupro-nickel	11.31 g	.925 silver	11.31 g		
10p from 1992	24.50 mm	cupro-nickel	6.50 g	.925 silver	6.50 g	.916 gold	12.65 g
20p	21.40 mm	cupro-nickel	5.00 g	.925 silver	5.00 g	.916 gold	9.74 g
25p	38.61 mm	cupro-nickel	28.28 g	.925 silver	28.28 g		
50p	30.00 mm	cupro-nickel	13.50 g	.925 silver	13.50 g	.916 gold	26.32 g
50p from 1997	27.30 mm	cupro-nickel	8.00 g	.925 silver	8.00 g	.916 gold	15.58 g
£1	22.50 mm	nickel-brass	9.50 g	.925 silver	9.50 g	.916 gold	19.61 g
£1 from 2016	23.03 mm	bi metal	8.75 g	.925 silver	10.47 g	.916 gold	17.72 g
£2	28.40 mm	nickel-brass	15.98 g	.925 silver	15.98 g	.916 gold	15.97 g
£2 bi-metal	28.40 mm	c-n/n-b	12.00 g	.925 silver	12.00 g	.916 gold	15.97 g
£5	38.61 mm	cupro-nickel	28.28 g	.925 silver	28.28 g	.916 gold	39.94 g

Maundy							
4p	17.63 mm			.925 silver	1.88 g	.916 gold	3.16 g
3p	16.26 mm			.925 silver	1.41 g	.916 gold	2.37 g
2p	13.44 mm			.925 silver	0.94 g	.916 gold	1.58 g
1p	11.15 mm			.925 silver	0.47 g	.916 gold	0.79 g

For Specifications of Gold Sovereign coins, Britannia silver, Britannia gold and Britannia platinum, see pages 156, 187 and 211 and 239.

BRONZE

HALF PENNY COINS
Obverse portrait by Arnold Machin

A1   A2

A1 **Half new penny.** R. The Royal Crown and the inscription '1/2 NEW PENNY'.
(Reverse design: Christopher Ironside.)

1971 .... £1	1975 ....£1	1979..............................£1
— Proof *FDC** £2	— Proof *FDC** £2	— Proof *FDC**.......... £2
1972 Proof *FDC** £5	1976 ....£1	1980..............................£1
1973.......................... £1	— Proof *FDC** £2	— Proof *FDC**...........£2
— Proof *FDC**...... £2	1977 ....£1	1981..............................£1
1974.......................... £1	— Proof *FDC** £2	— Proof *FDC** £2
— Proof *FDC**...... £2	1978 ....£1	
	— Proof *FDC** £2	

A2 **Half penny.** 'New' omitted. As illustration

1982.......................... £1	1983 ....£1	1984........Unc £2; BU* £3
— Proof *FDC** £2	— Proof *FDC** £3	— Proof *FDC**..........£3

ONE PENNY COINS
Obverse portrait by Arnold Machin

B1   B2   B3

B1 **One new penny.** R. A portcullis with chains royally crossed, being the badge of Henry
VII and his successors, and the inscription 'NEW PENNY' above and the figure '1' below.
(Design: Christopher Ironside.)

1971 .... £1	1975 ....£1	1979..............................£1
— Proof *FDC** £2	— Proof *FDC** £2	— Proof *FDC**...........£2
1972 Proof *FDC** £5	1976 ....£1	1980..............................£1
1973.......................... £1	— Proof *FDC** £2	— Proof *FDC**...........£2
— Proof *FDC** £3	1977 ....£1	1981..............................£1
1974.......................... £1	— Proof *FDC** £2	— Proof *FDC** £2
— Proof *FDC** £2	1978 ....£1	
	— Proof *FDC** £2	

B2 **One penny.** 'New' omitted, As illustration

1982.......................... £1	1983 ....£1	1984........Unc £1; BU* £2
— Proof *FDC**...... £2	— *FDC** £2	— Proof *FDC**...........£2

Obverse portrait by Raphael Maklouf
B3 **One penny.** R. Crowned portcullis with chains.

1985......Unc £1; BU* £2	1988 .... Unc £1; BU* £2	1991........Unc £1; BU* £2
— Proof *FDC** £2	— Proof *FDC** £2	— Proof *FDC**...........£2
1986......Unc £1; BU* £2	1989 .... Unc £1; BU* £2	1992........Unc £1; BU* £2
— Proof *FDC** £2	— Proof *FDC** £2	— Proof *FDC**...........£2
1987......Unc £1; BU* £2	1990 ...... Unc £1; BU* £2	
— Proof *FDC** £2	— Proof *FDC** £2	

* Coins marked thus were originally issued in Royal Mint sets.

COPPER PLATED STEEL

B4   **One penny** R. Crowned portcullis with chains.

1992......Unc £1; BU* £2	1995 .... Unc £1; BU* £2	1997........ Unc £1; BU* £2
1993..... Unc £1; BU* £2	— Proof *FDC* £2	— Proof *FDC* £2
— Proof *FDC* £2	1996........Unc £1; BU* £2	
1994......Unc £1; BU* £2	— Proof *FDC* £2	
— Proof *FDC* £2	— Proof in silver *FDC**£15	

Obverse portrait by Ian Rank-Broadley

B5

B5 One penny. R. Crowned portcullis with chains. (Illus. as B2.)

1998 .... Unc £1; BU* £2	2005 .... Unc £1; BU* £2
— Proof *FDC* £3	— Proof *FDC* £3
1999 .... Unc £1	2006 .... Unc £1; BU* £2
2000 .... Unc £1; BU* £2	— Proof *FDC* £3
— Proof *FDC* £3	— Proof in silver *FDC* (see PSS17)**£10
— Proof in silver *FDC* (see PSS08)**£10	2007 .... Unc £1; BU* £2
2001 .... Unc £1; BU* £2	— Proof *FDC* £3
— Proof *FDC* £3	2008 .... Unc £1; BU* £2
2002 .... Unc £1; BU* £2	— Proof *FDC* £3
— Proof *FDC* £3	— Proof in silver *FDC* (see PSS27)**£10
— Proof in gold *FDC*	— Proof in gold *FDC*
(see PGCS02)* £300	(see PGCS06)* £300
2003 .... Unc £1; BU* £2	— Proof in platinum *FDC*
— Proof *FDC* £3	(see PPLS1)* £300
2004 .... Unc £1; BU* £2	
— Proof *FDC* £3	

BRONZE

B5A One penny.

1999 BU* £3

—   Proof *FDC* £4

* Coins marked thus were originally issued in Royal Mint sets.

COPPER PLATED STEEL

B6

B6   **One penny.** R. A section of Our Royal Arms showing elements of the first and third
quartering accompanied by the words 'ONE PENNY'. (Reverse design: Matthew Dent.)

2008 .... Unc £1; BU* £2
— Proof *FDC* (in 2008 set, see PS96)* £3
— Proof in silver *FDC* (in 2008 set, see PSS28)* £10
— Proof piedfort in silver *FDC* (in 2008 set, see PSS29)* £15
— Proof in gold *FDC* (in 2008 set, see PGCS07)* £300
— Proof in platinum *FDC* (in 2008 set, see PPLS2)* £300

2009 .... Unc £1; BU* £2
— Proof *FDC* (in 2009 set, see PS97)* £3
— BU in silver (issued: 8,467) £15
— Proof in silver *FDC* (in 2009 set, see PSS 37)* £15

2010 .... Unc £1; BU* £2
— Proof *FDC* (in 2010 set, see PS101)* £3
— BU in silver (issued: 9,701) £15
— Proof in silver *FDC* (Edition: 3,500) (in 2010 set, see PSS41)* £15

2011 .... Unc £1; BU* £2
— Proof *FDC* (in 2011 set, see PS104) * £3
— BU in silver £15
— Proof in silver *FDC* (Edition: 2,500) (in 2011 set, see PSS44)* £15

2012 .... Unc £1; BU* £2
— Proof *FDC* (in 2012 set, see PS107) * £3
— BU in silver (issued: 5,548) £15
— Proof in silver *FDC* (Edition: 995) (see PSS47)* £15
— Proof in silver with selected gold plating *FDC* (Edition: 2,012) (see PSS48)* £15
— Proof in gold *FDC* (Edition: 150) (see PGCS1)* £300

2013 .... Unc £1; BU* £2
— Proof *FDC* (in 2013 set, see PS109)* £5
— BU in silver £10
— Proof in silver *FDC* (Edition: 2,013) (see PSS50)* £25
— Proof in gold *FDC* (Issued: 59) (see PGCS13)* £350

2014 .... Unc £1; BU* £2
— Proof *FDC* (in 2014 set, see PS112)*
— BU in silver £10
— Proof in silver *FDC* (Edition: 2014) (see PSS57)* £20

2015 .... Unc £1; BU* £2
— Proof *FDC* (in 2015 set, see PS115) * £5
— BU in silver £10
— Proof in silver *FDC* (Edition: 7,500) (see PSS62)* £25
— Proof in gold *FDC* (Edition: 500) (see PGCS18) * £300
— Proof in platinum *FDC* (Issued: 10) (see PPLS3) * £350

* Coins marked thus were originally issued in Royal Mint sets.

Obverse portrait by Jody Clark
B7   One penny. R. as B6 above.
2015 ....Unc £1; BU* £2
  — Proof *FDC* (in 2015 set, see PS116)* £5
  — BU in silver £10
  — Proof in silver *FDC* (Edition: 7,500) (see PSS63)* £20
  — Proof in gold *FDC* (Edition: 500) (see PGCS19) * £300
  — Proof in platinum *FDC* (Issued: 10) (see PPLS3) * £350
2016 ....Unc £1; BU* £2
  — Proof *FDC* (in 2016 set, see PS119)* £5
  — BU in silver £10
  — Proof in silver *FDC* (Edition: 1,500) (see PSS68)* £20
2017 ....Unc £1; BU* £2
  — Proof *FDC* (in 2017 set, see PS122)* £6
  — BU in silver £10
  — Proof in silver *FDC* (Edition: 1,500) (see PSS73)* £20
  — Proof in gold *FDC* (Issued: 24) (see PCGS25)* £300
2018 BU* £5
  — Proof *FDC* (in 2018 set, see PS125)* £10
  — Proof in silver *FDC* (Edition: 1,000) (see PSS78)* £20
2019 BU* £5
  — BU in silver £15
  — Proof *FDC* (in 2019 set, see PS128)* £10
  — Proof in silver *FDC* (Edition: 1,000) (see PSS84)* £20
2020 BU* £5
  — Proof *FDC* (in 2020 set, see PS132)* £10
  — Proof in silver *FDC* (Edition: 1,000) (see PSS90)* £20
B8   One penny. R. as B5 above.
2018 BU in silver £15
2019 BU in silver £15

BRONZE
TWO PENCE COINS
Obverse portrait by Arnold Machin

C1

C1   Two new pence. R. The badge of the Prince of Wales, being three ostrich feathers enfiling a coronet of cross pattee and fleur de lys, with the motto 'ICH DIEN', and the inscription '2 NEW PENCE'. (Reverse design: Christopher Ironside.)

1971 ....£1	1976 ....£1	1979...............................£1
— Proof *FDC*......£2	— Proof *FDC* £2	— Proof *FDC*...........£2
1972 Proof *FDC*......£5	1977 ....£1	1980...............................£1
1973 Proof *FDC*......£5	— Proof *FDC* £2	— Proof *FDC*...........£2
1974 Proof *FDC*......£5	1978 ....£1	1981...............................£2
1975...........................£1	— Proof *FDC* £2	— Proof *FDC*...........£3
— Proof *FDC*.......£2		

* Coins marked thus were originally issued in Royal Mint sets.

C2

C2 **Two pence.** 'New' omitted. As illustration.

1982*......................... £2   1983*..............................£1   1984 BU* £1
—   Proof *FDC*.......£3   —   Proof *FDC*.............£2   —   Proof *FDC*...........£2

C2A **— Error reverse.** The word 'new' was dropped from the reverse of the currency issues in 1982 but a number of 2 pence coins were struck in 1983 with the incorrect reverse die, similar to coins listed as C1. Reports suggest that the error coins, or 'Mules' were contained in some sets packed by the Royal Mint for Martini and Heinz issued in 1983 ....£1250

Obverse portrait by Raphael Maklouf

C3

C3 **Two pence.** R. Prince of Wales feathers.

1985......Unc £1; BU* £2   1988 ....Unc £1; BU* £2   1991........Unc £1; BU* £2
—   Proof *FDC*........£2   —   Proof *FDC* ....£2   —   Proof *FDC*...........£2
1986......Unc £1; BU* £2   1989 ....Unc £1; BU* £2   1992........Unc £1; BU* £2
—   Proof *FDC*........£2   —   Proof *FDC* ....£2   —   Proof *FDC*...........£3
1987......Unc £1; BU* £2   1990 ....Unc £1; BU* £2
—   Proof *FDC*........£2   —   Proof *FDC* £2

COPPER PLATED STEEL

C4 **Two pence** R. Plumes.

1992......Unc £1; BU* £2   1995 .... Unc £1; BU* £2   1997........Unc £1; BU* £2
1993......Unc £1; BU* £2   —   Proof *FDC* ....£3   —   Proof *FDC* £3
—   Proof *FDC* ....£3   1996 .... Unc £1; BU* £2
1994......Unc £1; BU* £2   —   Proof *FDC* £3
—   Proof *FDC*........£3   —   Proof in silver *FDC*£15

* Coins marked thus were originally issued in Royal Mint sets.

TWO PENCE COINS

Obverse portrait by Ian Rank-Broadley

C5   C6

C5 Two pence. R. Prince of Wales feathers.

1998...........................Unc £1; BU* £2	2005 ....Unc £1; BU* £2
— Proof *FDC*...................................£3	— Proof *FDC*...................................£3
1999...£1	2006...........................Unc £1; BU* £2
2000...........................Unc £1; BU* £2	— Proof *FDC*...................................£3
— Proof *FDC*...................................£3	— Proof in silver *FDC* (see PSS17)*£10
— Proof in silver *FDC* (see PSS08)* £10	2007 ....Unc £1; BU* £2
2001...........................Unc £1; BU* £2	— Proof *FDC*...................................£3
— Proof *FDC*...................................£3	2008 ....Unc £1; BU* £2
2002...........................Unc £1; BU* £2	— Proof *FDC*...................................£3
— Proof *FDC*...................................£3	— Proof in silver *FDC* (see PSS27)*£10
— Proof in gold *FDC*	— Proof in gold *FDC*
(see PGCS02)*..........................£600	(see PGCS06)*..........................£600
2003...........................Unc £1; BU* £2	— Proof in platinum *FDC*
— Proof *FDC*...................................£3	(see PPLS2)*............................£600
2004...........................Unc £1; BU* £2	
— Proof *FDC*...................................£3	

BRONZE

C5A Two pence. R. Prince of Wales feathers as C2 above.

1998..£3

1999 BU* £3

— Proof *FDC*..£3

COPPER PLATED STEEL

C6 Two pence. R. A section of Our Royal Arms showing elements of the second quartering accompanied by the words 'TWO PENCE'. (Reverse design: Matthew Dent.)

2008 ....Unc £1; BU* £2

— Proof *FDC* (in 2008 set, see PS96)* £3

— Proof in silver *FDC* (in 2008 set, see PSS28)* £10

— Proof piedfort in silver *FDC* (in 2008 set, see PSS29)* £20

— Proof in gold *FDC* (in 2008 set, see PGCS07)* £600

— Proof in platinum *FDC* (in 2008 set, see PPLS2)* £600

2009...Unc £1; BU* £2

— Proof *FDC* (in 2009 set, see PS97)* £1

— Proof in silver *FDC* (in 2009 set, see PSS 37)* £10

* Coins marked thus were originally issued in Royal Mint sets.

2010..Unc £1; BU* £2
— Proof *FDC* (in 2010 set, see PS101)*...£3
— Proof in silver *FDC* (Edition: 3,500) (in 2010 set, see PSS41)*.........................£10
2011..Unc £1; BU* £2
— Proof *FDC* (in 2011 set, see PS104)*...£3
— Proof in silver *FDC* (Edition: 2,500) (in 2011 set, see PSS44)*.........................£15
2012..Unc £1; BU* £2
— Proof *FDC* (in 2012 set, see PS107)*.. £3
— Proof in silver *FDC* (Edition: 995, see PSS47)*..£25
— Proof in silver with selected gold plating *FDC* (Edition: 2,012) (see PSS48)*.... £25
— Proof in gold *FDC* (Edition: 150) (see PGCS11)*...£500
2013.. Unc £1; BU* £2
— Proof *FDC* (in 2013 set, see PS110)*... £5
— Proof in silver *FDC* (Edition: 2,013) (see PSS50)*...£25
— Proof in gold *FDC* (Issued: 59) (see PGCAS)*... £500
2014..Unc £1; BU* £2
— Proof *FDC* (in 2014 set, see PS112)*... £5
— Proof in silver *FDC* (Edition: 2,014) (see PSS57)*
2015 ....Unc £1; BU* £2
— Proof *FDC* (in 2015 set, see PS115)*... £5
— Proof in silver *FDC* (Edition: 7,500) (see PSS62)*...£25
— Proof in gold *FDC* (Edition: 500) (see PGCS18)*... £500
— Proof in platinum *FDC* (issued: 10) (see PPLS3)*...£650

Obverse portrait by Jody Clark
C7   **Two pence.** R. as C6 above.
2015 ....Unc £1; BU* £2
— Proof *FDC* (in 2015 set, see PS116)*... £5
— Proof in silver *FDC* (Edition: 7,500) (see PSS63)*... £25
— Proof in gold *FDC* (Edition: 500) (see PGCS19)*... £500
— Proof in platinum *FDC* (issued: 10) (see PPLS3)*...£650
2016.. Unc £1; BU* £2
— Proof *FDC* (in 2016 set, see PS119)*...£5
— Proof in silver *FDC* (Edition: 1,500) (see PSS68)*..£25
2017..Unc £1; BU* £2
— Proof *FDC* (in 2017 set, see PS122)*...£5
— Proof in silver *FDC* (Edition: 1,500) (see PSS73)*ow..£25
— Proof in gold *FDC* (Issued: 24) (see PCGS25)*.......................................£500
2018 BU*.. £5
— Proof *FDC* (in 2018 set, see PS125)*...£5
— Proof in silver *FDC* (Edition: 1,000) (see PSS78)*...£25
2019 BU*...£4
— Proof *FDC* (in 2019 set, see PS128)*...£5
— Proof in silver *FDC* (Edition: 1,000) (see PSS84)*...£25
2020 BU*...£4
— Proof *FDC* (in 2020 set, see PS132*...£5
— Proof in silver *FDC* (Edition: 1,000) (see PSS90)*...£25

* Coins marked thus were originally issued in Royal Mint sets.

CUPRO-NICKEL

FIVE PENCE COINS
Obverse portrait by Arnold Machin

D1

D1   **Five new pence.** R. A thistle royally crowned, being the badge of Scotland, and the
inscription '5 NEW PENCE'. (Reverse design: Christopher Ironside.)

1968............................ £1	1974 Proof *FDC** £5	1979................................£1
1969............................ £1	1975 ....£1	— Proof *FDC** £3
1970............................ £1	— Proof *FDC** £5	1980................................£1
1971............................ £1	1976 Proof *FDC** £5	— Proof *FDC** £2
— Proof *FDC** £2	1977 ....£1	1981 Proof *FDC** £4
1972 Proof *FDC** £5	— Proof *FDC** £3	
1973 Proof *FDC** £5	1978 .... £1	
	— Proof *FDC** £3	

Obverse portrait by Raphael Maklouf

D2   D3   D4

D2   **Five pence.** 'New' omitted. As illustration.

1982*......................... £4	1983* £4	1984 BU* £4
— Proof *FDC** £5	— Proof *FDC** £5	— Proof *FDC** £5

D3   **Five pence.** R. Crowned thistle

1985 BU* £4	1988 ....Unc £2; BU* £2	1990 BU* £4
— Proof *FDC** £5	— Proof *FDC** £3	— Proof *FDC** £5
1986 BU*..................... £4	1989 ....Unc £2; BU* £2	— Proof in silver *FDC** £10
— Proof *FDC** £5	— Proof *FDC** £3	
1987......Unc £2; BU* £2		
— Proof *FDC** £3		

D4   **Five pence.** R. Crowned thistle: reduced diameter of 18 mm.

1990.......Unc £2; BU* £2	1992 ....Unc £2; BU* £2	— Proof *FDC** £4
— Proof *FDC** £4	— Proof *FDC** £4	1996........ Unc £2; BU* £2
— Proof in silver *FDC** £10	1993* £6	— Proof *FDC** £4
— Proof piedfort in silver	— Proof *FDC**..............£4	— Proof in silver *FDC** £15
FDC (Issued:20,000)£20	1994 ....Unc £2; BU* £2	1997................................£2
1991.......Unc £2; BU* £2	— Proof *FDC** £4	— Proof *FDC** £4
— Proof *FDC** £4	1995 ....Unc £2; BU* £2	

PSS03 - 1990 5p (D3 and D4) silver proofs (2) (Issued: 35,000) £25

* Coins marked thus were originally issued in Royal Mint sets.

Obverse portrait by Ian Rank-Broadley

| D5 | D6 |

D5   **Five pence.** R. Crowned thistle.

1998.................................Unc £1; BU* £2	2004 ....Unc £1; BU* £2
— Proof *FDC* * £3	— Proof *FDC* * £3
1999 ....Unc £1; BU* £2	2005 ....Unc £1; BU* £2
— Proof *FDC* * £3	— Proof *FDC* * £3
2000.................................Unc £1; BU* £2	2006 ....Unc £1; BU* £2
— Proof *FDC* * £3	— Proof *FDC* * £3
— Proof in silver *FDC* (see PSS08)* £12	— Proof in silver *FDC* (see PSS17)* £12
2001.................................Unc £1; BU* £2	2007 ....Unc £1; BU* £2
— Proof *FDC* * £3	— Proof *FDC* * £3
2002.................................Unc £1; BU* £2	2008 ....Unc £1; BU* £2
— Proof *FDC* * £3	— Proof *FDC* * £3
— Proof in gold *FDC*	— Proof in silver *FDC* (see PSS27)*....£12
(see PGCS02) £280	— Proof in gold *FDC* (see PGCS06)* £280
2003.................................Unc £1; BU* £2	— Proof in platinum *FDC*
— Proof *FDC* * £3	(see PPLS1)* £250

D6   **Five pence.** R. A section of Our Royal Arms showing elements of all four quarterings accompanied by the words 'FIVE PENCE'. (Reverse design: Matthew Dent.)

2008 .... Unc £1; BU* £2
— Proof *FDC* (in 2008 set, see PS96)* £3
— Proof in silver *FDC* (in 2008 set, see PSS28)* £12
— Proof piedfort in silver *FDC* (in 2008 set, see PSS29)* £25
— Proof in gold *FDC* (in 2008 set, see PGCS07)* £280
— Proof in platinum *FDC* (in 2008 set, see PPLS2)* £250
2009.. Unc £1; BU* £2
— Proof *FDC* (in 2009 set, see PS97)* £3
— Proof in silver *FDC* (in 2009 set, see PSS 37)* £12
2010.. Unc £1; BU* £2
— Proof *FDC* (in 2010 set, see PS101)* £3
— Proof in silver *FDC* (Edition: 3,500) (in 2010 set, see PSS41)* £12

NICKEL PLATED STEEL

D7   **Five pence.**

2011... Unc £1; BU* £2
— Proof *FDC* (in 2011 set, see PS104)* £3
— Proof in silver *FDC* (in 2011 set, Edition: 2,500) (see PSS44)* £12
2012...Unc £1; BU* £2
— Proof *FDC* (in 2012 set, see PS107)* £5
— Proof in silver *FDC* (Edition: 995) (see PSS47)* £30
— Proof in silver with selected gold plating *FDC* (Edition: 2,012) (see PSS48)* £30
— Proof in gold *FDC* (Edition: 150) (see PGCS11)* £280

* Coins marked thus were originally issued in Royal Mint sets.

2013.. Unc £1; BU* £2
— Proof *FDC* (in 2013 set, see PS109)*... £5
— Proof in silver *FDC* (Edition: 2,013) (see PSS50)*.................................£30
— Proof in gold *FDC* (Issued: 59) (see PGCS13)*....................................£300
2014.. Unc £1; BU* £2
— Proof *FDC* (in 2014 set, see PS112)*... £5
— Proof in silver *FDC* (Edition: 2,014) (see PSS57)*.................................£30
2015.. Unc £1; BU* £2
— Proof *FDC* (in 2015 set, see PS115)*... £5
— Proof in silver *FDC* (Edition: 7,500) (see PSS62)*.................................£30
— Proof in gold *FDC* (Edition: 500) (see PGCS18)*..................................£280
— Proof in platinum *FDC* (Issued: 10) (see PPLS3)*..................................£300

Obverse portrait by Jody Clark

D8

D8   Five pence.
2015...Unc £1; BU* £3
— Proof *FDC* (in 2015 set, see PS116)*..£5
— Proof in silver *FDC* (Edition: 7,500) (see PSS63)*.................................£20
— Proof in gold *FDC* (Edition: 500) (see PGC5P)*....................................£225
— Proof in platinum *FDC* (Issued: 10) (see PPLS3)*..................................£300
2016.. Unc £1; BU* £3
— Proof *FDC* (in 2016 set, see PS119)*..£5
— Proof in silver *FDC* (Edition: 1,500) (see PSS68)*.................................£30
2017 ....Unc £1; BU* £3
— Proof *FDC* (in 2017 set, see PS122)*..£5
— Proof in silver *FDC* (Edition: 1,500) (see PSS73)*.................................£30
— Proof in gold *FDC* (Issued: 24) (see PCGS25)*......................................£225
2018 BU*... £5
— Proof *FDC* (in 2018 set, see PS125)*..£7
— Proof in silver *FDC* (Edition: 1,000) (see PSS78)*.................................£30
2019 BU*...£4
— Proof *FDC* (in 2019 set, see PS128)*..£6
— Proof in silver *FDC* (Edition: 1,000) (see PSS84)*.................................£25
2020 BU*...£4
— Proof *FDC* (in 2020 set, see PS132)*..£6
— Proof in silver *FDC* (Edition: 500) (see PSS90)*....................................£25

* Coins marked thus were originally issued in Royal Mint sets.

SIX PENCE COIN

E1

E1 **Six pence.** (0.925 silver). R. A design of Our Royal Cypher surrounded by a floral motif with the inscription SIXPENCE' accompanied by the date of the year. (Reverse design: John Bergdahl.)
2016 BU in presentation box £30
2017 BU in presentation box £30
2018 BU in folder...£15
2019 BU in presentation box £30

TEN PENCE COINS
Obverse portrait by Arnold Machin

F1

F1 **Ten new pence.** R. Lion passant guardant being royally crowned, being part of the crest of England, and the inscription 'Ten New Pence'. (Reverse design: Christopher Ironside.)

1968 .... £2	1974 .... £2	1978 Proof *FDC* £4
1969 .... £2	— Proof *FDC* £3	1979 ....£2
1970 .... £3	1975 .... £2	— Proof *FDC* £3
1971 .... £3	— Proof *FDC* £3	1980 ....£2
— Proof *FDC* £3	1976 .... £2	— Proof *FDC* £3
1972 Proof *FDC* £5	— Proof *FDC* £3	1981 ....£3
1973 .... £2	1977 .... £2	— Proof *FDC* £4
— Proof *FDC* £3	— Proof *FDC* £3	

F2

F2 **Ten pence.** 'New' omitted. As illustration.

1982* £4	1983* £4	1984 BU* £4
— Proof *FDC* £4	— Proof *FDC* £4	— Proof *FDC* £4

* Coins marked thus were originally issued in Royal Mint sets.

Obverse portrait by Raphael Maklouf

F3

F3   **Ten pence.** R. Lion passant guardant.

1985 BU* £4	1988 BU* £4	1991 BU* £4
— Proof *FDC* * £4	— Proof *FDC** £4	— Proof *FDC** £5
1986 BU* £4	1989 BU* £4	1992 BU* £5
— Proof *FDC** £4	— Proof *FDC** £5	— Proof *FDC** £6
1987 BU* £4	1990 BU* £4	— Proof in silver *FDC** £14
— Proof *FDC** £4	— Proof *FDC** £5	

F4

F4   **Ten pence.** R Lion passant guardant: reduced diameter of 24.5 mm

1992............................ Unc £1; BU* £3	1995............................ Unc £1; BU* £3
— Proof *FDC** £3	— Proof *FDC** £3
— Proof in silver *FDC** £10	1996............................ Unc £1; BU* £3
— Proof piedfort in silver *FDC**	— Proof *FDC** £3
(Issued: 14,167) £30	— Proof in silver *FDC** £15
1993 BU* £4	1997............................ Unc £1; BU* £3
— Proof *FDC** £4	— Proof *FDC** £3
1994 BU* £4	
— Proof *FDC** £3	

PSS04 - 1992 10p (F3 and F4) silver proofs (2)...£30

* Coins marked thus were originally issued in Royal Mint sets.

Obverse portrait by Ian Rank-Broadley

F5

F5 **Ten pence.** R. Lion passant guardant. (Illus. as F4).

1998 BU*	£5	2005	Unc £1; BU* £3
— Proof *FDC**	£5	— Proof *FDC**	£3
1999 BU*	£5	2006	Unc £1; BU* £3
— Proof *FDC**	£5	— Proof *FDC**	£3
2000	Unc £1; BU* £3	— Proof in silver *FDC*	
— Proof *FDC**	£3	(see PSS17)*	£15
— Proof in silver *FDC*		2007	£1
(see PSS08)*	£15	— Proof *FDC*	£3
2001	Unc £1; BU* £3	2008	Unc £1; BU* £3
— Proof *FDC**	£3	— Proof *FDC**	£3
2002	Unc £1; BU* £3	— Proof in silver *FDC*	
— Proof in gold *FDC*		(see PSS27)*	£15
(see PGCS02)*	£550	— Proof in gold *FDC*	
2003	Unc £1; BU* £3	(see PGCS06)*	£550
— Proof *FDC**	£3	— Proof in platinum *FDC*	
2004	Unc £1; BU* £3	(see PPLS1)*	£500
— Proof *FDC**	£3		

F6

F6 **Ten pence.** R. A section of Our Royal Arms showing elements of the first quartering accompanied by the words 'TEN PENCE'. (Reverse design: Matthew Dent.)

2008	Unc £1; BU* £3
— Proof *FDC* (in 2008 set, see PS96)*	£6
— Proof in silver *FDC* (in 2008 set, see PSS28)*	£15
— Proof piedfort in silver *FDC* (in 2008 set, see PSS29)*	£25
— Proof in gold *FDC* (in 2008 set, see PGCS07)*	£550
— Proof in platinum *FDC* (in 2008 set, see PPLS2)*	£500
2009	Unc £1; BU* £3
— Proof *FDC* (in 2009 set, see PS97)*	£6
— Proof in silver *FDC* (in 2009 set, see PSS 37)*	£15
2010	Unc £1; BU* £3
— Proof *FDC* (in 2010 set, see PS101)*	£6
— Proof in silver *FDC* (Edition: 3,500) (in 2010 set, see PSS 41)*	£15

* Coins marked thus were originally issued in Royal Mint sets.

NICKEL PLATED STEEL

F7   **Ten pence.**

2011 .... Unc £1; BU* £3
  — Proof *FDC* (in 2011 set, see PS104)* £3
  — Proof in silver *FDC* (Edition: 2,500) (in 2011 set, see PSS44)* £15
2012 ....Unc £1; BU* £3
  — Proof *FDC* (in 2012 set, see PS107)* £3
  — Proof in silver *FDC* (Edition: 995) (see PSS47)* £30
  — Proof in silver with selected gold plating *FDC* (Edition: 2,012) (see PSS48)* £30
  — Proof in gold *FDC* (Edition: 150) (see PGCS11)* £550
2013 .... Unc £1; BU* £3
  — Proof *FDC* (in 2013 set, see PS109)* £5
  — Proof in silver *FDC* (Edition: 2,013) (see PSS50)* £30
  — Proof in gold *FDC* (Issued: 59) (see PGCS13)* £600
2014 .... Unc £1; BU* £3
  — Proof *FDC* (in 2014 set, see PS112)* £5
  — Proof in silver *FDC* (Edition: 2,014) (see PSS57)*
2015 .... Unc £1; BU* £3
  — Proof *FDC* (in 2015 set, see PS115)* £5
  — Proof in silver *FDC* (Edition: 7,500) (see PSS62)* £30
  — Proof in gold *FDC* (Edition: 500) (see PGCS18)* £550
  — Proof in platinum *FDC* (Issued: 10) (see PPLS3)* £550

Obverse portrait by Jody Clark

F8

F8   **Ten pence.**

2015 .... Unc £1; BU* £3
  — Proof *FDC* (in 2015 set, see PS116)* £5
  — Proof in silver *FDC* (Edition: 7,500) (see PSS63) £30
  — Proof in gold *FDC* (Edition: 500) (see PGCS19)* £550
  — Proof in platinum *FDC* (Issued: 10) (see PPLS3)* £550
2016 .... Unc £1; BU* £3
  — Proof *FDC* (in 2016 set, see PS119)* £5
  — Proof in silver *FDC* (Edition: 1,500) (see PSS68)* £30
2017 .... Unc £1; BU* £3
  — Proof *FDC* (in 2017 set, see PS122)* £6
  — Proof in silver *FDC* (Edition: 1,500) (see PSS73)* £30
  — Proof in gold *FDC* (Issued: 24) (see PCGS25)* £550
2018 .... BU* £4
  — Proof *FDC* (in 2018 set, see PS125)* £6
  — Proof in silver *FDC* (Edition: 1,000) (see PSS78)* £30
2019 .... BU* £4
  — Proof *FDC* (in 2019 set, see PS128)* £6
  — Proof in silver *FDC* (Edition: 1,000) (see PSS84)* £30
2020 .... BU* £4
  — Proof *FDC* (in 2020 set, see PS132)* £6
  — Proof in silver *FDC* (Edition: 500) (see PSS90)* £30

* Coins marked thus were originally issued in Royal Mint sets.

F9
Angel of the North

F10
Bond

F11
Cricket

F12
Double Decker Bus

F13
English Breakfast

F14
Fish and Chips

F15
Greenwich Mean Time

F16
Houses of Parliament

F17
Ice Cream

F18
Jubilee

F19
King Arthur

F20
Loch Ness Monster

F21
Mackintosh

F22
NHS

F23
Oak

F24
Post Box

F25
Queue

F26
Robin

F27
Stonehenge

F28
Tea

F29	F30	F31	F32
Union Flag	Villages	World Wide Web	X Marks the Spot

F33	F34
Yeoman Warder	Zebra Crossing

F9 to F34 Ten pence. A series of twenty-six coins depicting the letters of the Alphabet from A to Z. (Reverse designs: The Royal Mint Team.)

2018
- — Uncirculated (Issued: 220,000 of each coin) £1
- — BU, each coin £2
- — Proof in silver *FDC*, each coin £35
- — Proof in silver *FDC* in Acrylic block, each coin (Edition: 15,000) £45

2019
- — Uncirculated £1
- — BU, each coin £2
- — BU, set of 26 in folder £62

F11 — C (Cricket) proof in gold FDC (Edition: 256)..£700
This coin was issued to commemorate the England victory in the Cricket World Cup Final.

* Coins marked thus were originally issued in Royal Mint sets.

COINS OF ENGLAND & THE UNITED KINGDOM PRE-DECIMAL SERIES

SPINK

COINS OF ENGLAND 2021
E-book available on Amazon, iBookstore, Google, Kobo, OverDrive and across most other platforms

For more information or enquiries please contact
Tel: +44 (0)20 7563 4119 | Email: books@spink.com
69 Southampton Row, Bloomsbury, London WC1B 4ET

WWW.SPINKBOOKS.COM

CUPRO-NICKEL

TWENTY PENCE COINS
Obverse portrait by Arnold Machin

G1

G1 Twenty pence. R. The Royal Badge of the Rose of England represented as a double rose barbed and seeded, slipped and leaved and ensigned by a Royal Crown and the date of the year with the inscription 'TWENTY PENCE' and the figure '20' superimposed on the stem of the rose. (Reverse design: William Gardner.)

1982 ....£1
— Proof *FDC** £3
— Proof piedfort in silver *FDC* (Issued: 10,000) £30
1983 ....£1
1984 ....Unc £1; BU* £2
— Proof *FDC** £3

Obverse portrait by Raphael Maklouf

G2

G2 Twenty pence. R. Crowned double rose.

1985 ....Unc £1; BU* £2	1989 ....Unc £1; BU* £2
— Proof *FDC** £3	— Proof *FDC** £3
1986 BU* £5	1990 ....Unc £1; BU* £2
— Proof *FDC** £6	— Proof *FDC** £3
1987 ....Unc £1; BU* £2	1991 ....Unc £1; BU* £2
— Proof *FDC** £3	— Proof *FDC** £3
1988 ....Unc £1; BU* £2	
— Proof *FDC** £3	

G2A Twenty pence. Enhanced royal portrait.

1992 ....Unc £1; BU* £2	1996 ....Unc £1; BU* £2
— Proof *FDC** £3	— Proof *FDC** £3
1993 ....Unc £1; BU* £2	— Proof in silver *FDC** £18
— Proof *FDC** £3	1997 ....Unc £1; BU* £2
1994 ....Unc £1; BU* £2	— Proof *FDC** £3
— Proof *FDC** £3	
1995 ....Unc £1; BU* £2	
— Proof *FDC** £3	

* *Coins marked thus were originally issued in Royal Mint sets.*

Obverse portrait by Ian Rank-Broadley

G3

G3　**Twenty pence.** Ɍ. Crowned double rose.

1998....................Unc £1; BU* £2	2004 ....Unc £1; BU* £2
— 　Proof *FDC*...............................£3	— 　Proof *FDC* £3
1999....................Unc £1; BU* £2	2005 ....Unc £1; BU* £2
— 　Proof *FDC*...............................£3	— 　Proof *FDC* £3
2000....................Unc £1; BU* £2	2006 ....Unc £1; BU* £2
— 　Proof *FDC*...............................£3	— 　Proof *FDC* £3
— 　Proof in silver *FDC* (see PSS08) *£20	— 　Proof in silver *FDC* (see PSS17)* £20
2001...........................Unc £1; BU* £2	2007 ....Unc £1; BU* £2
— 　Proof *FDC*...............................£3	— 　Proof *FDC* £3
2002...........................Unc £1; BU* £2	2008 ....Unc £1; BU* £2
— 　Proof *FDC*...............................£3	— 　Proof *FDC* £3
— 　Proof in gold *FDC*	— 　Proof in silver *FDC* (see PSS27)*..........£20
(see PGCS02)*............................£450	— 　Proof in gold *FDC* (see PGCS06)* .£450
2003...........................Unc £1; BU* £2	— 　Proof in platinum *FDC*
— 　Proof *FDC*...............................£3	(see PPLS1)* £450

G4

G4　**Twenty pence.** R. A section of Our Royal Arms showing elements of the second and forth quartering accompanied by the words 'TWENTY PENCE'. (Reverse design: Matthew Dent.)

2008...Unc £1; BU* £2
— 　Proof *FDC* (in 2008 set, see PS96)* £3
— 　Proof in silver *FDC* (in 2008 set, see PSS28)* £20
— 　Proof piedfort in silver *FDC* (in 2008 set, see PSS29)* £40
— 　Proof in gold *FDC* (in 2008 set, see PGCS07)* £450
— 　Proof in platinum *FDC* (in 2008 set, see PPLS2)* £450
2009...Unc £1; BU* £2
— 　Proof *FDC* (in 2009 set, see PS97)* £6
— 　Proof in silver *FDC* (in 2009 set, see PSS 37)* £20
2010...Unc £1; BU* £2
— 　Proof *FDC* (in 2010 set, see PS101)* £6
— 　Proof in silver *FDC* (Edition: 3,500) (in 2010 set, see PSS 41)* £20
2011...Unc £1; BU* £2
— 　Proof *FDC* (in 2011 set, see PS104) * £3
— 　Proof in silver *FDC* (Edition: 2,500) (in 2011 set, see PSS44)* £15

* Coins marked thus were originally issued in Royal Mint sets.

2012 ....Unc £1; BU* £2
— Proof *FDC* (in 2012 set, see PS107)* £3
— Proof in silver *FDC* (Edition: 995) (see PSS47)* £30
— Proof in silver with selected gold plating *FDC* (Edition: 2,012) (see PSS48)* £30
— Proof in gold *FDC* (Edition: 150) (see PGCS11)*.. £450
2013.. Unc £1; BU* £2
— Proof *FDC* (in 2013 set, see PS109)* £5
— Proof in silver *FDC* (Edition: 2,013) (see PSS50)* £30
— Proof in gold *FDC* (Issued: 59) (see PGCS13)*...£500
2014..Unc £1; BU* £2
— Proof *FDC* (in 2014 set, see PS112)* £5
— Proof in silver *FDC* (Edition: 2,014) (see PSS57)*
2015.. Unc £1; BU* £2
— Proof *FDC* (in 2015 set, see PS115)* £5
— Proof in silver *FDC* (Edition: 7,500) (see PSS62)* £30
— Proof in gold *FDC* (Edition: 500) (see PGCS18)* £450
— Proof in platinum *FDC* (Issued: 10) (see PPLS3)*..£500

G4A — **Error obverse – known as a Mule.** The new reverse design by Matthew Dent does not include the year date and this should have appeared on the obverse. A number of coins were struck using the undated obverse die that had previously been used with the dated reverse of the crowned double rose. (See Illus. G3.)
VF...£45
UNC £75

Obverse portrait by Jody Clark

G5

G5 **Twenty pence.**
2015.. Unc £1; BU* £2
— Proof *FDC* (in 2015 set, see PS116)* £5
— Proof in silver *FDC* (Edition: 7,500) (see PSS63)* £30
— Proof in gold *FDC* (Edition: 500) (see PGCS19)* £450
— Proof in platinum *FDC* (Issued: 10) (see PPLS3)*...£500
2016..Unc £1; BU* £2
— Proof *FDC* (in 2016 set, see PS119)* £5
— Proof in silver *FDC* (Edition: 1,500) (see PSS68)* £30
2017 BU* £6
— Proof *FDC* (in 2017 set, see PS122)* £10
— Proof in silver *FDC* (Edition: 1,500) (see PSS73)* £30
— Proof in gold *FDC* (Issued: 24) (see PCGS25)* £450
2018 BU* £6
— Proof *FDC* (in 2018 set, see PS125)*...£10
— Proof in silver *FDC* (Edition: 1,000) (see PSS78)* £30
2019 .... Unc £1; BU* £4
— Proof *FDC* (in 2019 set, see PS128)*...£10
— Proof in silver *FDC* (Edition: 1,000) (see PSS84)* £30
2020 BU* £4
— Proof *FDC* (in 2020 set, see PS132)*...£10
— Proof in silver *FDC* (Edition: 500) (see PSS90)* £30

* Coins marked thus were originally issued in Royal Mint sets.

FIFTY PENCE COINS
Obverse portrait by Arnold Machin

H1

H1   **Fifty new pence** (seven-sided). R. A figure of Britannia seated beside a lion, with a shield resting against her right side, holding a trident in her right hand and an olive branch in her left hand; and the inscription '50 NEW PENCE'. (Reverse design: Christopher Ironside.)

1969	£2	1976	£2	1979	£2
1970	£5	— Proof *FDC**	£3	— Proof *FDC**	£3
1971 Proof *FDC**	£7	1977	£2	1980	£2
1972 Proof *FDC**	£7	— Proof *FDC**	£3	— Proof *FDC**	£3
1974 Proof *FDC**	£8	1978	£2	1981	£2
1975 Proof *FDC**	£8	— Proof *FDC**	£3	— Proof *FDC**	£3

H2   H3

H2   **Fifty pence.** Accession to European Economic Community. R. The inscription 'FIFTY PENCE' and the date of the year, surrounded by nine hands, symbolizing the nine members of the community, clasping one another in a mutual gesture of trust, assistance and friendship. (Reverse design: David Wynne.)

1973 ....£3
— Proof *FDC*** £6

H2A —Design as H2 above, but struck in very small numbers in silver on thicker blank. Sometimes referred to as a piedfort but not twice the weight of the regular cupro-nickel currency issue. The pieces were presented to EEC Finance Ministers and possibly senior officials on the occasion of the United Kingdom joining the European Economic Community...£3000

H3   **Fifty pence.** 'New' omitted. As illustration

1982	£3	1983	£2	1984 BU*	£5
— Proof *FDC**	£3	— Proof *FDC**	£3	— Proof *FDC**	£7

* Coins marked thus were originally issued in Royal Mint sets
** Issued as an individual proof coin and in the year set

Obverse portrait by Raphael Maklouf

H4

H4   Fifty pence. R. Britannia.

1985.....Unc £4; BU* £5	1990 BU*........................£5	1996 BU* £5
— Proof *FDC*........£5	— Proof *FDC* £5	— Proof *FDC*...........£5
1986 BU* £5	1991 BU* £5	— Proof in silver *FDC** £20
— Proof *FDC*........£5	— Proof *FDC* £5	1997 BU* £5
1987 BU* £5	1992 BU*........................£5	— Proof *FDC*...........£6
— Proof *FDC* £5	— Proof *FDC*.................£5	— Proof in silver *FDC**£20
1988 BU* £5	1993 BU*........................£5	
— Proof *FDC*........£5	— Proof *FDC* £5	
1989 BU* £5	1995 BU*........................£5	
— Proof *FDC*........£5	— Proof *FDC* £5	

H5

H5   Fifty pence Presidency of the Council of European Community Ministers and completion of the Single Market. R A representation of a table on which are placed twelve stars, linked by a network of lines to each other and also to twelve chairs, around the table, on one of which appear the letters 'UK', and with the dates '1992' and '1993' above and the value '50 PENCE' below. (Reverse design: Mary Milner Dickens.)

1992-1993 ....VF £30; Unc £50; BU* £75
— Proof *FDC** £75
— Proof in silver *FDC** (Issued: 26,890).. £75
— Proof piedfort in silver *FDC* (Issued: 10,993) £90
— Proof in gold *FDC* (Issued: 1,864)...£1300

US13 - 1992 50p (H4 and H5) BU in folder (2) £75

* Coins marked thus were originally issued in Royal Mint sets

H6

H6   **Fifty pence** 50th Anniversary of the Normandy Landings on D-Day. R: A design
       representing the Allied invasion force of the D-Day landings heading for Normandy and
       filling the sea and sky, together with the value '50 PENCE'. (Reverse design: John Mills.)
       1994... Unc £2; BU* £3
       —   BU in presentation folder £5
       —   Proof *FDC** £5
       —   Proof in silver *FDC* (Issued: 40,000) £35
       —   Proof piedfort in silver *FDC* (Issued: 10,000) £60
       —   Proof in gold *FDC* (Issued: 1,877)...£1400
H7   **Fifty penc**e R. Britannia: reduced diameter of 27.3mm
       1997.. Unc £2; BU* £2
       —   Proof *FDC** £4
       —   Proof in silver *FDC* (Issued: 1,632)...£25
       —   Proof piedfort in silver *FDC* (Issued: 7,192) £40

PSS06 - 1997 50p (H4 and H7) silver proofs (2) (Issued: 10,304) £45

Obverse portrait by Ian Rank-Broadley

H8

H8   **Fifty pence.** R. Britannia. (Illus. as H4.)
       1998.. Unc £2; BU* £3
       —   Proof *FDC** £3
       1999.. Unc £2; BU* £3
       —   Proof *FDC** £3
       2000.. Unc £2; BU* £3
       —   Proof *FDC** £3
       —   Proof in silver *FDC* (see PSS08)* £25
       2001.. Unc £2; BU* £3
       —   Proof *FDC** £3
       2002.. Unc £2; BU* £3
       —   Proof *FDC** £3
       —   Proof in gold *FDC* (see PGCS02)* £700
       2003 .... Unc £2; BU* £3
       —   Proof *FDC** £3

* Coins marked thus were originally issued in Royal Mint sets.

2004 .... Unc £2; BU* £3
— Proof *FDC** £3
2005 .... Unc £2; BU* £3
— Proof *FDC** £3
2006 .... Unc £2; BU* £3
— Proof *FDC** £3
— Proof in silver *FDC* (see PSS17)* £25
2007 .... Unc £2; BU* £3
— Proof *FDC** £3
2008 .... Unc £2; BU* £3
— Proof *FDC** £3
— Proof in silver *FDC* (see PSS27)* £30
— Proof in gold *FDC* (see PGCS06)* £700
— Proof in platinum *FDC* (see PPLS1)* £600
2009
— Proof *FDC* (in 2009 set, see PS100)* £15
— Proof in silver *FDC* (in 2009 set, see PSS40)* £30
— Proof in gold *FDC* (in 2009 set, see PGCS09)* £700
— Proof piedfort in gold *FDC* (Issued: 40) (see PGCS10)* £1600

H9

H9   **Fifty pence.** 25th Anniversary of the United Kingdom's Membership of the European
Union and Presidency of the Council of Ministers. R. Celebratory pattern of twelve stars
reflecting the European flag with the dates 1973 and 1998. (Reverse design: John Mills.)
1998 .... Unc £2; BU* £3
— Proof *FDC** £5
— Proof in silver *FDC* (Issued: 8,859) £30
— Proof piedfort in silver *FDC* (Issued: 8,440) £50
— Proof in gold *FDC* (Issued: 1,177) £750
2009
— Proof *FDC* (in 2009 set, see PS100)* £15
— Proof in silver *FDC* (in 2009 set, see PSS40)* £30
— Proof in gold *FDC* (in 2009 set, see PGCS09)* £750
— Proof piedfort in gold *FDC* (Issued: 40) (see PGCS10)* £1600

US20 - 1998 50p (H8 and H9) BU in folder (2) £6

* Coins marked thus were originally issued in Royal Mint sets.

H10   H11

H10 Fifty pence. 50th Anniversary of the National Health Service. ℞. A pair of hands set against a pattern of radiating lines with the words 'FIFTIETH ANNIVERSARY' and the value '50 PENCE' accompanied by the initials 'NHS' which appear five times on the outer border. (Reverse design: David Cornell.)

1998 ....£2
—   BU in presentation folder £5
—   Proof in silver *FDC* (Issued: 9,032)..£30
—   Proof piedfort in silver *FDC* (Issued: 5,117) £50
—   Proof in gold *FDC* (Issued: 651)...£750
2009
—   Proof *FDC* (in 2009 set, see PS100)* £15
—   Proof in silver *FDC* (in 2009 set, see PSS40)* £30
—   Proof in gold *FDC* (in 2009 set, see PGCS09)* £750
—   Proof piedfort in gold *FDC* (Issued: 40) (see PGCS10)* £1600

PSS07 - 1998 50p (H9 and H10) silver proofs (2) £60

H11 Fifty pence. 150th Anniversary of the Public Libraries Act. ℞. The turning pages of a book above the dates '1850 – 2000'and the value '50 PENCE', all above a classical library building on which the words 'PUBLIC LIBRARY' and, within the pediment, representations of compact discs. (Reverse design: Mary Milner Dickens.)

2000 .... Unc £2; BU* £3
—   BU in presentation folder £7
—   Proof *FDC** £5
—   Proof in silver *FDC* (Issued: 7,634)..£28
—   Proof piedfort in silver *FDC* (Issued: 5,721) £50
—   Proof in gold *FDC* (Issued: 710)...£750
2009
—   Proof *FDC* (in 2009 set, see PS100)* £15
—   Proof in silver *FDC* (in 2009 set, see PSS40)* £30
—   Proof in gold *FDC* (in 2009 set, see PGCS09)* £750
—   Proof piedfort in gold *FDC* (Issued: 40) (see PGCS10)* £1600

* Coins marked thus were originally issued in Royal Mint sets.

H12   H13

H12   Fifty pence. Centenary of the Suffragette Movement. ℞. The figure of a suffragette chained to railings and holding a banner on which appear the letters 'WSPU', to the right a ballot paper marked with a cross and the words 'GIVE WOMEN THE VOTE', to the left the value '50 PENCE' and below and to the far right the dates '1903' and '2003'. (Reverse design: Mary Milner Dickens.)

2003 .... Unc £3; BU* £4
— BU in presentation folder (Issued: 9,582) £7
— Proof *FDC* (in 2003 set, see PS78)* £5
— Proof in silver *FDC* (Issued: 6,267) £28
— Proof piedfort in silver *FDC* (Issued 6,795) £50
— Proof in gold *FDC* (Issued: 942)..£750

2009
— Proof *FDC* (in 2009 set, see PS100)* £15
— Proof in silver *FDC* (in 2009 set, see PSS40)* £30
— Proof in gold *FDC* (in 2009 set, see PGCS09)* £750
— Proof piedfort in gold *FDC* (Issued: 40) (see PGCS10)[th] £1600

H13   Fifty pence. 50th Anniversary of the First Sub Four-minute Mile. ℞. The legs of a running athlete with a stylised stopwatch in the background and, below, the value '50 PENCE'. (Reverse design: James Butler.)

2004 .... Unc £2; BU* £3
— BU in presentation folder (Issued: 10,371) £7
— Proof *FDC* (in 2004 set, see PS81)* £5
— Proof in silver *FDC* (Issued: 4,924)..£28
— Proof piedfort in silver *FDC* (Issued: 4,054) £60
— Proof in gold *FDC* (Issued: 644)..£750

2009
— Proof *FDC* (in 2009 set, see PS100)* £15
— Proof in silver *FDC* (in 2009 set, see PSS40)* £30
— Proof in gold *FDC* (in 2009 set, see PGCS09)* £750
— Proof piedfort in gold *FDC* (Issued: 40) (see PGCS10)* £1600

* Coins marked thus were originally issued in Royal Mint sets.

H14   H15

H14   **Fifty pence**. 250th Anniversary of the Publication of Samuel Johnson's Dictionary of the English Language. ℞. Entries from Samuel Johnson's Dictionary of the English Language for the words 'FIFTY' and 'PENCE', with the figure '50' above, and the inscription 'JOHNSON'S DICTIONARY 1755' below. (Reverse design: Tom Phillips.)

2005 ....Unc £2; BU* £3
—   Proof *FDC* (in 2005 set, see PS84)* £7
—   Proof in silver *FDC* (Issued: 4,029) £28
—   Proof piedfort in silver *FDC* (Issued: 3,808) £60
—   Proof in gold *FDC* (Issued: 584)..£750
2009
—   Proof *FDC* (in 2009 set, see PS100)* £15
—   Proof in silver *FDC* (in 2009 set, see PSS40)* £30
—   Proof in gold *FDC* (in 2009 set, see PGCS09)* £750
—   Proof piedfort in gold *FDC* (Issued: 40) (see PGCS10)* £1600

H15   **Fifty pence.** 150th Anniversary of the Institution of the Victoria Cross. ℞. A depiction of the obverse and reverse of a Victoria Cross with the date '29. JAN 1856' in the centre of the reverse of the Cross, the letters 'VC' to the right and the value 'FIFTY PENCE'. (Reverse design: Claire Aldridge.)

2006 ....Unc £2; BU* £3
—   Proof *FDC* (in 2006 set, see PS87)* £5
—   Proof in silver *FDC* (Issued: 6,310) £30
—   Proof piedfort in silver *FDC* (Issued: 3,532) (see PSS27) £60
—   Proof in gold *FDC* (Issued: 866)..£750
2009
—   Proof *FDC* (in 2009 set, see PS100)* £15
—   Proof in silver *FDC* (in 2009 set, see PSS40)* £30
—   Proof in gold *FDC* (in 2009 set, see PGCS09)* £750
—   Proof piedfort in gold *FDC* (Issued: 40) (see PGCS10)* £1600

* Coins marked thus were originally issued in Royal Mint sets.

SPINK

COINS OF ENGLAND 2021
E-book available on Amazon, iBookstore,
Google, Kobo, OverDrive
and across most other platforms
For more information or enquiries please contact
Tel: +44 (0)20 7563 4119 | Email: books@spink.com
69 Southampton Row, Bloomsbury, London WC1B 4ET
WWW.SPINKBOOKS.COM

H16   H17

H16 **Fifty pence.** 150th Anniversary of the Institution of the Victoria Cross. R. A Depiction of a soldier carrying a wounded comrade with an outline of the Victoria Cross surrounded by a sunburst effect in the background and the value 'FIFTY PENCE'. (Reverse design: Clive Duncan.)

2006 ....Unc £2; BU* £3
— Proof *FDC* (in 2006 set, see PS87)* £5
— Proof in silver *FDC* (Issued: 6,872) £30
— Proof piedfort in silver *FDC* (Issued: 3,415) (see PSS27) £60
— Proof in gold *FDC* (Issued: 804) £750
2009
— Proof *FDC* (in 2009 set, see PS100)* £15
— Proof in silver *FDC* (in 2009 set, see PSS40)* £30
— Proof in gold *FDC* (in 2009 set, see PGCS09)* £750
— Proof piedfort in gold *FDC* (Issued: 40) (see PGCS10)* £1600

US34 - 2006 50p (H15 and H16) BU in folder (2) £7
PSS20 - 2006 50p (H15 and H16) silver proofs (2) £65
PSS21 - 2006 50p (H15 and H16) silver piedfort proofs (2)................................£115
PGCS04 - 2006 50p (H15 and H16) gold proofs (2) £1500

H17 **Fifty pence.** Centenary of the Founding of the Scouting Movement. R. A Fleur-de-lis superimposed over a globe and surrounded by the inscription 'BE PREPARED', and the dates '1907' and '2007' and the denomination 'FIFTY PENCE'. (Reverse design: Kerry Jones.)

2007 ....Unc £2; BU* £3
— BU in presentation folder £7
— Proof *FDC* (in 2007 set, see PS90)* £5
— Proof in silver *FDC* (Issued: 10,895) £30
— Proof piedfort in silver *FDC* (Issued; 1,555)* £60
— Proof in gold *FDC* (Issued: 1,250) £750
2009
— Proof *FDC* (in 2009 set, see PS100)* £15
— Proof in silver *FDC* (in 2009 set, see PSS40)* £30
— Proof in gold *FDC* (in 2009 set, see PGCS09)* £750
— Proof piedfort in gold *FDC* (Issued: 40) (see PGCS10)* £1600

* Coins marked thus were originally issued in Royal Mint sets.

H18

H18 Fifty pence. ℞. A section of Our Royal Arms showing elements of the third and
fourth quarterings accompanied by the words 'FIFTY PENCE'. (Reverse design:
Matthew Dent.)

2008 ....Unc £2; BU* £3
— Proof *FDC* (in 2008 set, see PS96)* £5
— Proof in silver *FDC* (in 2008 set, see PSS28)* £30
— Proof piedfort in silver *FDC* (in 2008 set, see PSS29)* £60
— Proof in gold *FDC* (in 2008 set, see PGCS07)* £750
— Proof in platinum *FDC* (in 2008 set, see PPLS2)* £600
2009 (in 2009 set, see US39) BU* £20
— Proof *FDC* (in 2009 set, see PS97)* £20
— Proof in silver *FDC* (in 2009 set, see PSS37)* £30
— Proof in gold *FDC* (in 2009 set, see PGCS09)* £750
— Proof piedfort in gold *FDC* (Issued: 40) (see PGCS10)* £1600
2010 BU* £20
— Proof *FDC* (in 2010 set, see PS101)* £20
— Proof in silver *FDC* (in 2010 set, Edition: 3,500) (see PSS41)* £30
2011 BU* £20
— Proof *FDC* (in 2010 set, see PS104)* £20
— Proof in silver *FDC* (in 2011 set, Edition: 2,500) (see PSS44) * £30
2012 ....Unc £2; BU* £3
— Proof *FDC* (in 2012 set, see PS107)* £5
— Proof in silver *FDC* (Edition: 995, see PSS47)* £30
— Proof in silver with selected gold plating *FDC* (Edition: 2,012) (see PSS48) £35
— Proof in gold *FDC* (Edition: 150) (see PGCS11)* £750
2013 .... Unc £2; BU* £3
— Proof *FDC* (in 2013 set, see PS109) * £8
— Proof in silver *FDC* (Edition: 2,013) (see PSS50)* £30
— Proof in gold *FDC* (Issued: 59) (see PGCS13)* £800
2014 ....Unc £2; BU* £3
— Proof *FDC* (in 2014 set, see PS112)* £7
— Proof in silver *FDC* (Edition: 2,014) (see PSS57)* £30
2015 ....Unc £2; BU* £3
— Proof *FDC* (in 2015 set, see PS115) * £7
— Proof in silver *FDC* (Edition: 7,500) (see PSS62)* £30
— Proof in gold *FDC* (Edition: 500) (see PGCS18) * £750
— Proof in platinum *FDC* (Issued: 10) (see PPLS3) * £650

* Coins marked thus were originally issued in Royal Mint sets.

H19

H19   Fifty pence. 250th Anniversary of the Foundation of the Royal Botanical Gardens, Kew.
R. A design showing the pagoda, a building associated with the Royal Botanical Gardens
at Kew, encircled by a vine and accompanied by the dates '1759' and '2009', with the
word 'KEW' at the base of the pagoda. (Reverse design: Christopher Le Brun.)
2009 .... VF £50; BU £90
   —   BU in presentation pack (Issued: 128,364) £100
   —   Proof *FDC* (in 2009 set, see PS97)* £100
   —   Proof in silver *FDC* (Issued: 7,575) £100
   —   Proof piedfort in silver *FDC* (Issued: 2,967)) £150
   —   Proof in gold *FDC* (Issued: 629)..£2500
   —   Proof piedfort in gold *FDC* (Issued: 40) (see PGCS10)* £4000

H20   Fifty new pence. R. Britannia (see H1). Reduced size 27.3 mm.
2009
   —   Proof *FDC* (in 2009 set, see PS100)* £15
   —   Proof in silver *FDC* (in 2009 set, see PSS40)* £30
   —   Proof in gold *FDC* (in 2009 set, see PGCS09)* £750
   —   Proof piedfort in gold *FDC* (Issued: 40) (in 2009 set, see PGCS10)* £1600

H21   Fifty new pence. Accession to European Economic Community R. Clasped hands
(see H2). Reduced size 27.3 mm.
2009
   —   Proof *FDC* (in 2009 set, see PS100)* £15
   —   Proof in silver *FDC* (in 2009 set, see PSS40)* £30
   —   Proof in gold *FDC* (in 2009 set, see PGCS09)* £750
   —   Proof piedfort in gold *FDC* (Issued: 40) (in 2009 set, see PGCS10)* £1600

H22   Fifty pence. Presidency of the Council of European Community Ministers and
Completion of the Single Market. R. Conference table top and twelve stars (see H5).
Reduced size 27.3 mm.
2009
   —   Proof *FDC* (in 2009 set, see PS100)* £15
   —   Proof in silver *FDC* (in 2009 set, see PSS40)* £30
   —   Proof in gold *FDC* (in 2009 set, see PGCS09)* £750
   —   Proof piedfort in gold *FDC* (Issued: 40) (in 2009 set, see PGCS10)* £1600

H23   Fifty pence. 50th Anniversary of the Normandy Landings on D-Day. R. Allied Invasion
Force (see H6). Reduced size 27.3 mm.
2009
   —   Proof *FDC* (in 2009 set, see PS100)* £15
   —   Proof in silver *FDC* (in 2009 set, see PSS40)* £30
   —   Proof in gold *FDC* (in 2009 set, see PGCS09)* £750
   —   Proof piedfort in gold *FDC* (Issued: 40) (in 2009 set, see PGCS10)* £1600

2009 40th Anniversary of the Introduction of the 50p Coin
PS100 - 2009 50p Set with reverse designs 1973-2009 c/n proofs (16) (Issued: 1,039)........£240
PSS40 - 2009 50p Set with reverse designs 1973-2009 silver proofs (16) (Issued: 1,168) ...£425
PGCS09 - 2009 50p Set with reverse designs 1973-2009 gold proofs (16) (Issued: 70) ..£12000
PGCS10 - 2009 50p Set with reverse designs 1973-2009 gold proofs piedfort (16)
            (Issued: 40)..£26000

* Coins marked thus were originally issued in Royal Mint sets.

H24   H25

H24 **Fifty pence.** 100th Anniversary of Girl Guides. R. A design which depicts a repeating
pattern of the current identity of Girl Guiding, UK, accompanied by the inscription
'CELEBRATING ONE HUNDRED YEARS OF GIRLGUIDING UK' and the
denomination 'FIFTY PENCE'. (Reverse design: Jonathan Evans and Donna Hainan.)
2010...Unc £2; BU* £3
— BU on presentation card (Issued: 99,075))...£7
— BU in presentation folder (Edition: 50,000)..£8
— Proof *FDC* (in 2010 set, see PS101)* £7
— Proof in silver *FDC* (Issued: 5,271))..£30
— Proof piedfort in silver *FDC* (Issued: 2,879) £55
— Proof in gold *FDC* (Issued: 355)...£750

H25 **Fifty pence.** Fiftieth Anniversary of the World Wildlife Fund. R. A design which features
50 different icons symbolising projects and programmes that the World   Wildlife
Fund has supported over the course of the last 50 years, with the Panda logo of the
organisation in the centre and the date '2011' below. (Reverse design: Matthew Dent.)
2011 ....Unc £3; BU* £4
— BU in presentation folder (Issued: 67,299) £7
— Proof *FDC* (in 2011 set, see PS104)*...£7
— Proof in silver *FDC* (Issued: 24,870) £40
— Proof piedfort in silver *FDC* (Issued: 2,244)..£65
— Proof in gold *FDC* (Issued: 243) £1000

H26

H26 **Fifty pence.** R. A version of the Royal Arms with the inscription 'FIFTY PENCE'
above and the denomination '50' below. (Reverse design: Christopher Ironside.)
2013 ....Unc £3; BU* £8
— BU in presentation folder £12
— Proof *FDC* (in 2013 set, see PS109)*...£5
— Proof silver *FDC* (Issued: 1,823) £55
— Proof piedfort in silver *FDC* (Issued: 816)...£100
— Proof in gold *FDC* (Issued: 198) £800

* *Coins marked thus were originally issued in Royal Mint sets.*

H27

H27 Fifty pence. Centenary of the Birth of Benjamin Britten. R. In the centre the name 'BENJAMIN BRITTEN' superimposed over musical staves with the inscription 'BLOW BUGLE BLOW' above and 'SET THE WILD ECHOES FLYING' below. (Reverse design: Tom Phillips.)

2013 ....Unc £3; BU* £8
— BU in presentation folder £12
— Proof silver *FDC* (Issued: 717) £45
— Proof piedfort in silver *FDC* (Issued: 515)...£90
— Proof in gold *FDC* (Issued: 70) £1250

H28 H29

H28 Fifty pence. Commonwealth Games R. A design of a cyclist and a sprinter with the Scottish Saltire bisecting the coin and the inscription 'XX COMMONWEALTH GAMES GLASGOW' and the date'2014'. (Reverse design: Alex Loudon with Dan Flashman.)

2014 ....Unc £3; BU* £4
— BU in presentation folder £10
— Proof *FDC* (in 2014 set, see PS112)*..£5
— Proof silver *FDC* (Issued: 2,610 including coins in sets)...........................£45
— Proof piedfort in silver *FDC* (Issued: 992 including coins in sets) £90
— Proof in gold *FDC* (Issued: 233) £800

H29 Fifty pence. 75th Anniversary of the Battle of Britain. R. A design showing airmen running to their planes with enemy aircraft overhead with the inscription 'THE BATTLE OF BRITAIN 1940'. (Reverse design: Gary Breeze.) N.B. With no denomination.

2015 BU*..£5
— BU in presentation folder £25
— Proof *FDC* (in 2015 set, see PS116)*..£25
— Proof in silver *FDC* (Edition: 3,000) (see PSS64 and PSS65) £50
— Proof piedfort in silver *FDC* (Edition: 1,500) (see PSS66).....................£100
— Proof in gold *FDC* (Edition: 100) (see PGCS20).....................................£1000

* Coins marked thus were originally issued in Royal Mint sets.

Obverse portrait by Jody Clark

H30

H30   Fifty pence.

2015 ....Unc £2; BU* £3
—   Proof *FDC* (in 2015 set, see PS116)*...£15
—   Proof in silver *FDC* (Edition: 7,500) (see PSS63)* £30
—   Proof in gold *FDC* (Edition: 500) (see PGCS19)*...£750
—   Proof in platinum *FDC* (Issued: 10) (see PPLS3)* £650
2016 BU*..£10
—   Proof *FDC* (in 2016 set, see PS119)*...£15
—   Proof in silver *FDC* (Edition: 1,500) (see PSS68)* £30
2017 ....Unc £3; BU* £3
—   Proof *FDC* (in 2017 set, see PS122)...£10
—   Proof in silver *FDC* (Edition: 1,500) (see PSS72) £30
—   Proof in gold *FDC* (Issued: 24) (see PCGS25)* £750
2018 BU*..£10
—   Proof *FDC* (in 2018 set, see PS125)...£15
—   Proof in silver *FDC* (Edition: 1,000) (see PSS75) £30
2019 ....Unc £2; BU* £8
—   Proof *FDC* (in 2019 set, see PS128)...£15
—   Proof in silver *FDC* (Edition: 1,000) (see PSS84) £35
2020 BU*.. £8
—   Proof *FDC* (in 2020 set, see PS132)...£15
—   Proof in silver *FDC* (Edition: 500) (see PSS90) £35

H31

H31   Fifty pence. 75th Anniversary of the Battle of Britain. R.A design showing airmen
running to their planes with enemy aircraft overhead with the inscription 'THE
BATTLE OF BRITAIN 1940'. (Reverse design: Gary Breeze.) N.B. With denomination
only for circulation coins.

2015 ....£2
—   Proof in silver *FDC* (Edition: 4,200)...£50
—   Proof piedfort in silver *FDC* (Edition: 1,940) £100
—   Proof in gold *FDC* (Edition: 520)...£900

* Coins marked thus were originally issued in Royal Mint sets.

H32

H32   Fifty pence. Nine hundred and fiftieth anniversary of the Battle of Hastings. R. A
design showing the scene from the Bayeux tapestry depicting King Harold with an
arrow in his eye accompanied by the inscription 'BATTLE OF HASTINGS 1066'and
the date of the year. (Reverse design John Bergdahl.)

2016 ....Unc £3; BU* £4
— BU in presentation folder (Issued: 34,734) £10
— Proof *FDC* (in 2016 set, see PS119)* £15
— Proof in silver *FDC* (Issued: 3,379 including coin sets) £50
— Proof piedfort in silver *FDC* (Issued: 1,925 including coin sets).........................£100
— Proof in gold *FDC* (Issued: 319 including coin sets) £800

H33

H33   Fifty pence. One hundred and fiftieth anniversary of the birth of Beatrix Potter.
R. A silhouette of Beatrix Potter accompanied by an image of Peter Rabbit surrounded
by a floral motif with the inscription 'BEATRIX POTTER 1866 1943'. (Reverse design:
Emma Noble.)

2016 Unc (Issued 6,900,000)...£3
— BU (Issued: 48,650)...£4
— BU in presentation folder (Issued: 61,658) £12
— Proof in silver *FDC* (Issued: 7,471) £200
— Proof piedfort in silver *FDC* (Issued : 2,486)...£300
— Proof in gold *FDC* (Issued: 732) £1250

* Coins marked thus were originally issued in Royal Mint sets.

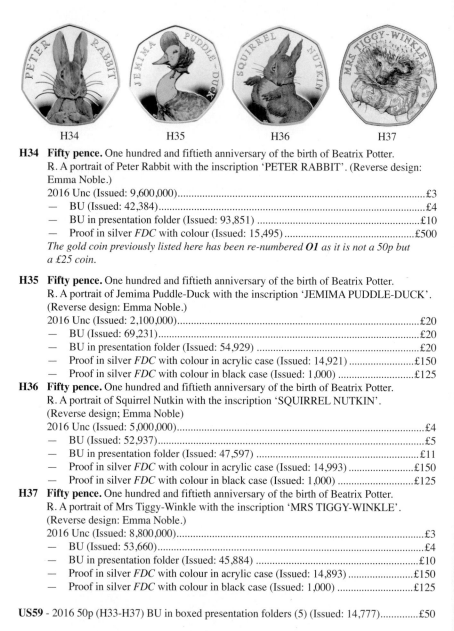

| H34 | H35 | H36 | H37 |

H34   **Fifty pence.** One hundred and fiftieth anniversary of the birth of Beatrix Potter.
R. A portrait of Peter Rabbit with the inscription 'PETER RABBIT'. (Reverse design: Emma Noble.)

2016 Unc (Issued: 9,600,000)..£3
—   BU (Issued: 42,384)..£4
—   BU in presentation folder (Issued: 93,851) £10
—   Proof in silver *FDC* with colour (Issued: 15,495)..£500

*The gold coin previously listed here has been re-numbered **O1** as it is not a 50p but a £25 coin.*

H35   **Fifty pence.** One hundred and fiftieth anniversary of the birth of Beatrix Potter.
R. A portrait of Jemima Puddle-Duck with the inscription 'JEMIMA PUDDLE-DUCK'. (Reverse design: Emma Noble.)

2016 Unc (Issued: 2,100,000)..£20
—   BU (Issued: 69,231)..£20
—   BU in presentation folder (Issued: 54,929) £20
—   Proof in silver *FDC* with colour in acrylic case (Issued: 14,921).....................£150
—   Proof in silver *FDC* with colour in black case (Issued: 1,000) £125

H36   **Fifty pence.** One hundred and fiftieth anniversary of the birth of Beatrix Potter.
R. A portrait of Squirrel Nutkin with the inscription 'SQUIRREL NUTKIN'. (Reverse design; Emma Noble)

2016 Unc (Issued: 5,000,000)..£4
—   BU (Issued: 52,937)..£5
—   BU in presentation folder (Issued: 47,597) £11
—   Proof in silver *FDC* with colour in acrylic case (Issued: 14,993).....................£150
—   Proof in silver *FDC* with colour in black case (Issued: 1,000) £125

H37   **Fifty pence.** One hundred and fiftieth anniversary of the birth of Beatrix Potter.
R. A portrait of Mrs Tiggy-Winkle with the inscription 'MRS TIGGY-WINKLE'. (Reverse design: Emma Noble.)

2016 Unc (Issued: 8,800,000)..£3
—   BU (Issued: 53,660)..£4
—   BU in presentation folder (Issued: 45,884) £10
—   Proof in silver *FDC* with colour in acrylic case (Issued: 14,893).....................£150
—   Proof in silver *FDC* with colour in black case (Issued: 1,000) £125

US59 - 2016 50p (H33-H37) BU in boxed presentation folders (5) (Issued: 14,777)..............£50

Colour Coins - *Some 50p silver proof coins are issued with colour and this is noted in the catalogue text. Uncirculated pieces of some issues are available in the market with colour but these are private productions so are not listed in this catalogue.*

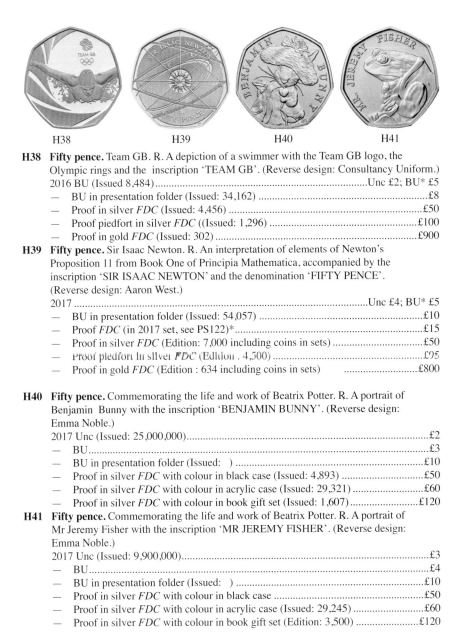

H38   H39   H40   H41

H38 **Fifty pence.** Team GB. R. A depiction of a swimmer with the Team GB logo, the
Olympic rings and the inscription 'TEAM GB'. (Reverse design: Consultancy Uniform.)
2016 BU (Issued 8,484)..Unc £2; BU* £5
— BU in presentation folder (Issued: 34,162) £8
— Proof in silver *FDC* (Issued: 4,456) £50
— Proof piedfort in silver *FDC* ((Issued: 1,296) £100
— Proof in gold *FDC* (Issued: 302) £900

H39 **Fifty pence.** Sir Isaac Newton. R. An interpretation of elements of Newton's
Proposition 11 from Book One of Principia Mathematica, accompanied by the
inscription 'SIR ISAAC NEWTON' and the denomination 'FIFTY PENCE'.
(Reverse design: Aaron West.)
2017 ....Unc £4; BU* £5
— BU in presentation folder (Issued: 54,057) £10
— Proof *FDC* (in 2017 set, see PS122)*...£15
— Proof in silver *FDC* (Edition: 7,000 including coins in sets) £50
— Proof piedfort in silver *FDC* (Edition : 4,500) £95
— Proof in gold *FDC* (Edition : 634 including coins in sets) £800

H40 **Fifty pence.** Commemorating the life and work of Beatrix Potter. R. A portrait of
Benjamin Bunny with the inscription 'BENJAMIN BUNNY'. (Reverse design:
Emma Noble.)
2017 Unc (Issued: 25,000,000)...£2
— BU...£3
— BU in presentation folder (Issued:) £10
— Proof in silver *FDC* with colour in black case (Issued: 4,893) £50
— Proof in silver *FDC* with colour in acrylic case (Issued: 29,321) £60
— Proof in silver *FDC* with colour in book gift set (Issued: 1,607)........................£120

H41 **Fifty pence.** Commemorating the life and work of Beatrix Potter. R. A portrait of
Mr Jeremy Fisher with the inscription 'MR JEREMY FISHER'. (Reverse design:
Emma Noble.)
2017 Unc (Issued: 9,900,000)...£3
— BU...£4
— BU in presentation folder (Issued:) £10
— Proof in silver *FDC* with colour in black case £50
— Proof in silver *FDC* with colour in acrylic case (Issued: 29,245) £60
— Proof in silver *FDC* with colour in book gift set (Edition: 3,500) £120

* Coins marked thus were originally issued in Royal Mint sets.

H42   H43   H44   H45

H42 **Fifty pence.** Commemorating the life and work of Beatrix Potter. R̟. A portrait of Tom Kitten with the inscription 'TOM KITTEN'. (Reverse design: Emma Noble.)

    2017 Unc (Issued: 9,500,000)..£3
- BU..£4
- BU in presentation folder (Issued:) £10
- Proof in silver *FDC* with colour in black case (Issued: 5070) £50
- Proof in silver *FDC* with colour in acrylic case (Issued: 27,643) £60
- Proof in silver *FDC* with colour in book gift set (Issued: 1,427) £120

H43 **Fifty pence.** Commemorating the life and work of Beatrix Potter. R̟. A portrait of Peter Rabbit running with the inscription 'THE TALE OF PETER RABBIT'. (Reverse design: Emma Noble.)

    2017 Unc (Issued: 19,900,000)..£2
- BU..£3
- BU in presentation folder (Issued:) £10
- Proof in silver *FDC* with colour in black case £60
- Proof in silver *FDC* with colour in acrylic case (Issued: 29,065) £75
- Proof in silver *FDC* with colour in book gift set (Issued: 2,623) £120
- Proof in gold *FDC* in book gift set (Edition: 450) £1400

H44 **Fifty pence.** Commemorating the life and work of Beatrix Potter. R̟. A depiction of Peter Rabbit with the inscription 'PETER RABBIT'. (Reverse design: Emma Noble.)

    2018 Unc (Issued: 1,400,000)..£3
- BU..£4
- BU in presentation folder £10
- Proof in silver *FDC* with colour in black case (Edition: 6,500)...........................£50
- Proof in silver *FDC* with colour in acrylic case (Edition: 35,000).......................£60
- Proof in silver *FDC* with colour in book gift set (Edition: 3,500) £120
- Proof in gold *FDC* (Edition: 450)..£1000
- Proof in gold *FDC* in book gift set £1200

H45 **Fifty pence.** Commemorating the life and work of Beatrix Potter. R̟. A depiction of Flopsy Bunny with the inscription 'FLOPSY BUNNY. (Reverse design: Emma Noble).

    2018 Unc (Issued: 1,400,000)..£3
- BU..£4
- BU in presentation folder £10
- Proof in silver *FDC* with colour in black case (Edition: 6,500)...........................£50
- Proof in silver *FDC* with colour in acrylic case (Edition: 35,000).......................£60
- Proof in silver *FDC* with colour in book gift set (Edition: 3,500) £120

H46   H47

H46   Fifty pence. Commemorating the life and work of Beatrix Potter. ℞. A depiction of
Mrs Tittlemouse with the inscription. 'MRS TITTLEMOUSE'. (Reverse design:
Emma Noble.)

2018 Unc (Issued: 1,700,000)...£3
— BU...£4
— BU in presentation folder £10
— Proof in silver *FDC* with colour in black case (Edition: 6,500)............................£50
— Proof in silver *FDC* with colour in acrylic case (Edition: 30,000)........................£60
— Proof in silver *FDC* with colour in book gift set (Edition: 3,500) £120

H47   Fifty pence. Commemorating the life and work of Beatrix Potter. ℞. A depiction of the
Tailor of Gloucester with the inscription 'THE TAILOR OF GLOUCESTER'.
(Reverse design: Emma Noble.)

2018 Unc (Issued: 3,900,000)...£3
— BU...£4
— BU in presentation folder £10
— Proof in silver *FDC* with colour in black case (Edition: 6,500)............................£50
— Proof in silver *FDC* with colour in acrylic case (Edition: 30,000)........................£60
— Proof in silver *FDC* with colour in book gift set (Edition: 3,500) £120

H48

H48   Fifty pence. 100th Anniversary of the Representation of the People Act. ℞.A depiction
of a line of people accompanied by the inscription '1918 REPRESENTATION OF THE
PEOPLE ACT'. (Reverse design: Stephen Taylor.)

2018 ....Unc £2; BU £3
— BU in presentation folder £10
— Proof *FDC* (in 2018 set, see PS125)* £15
— Proof in silver *FDC* (Edition: 6,500 including coins in sets)................................£50
— Proof piedfort in silver *FDC* (Edition: 2,918)..£100
— Proof in gold *FDC* (Edition: 500 including coins in sets)...................................£800

* Coins marked thus were originally issued in Royal Mint sets.

H49   H50   H51

H49 Fifty pence. Paddington Bear at the Station. ℞ A design depicting Paddington Bear
sitting on a suitcase inside Paddington Station. (Reverse design: David Knapton.)
2018...Unc £2; BU £3
— BU in presentation folder £10
— Proof in silver *FDC* with colour (Edition: 75,000) £60
— Proof in gold *FDC* (Edition: 1,250) £800

H50 Fifty pence. Paddington Bear at Buckingham Palace. ℞. A design depicting
Paddington Bear waving a Union Flag outside Buckingham Palace. (Reverse design:
David Knapton.)
2018...Unc £2; BU £3
— BU in presentation folder £10
— Proof in silver *FDC* with colour (Edition: 72,000) £60
— Proof in silver *FDC* with colour in book gift set (Edition: 3,000) £120
— Proof in gold *FDC* (Edition: 1,150) £800
— Proof in gold *FDC* with colour in book gift set (Edition: 100).......................£1000

*There are no prices given for some 50p coins in uncirculated condition from 2018 onwards as
none were issued for circulation so base metal pieces are only available in BU packs or year
sets. Loose coins can be found of some issues where the Royal Mint has supplied distributors
with BU coins in tubes at a premium.*

H51 Fifty pence. 40th Anniversary of the Snowman. (Reverse design: Natasha Radcliffe.)
2018
— BU in folder...£10
— Proof in silver *FDC* (Edition: 20,000) £70
— Proof in gold *FDC* (Edition: 400) £1000

H52

H52 Fifty pence. 160th Anniversary of the Birth of Sir Arthur Conan Doyle.
(Reverse design: Stephen Raw.)
2019..Unc £2; BU £5
BU in folder...£10
— Proof *FDC*
— Proof in silver *FDC* (Edition: 7,500 including coins in sets).............................£60
— Proof piedfort in silver *FDC* (Edition 3,500 including coins in sets) £100
— Proof in gold *FDC* (Edition: 600 including coins in sets)..................................£850

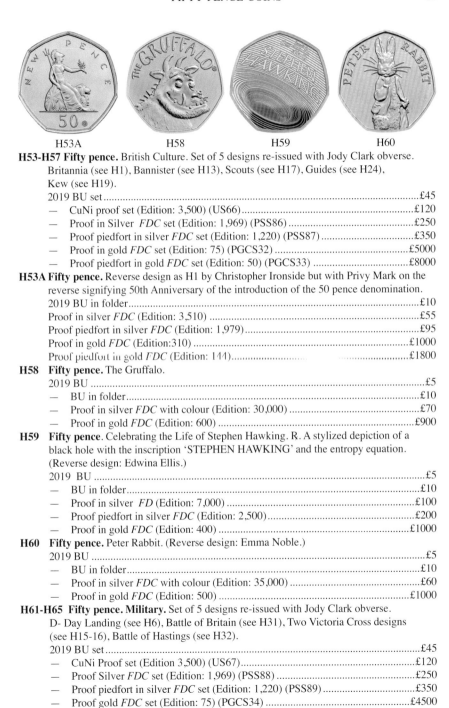

| H53A | H58 | H59 | H60 |

H53-H57 Fifty pence. British Culture. Set of 5 designs re-issued with Jody Clark obverse.
Britannia (see H1), Bannister (see H13), Scouts (see H17), Guides (see H24),
Kew (see H19).
- 2019 BU set £45
- — CuNi proof set (Edition: 3,500) (US66) £120
- — Proof in Silver *FDC* set (Edition: 1,969) (PSS86) £250
- — Proof piedfort in silver *FDC* set (Edition: 1,220) (PSS87) £350
- — Proof in gold *FDC* set (Edition: 75) (PGCS32) £5000
- — Proof piedfort in gold *FDC* set (Edition: 50) (PGCS33) £8000

H53A Fifty pence. Reverse design as H1 by Christopher Ironside but with Privy Mark on the
reverse signifying 50th Anniversary of the introduction of the 50 pence denomination.
- 2019 BU in folder £10
- Proof in silver *FDC* (Edition: 3,510) £55
- Proof piedfort in silver *FDC* (Edition: 1,979) £95
- Proof in gold *FDC* (Edition:310) £1000
- Proof piedfort in gold *FDC* (Edition: 144) £1800

H58 Fifty pence. The Gruffalo.
- 2019 BU £5
- — BU in folder £10
- — Proof in silver *FDC* with colour (Edition: 30,000) £70
- — Proof in gold *FDC* (Edition: 600) £900

H59 Fifty pence. Celebrating the Life of Stephen Hawking. R. A stylized depiction of a
black hole with the inscription 'STEPHEN HAWKING' and the entropy equation.
(Reverse design: Edwina Ellis.)
- 2019 BU £5
- — BU in folder £10
- — Proof in silver *FD* (Edition: 7,000) £100
- — Proof piedfort in silver *FDC* (Edition: 2,500) £200
- — Proof in gold *FDC* (Edition: 400) £1000

H60 Fifty pence. Peter Rabbit. (Reverse design: Emma Noble.)
- 2019 BU £5
- — BU in folder £10
- — Proof in silver *FDC* with colour (Edition: 35,000) £60
- — Proof in gold *FDC* (Edition: 500) £1000

H61-H65 Fifty pence. Military. Set of 5 designs re-issued with Jody Clark obverse.
D- Day Landing (see H6), Battle of Britain (see H31), Two Victoria Cross designs
(see H15-16), Battle of Hastings (see H32).
- 2019 BU set £45
- — CuNi Proof set (Edition 3,500) (US67) £120
- — Proof Silver *FDC* set (Edition: 1,969) (PSS88) £250
- — Proof piedfort in silver *FDC* set (Edition: 1,220) (PSS89) £350
- — Proof gold *FDC* set (Edition: 75) (PGCS34) £4500
- — Proof piedfort in gold *FDC* set (Edition: 50) (PGCS35) £7500

H66   H67

H66 **Fifty pence.** Paddington Bear. Tower of London. (Reverse design: Dave Knapton.)
2019 ....Unc £3; BU £5
— BU in folder...£10
— Proof in silver *FDC* with colour (Edition: 32,500) £65
— Proof in gold *FDC* (Edition: 650) £900

H67 **Fifty pence.** Paddington Bear. St Pauls. (Reverse design: Dave Knapton.)
2019 ....Unc £3; BU £5
— BU in folder...£10
— Proof in silver *FDC* with colour (Edition: 35,000) £65
— Proof in gold *FDC* (Edition: 650) £900

H68   H69

H68 **Fifty pence.** R.The Gruffalo confronting a mouse in a wood with the inscription
'THE GRUFFALO'. (Reverse design: Magic Light Pictures.)
2019 BU £5
— BU in folder - £10
— Proof in silver *FDC* with colour (Edition: 30,000) £65
— Proof in gold *FDC* (Edition: 600) £900

H69 **Fifty pence.** R. The figures of Wallace and Gromit with the inscription 'CASEUS
PRAESTANS' and 'WALLACE GROMIT'. (Reverse design: Nick Park.)
2019 BU in folder..10
— Proof in silver *FDC* with colour (Edition: 27,500) £65
— Proof in gold *FDC* (Edition: 640) £900

H70   H71   H72

H70 **Fifty pence.** Snowman II. R. The snowman with James. (Reverse design:
Snowman Enterprises.)
2019
— BU in folder £10
— Proof in silver *FDC* in acrylic case with colour (Edition: 27,500).........................£65
— Proof in gold *FDC* (Edition: 600)...£1075

H71 **Fifty pence.** Team GB 2020. R. Symbols of medal winning sports, the Team GB logo
and date '2020'. (Reverse design: David Knapton.)
2020 BU*...£10
— Proof (Edition: 5,000)*x £25
— Proof in silver *FDC* (Edition: 500)* £100
— Proof piedfort in silver *FDC* (Edition: 300)* £200
— Proof in gold *FDC* (Edition: 75)*..£1500

*This coin has been issued to celebrate the country's participation in the Tokyo Olympic Games
which have now been postponed until 2021. Single coins will not be issued until that year and
are expected to be dated 2021.*

H72 **Fifty pence.** Brexit, the UK's withdrawal from the European Union. R.'Peace,
prosperity and friendship with all nations' and the date '31 January 2020'. (Reverse
design: The Royal Mint.)
2020 .... Unc £2
— BU in folder £10
— Proof in silver *FDC* (Edition:47,000)..£65
— Proof in gold *FDC* (Edition: 1,500)...£1250
— Proof piedfort in gold *FDC* (Edition: 1,000) £2200

* Coins marked thus were originally issued in Royal Mint sets.

H73   H74   H75

H73 **Fifty pence.** Dinosaurs I. ℞. Megalosaurus. (Reverse design: Robert Nicholls.)
2020 BU in folder £10
—   BU with colour in folder (Edition: 50,000) £20
—   Proof in silver *FDC* (Edition: 3,000)..£60
—   Proof in silver *FDC* with colour (Edition: 7,000) £65
—   Proof in gold *FDC* (Edition: 350)...£1000

H74 **Fifty pence.** Dinosaurs II. ℞. Iguanodon. (Reverse design: Robert Nicholls.)
2020 BU in folder £10
—   BU with colour in folder (Edition: 50,000) £20
—   Proof in silver *FDC* (Edition: 3,000)..£60
—   Proof in silver *FDC* with colour (Edition: 7,000) £65
—   Proof in gold *FDC* (Edition: 350)...£1000

H75 **Fifty pence.** Dinosaurs III. ℞. Hylaeosaurus. (Reverse design: Robert Nicholls.)
2020 BU in folder £10
—   BU with colour in folder (Edition: 50,000) £20
—   Proof in silver *FDC* (Edition: 3,000)..£60
—   Proof in silver *FDC* with colour (Edition: 7,000) £65
—   Proof in gold *FDC* (Edition: 350)...£1000

H76   H77

H76 **Fifty pence.** Peter Rabbit. ℞. Peter Rabbit in his trademark blue jacket sneaking under
the gate in search of lettuces. (Reverse design: Emma Noble.)
2020 BU in folder £10
—   Proof in silver *FDC* with colour in acrylic case (Edition: 15,000)........................£65
—   Proof in gold *FDC* (Edition: 500)...£1000

H77 **Fifty pence.** Centenary of Birth of Rosalind Franklin. ℞. Depictions of printing
techniques from the 1950s with a graphic representation of photograph 51 – one of the
most important images in biological science demonstrating the double helix structure of
DNA. (Reverse design: David Knapton.)
2020 BU in folder £10
—   Proof in silver *FDC* (Edition: 3,500)..£55
—   Proof piedfort in silver *FDC* (Edition: 1,500) £95
—   Proof in gold *FDC* (Edition: 250)...£1075

H78 H79 H80

H78 Fifty pence. Characters from A. A. Milne's 'Winnie-the-Pooh' books I.
R. Winnie-the-Pooh. (Reverse design: The Walt Disney Company.)
2020 BU in folder £10
— BU in folder with colour (Edition: 45,000) £20
— Proof in silver *FDC* with colour (Edition: 18,010) £68
— Proof in gold *FDC* (Edition: 535)...£1125

H79 Fifty pence. Characters from A. A. Milne's 'Winnie-the-Pooh' books II.
R. Christopher Robin. (Reverse design: The Walt Disney Company.)
2020 BU in folder £10
— BU in folder with colour £20
— Proof in silver *FDC* £68
— Proof in gold *FDC* £1125

H80 Fifty pence. Characters from A. A. Milne's 'Winnie-the-Pooh' books III.
R. Piglet. (Reverse design: The Walt Disney Company.)
2020 BU in folder £10
— BU in folder with colour.. £20
— Proof in silver *FDC* £68
— Proof in gold *FDC* £1125

H81 Fifty pence. The Snowman III.
2020 BU in folder £10
--- Proof in silver *FDC* with colour £55
--- Proof in gold *FDC* £1075

H82 Fifty pence. 50th Anniversary of Decimal Day, 1971.
2021 BU*.. £8
--- BU in folder £10
--- Proof* £20
--- Proof in silver *FDC* £55
--- Proof piedfort in silver *FDC* £100
--- Proof in gold *FDC* £1075
--- Proof piedfort in gold *FDC* £2000

H83 Fifty pence. Dinosaurs IV. R. Ichthyosaur.
2021 BU in folder £10
--- Proof in silver *FDC* £60
--- Proof in silver *FDC* with colour £65
--- Proof in gold *FDC* £1075

H84 Fifty pence. Dinosaurs V. R. Plesiosaurus.
2021 BU in folder £10
--- Proof in silver *FDC* £60
--- Proof in silver *FDC* with colour £65
--- Proof in gold *FDC* £1075

* Coins marked thus were originally issued in Royal Mint sets.

NICKEL-BRASS

ONE POUND COINS
Obverse portrait by Arnold Machin

J1   J2

J1   **One pound.** ℞. The Ensigns Armorial of Our United Kingdom of Great Britain and
Northern Ireland with the value 'ONE POUND' below. Edge inscription 'DECUS ET
TUTAMEN'. (Reverse design: Eric Sewell.)
1983 ....£3
—   Unc in presentation folder (Issued: 484,900) £5
—   Proof *FDC* (in 1983 set, see PS33)* £5
—   Proof in silver *FDC* (Issued: 50,000) £35
—   Proof piedfort in silver *FDC* (Issued: 10,000) £125

J2   **One pound.** (Scottish design.) ℞. A thistle eradicated enfiling a representation
of Our Royal Diadem with the value 'ONE POUND' below. Edge inscription 'NEMO
ME IMPUNE LACESSIT'. (Reverse design: Leslie Durbin.)
1984 ....Unc £3; BU* £4
—   BU in presentation folder (Issued: 27,960) £5
—   Proof *FDC* (in 1984 set, see PS34)* £5
—   Proof in silver *FDC* (Issued: 44,855) £30
—   Proof piedfort in silver *FDC* (Issued: 15,000) £60

Obverse portrait by Raphael Maklouf

J3

J3   **One pound.** (Welsh design.) ℞. A leek eradicated enfiling a representation of Our Royal
Diadem with the value 'ONE POUND' below. Edge inscription 'PLEIDIOL WYF I'M
GWLAD'. (Reverse design: Leslie Durbin.)
1985 ....Unc £2; BU* £3
—   BU in presentation folder (Issued: 24,850) £4
—   Proof *FDC* (in 1985 set, see PS35)* £5
—   Proof in silver *FDC* (Issued: 50,000) £30
—   Proof piedfort in silver *FDC* (Issued: 15,000) £60
1990 ....Unc £2; BU* £3
—   Proof *FDC* (in 1990 set, see PS45)* £6
—   Proof in silver *FDC* (Issued: 23,277) £28

* Coins marked thus were originally issued in Royal Mint sets.

J4   J5   J6

J4   **One pound.** (Northern Irish design.) R. A flax plant eradicated enfiling a representation
of Our Royal Diadem with value 'ONE POUND' below. Edge inscription 'DECUS ET
TUTAMEN'. (Reverse design: Leslie Durbin.)
1986 ....Unc £2; BU* £3
— BU in presentation folder (Issued: 19,908) £5
— Proof *FDC* (in 1986 set, see PS37)* £4
— Proof in silver *FDC* (Issued: 37, 958) £30
— Proof piedfort in silver *FDC* (Issued: 15,000) £60
1991 ....Unc £2; BU* £5
— Proof *FDC* (in 1991 set, see PS47)* £6
— Proof in silver *FDC* (Issued: 22,922) £28

J5   **One pound.** (English design.) R. An oak tree enfiling a representation of Our
Royal Diadem with the value 'ONE POUND' below. Edge inscription 'DECUS ET
TUTAMEN'. (Reverse design: Leslie Durbin.)
1987 ....Unc £2; BU* £3
— BU in presentation folder (Issued: 72,607) £4
— Proof *FDC* (in 1987 set, see PS39)* £6
— Proof in silver *FDC* (Issued: 50,000) £30
— Proof piedfort in silver *FDC* (Issued: 15,000) £60
1992 ....Unc £2; BU* £3
— Proof *FDC* (in 1992 set, see PS49)* £6
— Proof in silver *FDC* (Issued: 13,065) £30

J6   **One pound.** (Royal Shield.) R. A Crowned Shield of Our Royal Arms ensigned by a
representation of Our Royal Crown with the value 'ONE POUND' below. Edge
inscription 'DECUS ET TUTAMEN'. (Reverse design: Derek Gorringe.)
1988 ....Unc £4; BU* £5
— BU in presentation folder (Issued: 29,550) £6
— Proof *FDC* (in 1988 set, see PS41)* £6
— Proof in silver *FDC* (Issued: 50,000) £35
— Proof piedfort in silver *FDC* (Issued: 10,000) £60

J7   **One pound.** (Scottish design.) Edge inscription 'NEMO ME IMPUNE LACESSIT'.
(Illus. as J2.)
1989 ....Unc £2; BU* £3
— Proof *FDC* (in 1989 set, see PS43)* £6
— Proof in silver *FDC* (Issued: 22,275) £30
— Proof piedfort in silver *FDC* (Issued: 10,000) £60

J8   **One pound.** (Royal Arms design.) Edge inscription 'DECUS ET TUTAMEN'.
(Illus. as J1.)
1993 ....Unc £2; BU* £3
— Proof *FDC* (in 1993 set, see PS51)* £6
— Proof in silver *FDC* (Issued: 16,526) £30
— Proof piedfort in silver *FDC* (Issued: 12,500) £60

* Coins marked thus were originally issued in Royal Mint sets.

J9 J10 J11 J12

J9 **One pound.** (Scottish design.) ℝ. A Lion rampant within a double tressure flory counter-flory, being that quartering of Our Royal Arms known heraldically as Scotland with the value 'ONE POUND' below. Edge inscription 'NEMO ME IMPUNE LACESSIT'. (Reverse design: Norman Sillman.)

1994 ....Unc £2; BU* £3
— BU in presentation folder £5
— Proof *FDC* (in 1994 set, see PS53)* £6
— Proof in silver *FDC* (Issued: 25,000) £30
— Proof piedfort in silver *FDC* (Issued: 11,722) £60

J10 **One pound.** (Welsh design.) ℝ. A dragon passant, being Our badge for Wales with the value 'ONE POUND' below. Edge inscription 'PLEIDIOL WYF I'M GWLAD'. (Reverse design: Norman Sillman.)

1995 ....Unc £2; BU* £3
— BU in presentation folder, English version £5
— BU in presentation folder, Welsh version...£10
— Proof *FDC* (in 1995 set, see PS55)* £5
— Proof in silver *FDC* (Issued: 27,445) £30
— Proof piedfort in silver *FDC* (Issued: 8,458) £70

J11 **One pound.** (Northern Irish design.) ℝ. A Celtic cross charged at the centre with an Annulet therein a Pimpernel flower and overall an ancient Torque, symbolizing that part of Our Kingdom known as Northern Ireland with the value 'ONE POUND' below. Edge inscription 'DECUS ET TUTAMEN'. (Reverse design: Norman Sillman.)

1996 ....Unc £2; BU* £3
— BU in presentation folder £6
— Proof *FDC* (in 1996 set, see PS57)* £6
— Proof in silver *FDC* (Issued: 25,000) £30
— Proof piedfort in silver *FDC* (Issued: 10,000....................................... £60

J12 **One pound.** (English design.) ℝ. Three lions passant guardant, being that quartering of Our Royal Arms known heraldically as England, with the value 'ONE POUND' below. Edge inscription 'DECUS ET TUTAMEN. (Reverse design: Norman Sillman.)

1997 ....Unc £2; BU* £3
— BU in presentation folder (Issued 56,996) £5
— Proof *FDC* (in 1997 set, see PS59)* £5
— Proof in silver *FDC* (Issued: 20,137) £30
— Proof piedfort in silver *FDC* (Issued: 10,000) £60

* Coins marked thus were originally issued in Royal Mint sets.

Obverse portrait by Ian Rank-Broadley

J13

J13   **One pound.** (Royal Arms design.) Edge inscription 'DECUS ET TUTAMEN'. (Rev. as J1.)
1998 BU* £12
— Proof *FDC* (in 1998 set, see PS61)* £15
— Proof in silver *FDC* (Issued: 13,863) £35
— Proof piedfort in silver *FDC* (Issued: 7,894) £60
2003 ....Unc £2; BU* £3
— BU in presentation folder (Issued: 23,760) £5
— Proof *FDC* (in 2003 set, see PS78)* £6
— Proof in silver *FDC* (Issued: 15,830) £30
— Proof piedfort in silver *FDC* (Issued: 9,871) £60
2008 ....Unc £2; BU* £3
— BU in presentation folder (Issued: 18,336) £7
— Proof *FDC* (in 2008 set, see PS93)* £6
— Proof in silver *FDC* (Issued: 8,441) £30
— Proof in gold *FDC* (Issued: 674) £900
— Proof in platinum *FDC* (in 2008 set, see PPLS1)* £800
2013. 30th Anniversary of the introduction of the £1 coin
— Proof silver *FDC* (Issued: 1,311 in 3 coin sets, see after J27)* £60
— Proof in gold *FDC* (Issued: 17 in 3 coin sets, see after J27)* £1250
J13A   2008
— Proof in silver with selected gold plating on reverse *FDC*
(in 2008 set, see PSS30)* £40
J14   **One pound.** (Scottish lion design). Edge inscription 'NEMO ME IMPUNE LACESSIT'.
(Rev. as J9.)
1999 BU* £12
— BU in presentation folder £15
— Proof *FDC* (in 1999 set, see PS63)* £25
— Proof in silver *FDC* (Issued: 16,328) £35
— Proof piedfort in silver *FDC* (Issued: 9,975) £60
2008
— Proof in gold *FDC* (in 2008 set, see PGCS08)* £900
J14A   1999
— Proof in silver *FDC*, with reverse frosting, (Issued: 1,994)* £50
J14B   2008
—   Proof in silver with selected gold plating on reverse *FDC* (in 2008 set, see PSS30)*
£40
J15   **One pound.** (Welsh design.) Edge inscription 'PLEIDIOL WYF I'M GWLAD'. (Rev. as J10.)
2000 ....Unc £2; BU* £3
— Proof *FDC* (in 2000 set, see PS65)* £6
— Proof in silver *FDC* (Issued: 15,913) £30
— Proof piedfort in silver *FDC* (Issued: 9,994) £60
2008
— Proof in gold *FDC* (in 2008 set, see PGCS08)* £900

* *Coins marked thus were originally issued in Royal Mint sets.*

J15A 2000
— Proof in silver *FDC*, with reverse frosting, (Issued: 1,994)* £50

PSS07A - 1999-2000 £1 (J14A and J15A) silver proofs with reverse frosting (2)
(Issued: 1,994)...£75

J15B 2008
— Proof in silver with selected gold plating on reverse *FDC*
(in 2008 set, see PSS30)* £40

J16   **One pound.** (Northern Irish design.) Edge inscription 'DECUS ET TUTAMEN'.
(Rev. as J11.)
2001 ....Unc £2; BU* £3
— Proof *FDC* (in 2001 set, see PS68)* £6
— Proof in silver *FDC* (Issued: 11,697) £30
— Proof piedfort in silver *FDC* (Issued: 8,464) £60
2008
— Proof in gold *FDC* (in 2008 set, see PGCS08)* £900

J16A 2001
— Proof in silver *FDC*, with reverse frosting, (Issued: 1,540)* £60

J16B 2008
— Proof in silver with selected gold plating on reverse *FDC*
(in 2008 set, see PSS30)* £40

J17   **One pound.** (English design.) Edge inscription 'DECUS ET TUTAMEN'.
(Rev. as J12.)
2002 ....Unc £2; BU* £3
— Proof *FDC* (in 2002 set, see PS72)* £6
— Proof in silver *FDC* (Issued: 17,693) £30
— Proof piedfort in silver *FDC* (Issued: 6,599) £60
— Proof in gold *FDC* (in 2002 set, see PGCS02)* £900
2008
— Proof in gold *FDC* (in 2008 set, see PGCS08)* £900

J17A 2002
— Proof in silver *FDC*, with reverse frosting, (Issued: 1,540)* £60

PSS10A - 1999-2002 £1 (J14A and J17A) silver proofs with reverse frosting (4)
(Issued: 1,540) £150
Purchasers of PSS07A were given the opportunity to purchase J16A and J17A
in a 4 coin case.

J17B 2008
— Proof in silver with selected gold plating on reverse *FDC*
(in 2008 set, see PSS30)* £40

* *Coins marked thus were originally issued in Royal Mint sets.*

| J18 | J18B | J19 | J19B |

J18 **One pound.** (Scotland.) R. A representation of the Forth Railway Bridge with a border
of railway tracks and beneath, the value 'ONE POUND' and an incuse decorative feature
on the edge symbolising bridges and pathways. (Reverse design: Edwina Ellis.)
2004 ....Unc £2; BU* £3
— BU in presentation folder (Issued: 24,014) £5
— Proof *FDC* (in 2004 set, see PS81)* £6
— Proof in silver *FDC* (Issued: 11,470) £30
— Proof piedfort in silver *FDC* (Issued: 7,013) £60
— Proof in gold *FDC* (Issued: 2,618)...£900
2008
— Proof in gold *FDC* (in 2008 set, see PGCS08)* £900

J18A One pound pattern. (Scotland.) R. Forth Railway Bridge but dated 2003 with plain
edge and hallmark, reading 'PATTERN' instead of 'ONE POUND'.
— Proof in silver *FDC* (in 2003 set, see PPS1)* £25
— Proof in gold *FDC* (in 2003 set, see PPS2)* £850

J18B One pound pattern. (Scotland.) R. Unicorn with the word 'PATTERN' below with
plain edge and hallmark and dated 2004. (Reverse design: Timothy Noad.)
— Proof in silver *FDC* (in 2004 set, see PPS3)* £25
— Proof in gold *FDC* (in 2004 set, see PPS4)* £850

J18C 2008
— Proof in silver with selected gold plating on reverse *FDC*
(in 2008 set, see PSS30)* £40

J19 **One pound.** (Wales.) R. A representation of the Menai Straits Bridge with a border of
railings and stanchions, the value 'ONE POUND' and an incuse decorative feature on
the edge symbolising bridges and pathways. (Reverse design: Edwina Ellis.)
2005 ....Unc £2; BU* £3
— BU in presentation folder (Issued: 24,802) £6
— Proof *FDC* (in 2005 set, see PS84)* £6
— Proof in silver *FDC* (Issued: 8,371) £35
— Proof piedfort in silver *FDC* (Issued: 6,007) £60
— Proof in gold *FDC* (Issued: 1,195)...£900
2008
— Proof in gold *FDC* (in 2008 set, see PGCS08)* £900

J19A One pound pattern. (Wales.) R. Menai Straits Bridge but dated 2003 with plain edge
and hallmark.
— Proof in silver *FDC* (in 2003 set, see PPS1)* £25
— Proof in gold *FDC* (in 2003 set, see PPS2)* £850

J19B One pound pattern. (Wales.) R. Dragon and the word 'PATTERN' below with plain
edge and hallmark and dated 2004. (Reverse design: Timothy Noad.)
— Proof in silver *FDC* (in 2004 set, see PPS3)* £25
— Proof in gold *FDC* (in 2004 set, see PPS4)* £900

J19C 2008
— Proof in silver as J19 with selected gold plating on reverse *FDC*
(in 2008 set, see PSS30)* £40

* Coins marked thus were originally issued in Royal Mint sets.

J20   J20B   J21

J21A   J21B

J20   **One pound.** (Northern Ireland.) R. A representation of the Egyptian Arch Railway
Bridge in County Down with a border of railway station canopy dags, the value
'ONE POUND' and an incuse decorative feature on the edge symbolising bridges
and pathways. (Reverse design: Edwina Ellis.)
2006 ....Unc £2; BU* £3
—   BU in presentation folder £6
—   Proof *FDC* (in 2006 set, see PS87)* £8
—   Proof in silver *FDC* (Edition: 20,000) £30
—   Proof piedfort in silver *FDC* (Edition: 7,500)...£60
—   Proof in gold *FDC* (Edition: 1,500) £900
2008
—   Proof in gold *FDC* (in 2008 set, see PGCS08)* £900

J20A **One pound pattern.** (Northern Ireland.) R. MacNeill's Egyptian Arch Railway Bridge
but dated 2003 with plain edge and hallmark.
—   Proof in silver *FDC* (in 2003 set, see PPS1)* £25
—   Proof in gold *FDC* (in 2003 set, see PPS2)*..£850

J20B **One pound pattern.** (Northern Ireland.) R. Stag and the word 'PATTERN' below with
plain edge and hallmark and dated 2004. (Reverse design: Timothy Noad.)
—   Proof in silver *FDC* (in 2004 set, see PPS3)* £25
—   Proof in gold *FDC* (in 2004 set, see PPS4)*..£850

J20C 2008
—   Proof in silver as J20 with selected gold plating on rev. *FDC* (in 2008 set,
see PSS30)*...£40

J21   **One pound.** (England.) R. A representation of the Gateshead Millennium Bridge with
a border of struts, the value 'ONE POUND' and an incuse decorative feature on the
edge symbolising bridges and pathways. (Reverse design: Edwina Ellis.)
2007 ....Unc £2; BU* £3
—   BU in presentation folder £7
—   Proof *FDC*￼ (in 2007 set, see PS90) £8
—   Proof in silver *FDC* (Issued: 10,110) £30
—   Proof piedfort in silver *FDC* (Issued: 5,739) £60
—   Proof in gold *FDC* (Issued: 1,112)..£900
2008
—   Proof in gold *FDC* (in 2008 set, see PGCS08)* £900

* *Coins marked thus were originally issued in Royal Mint sets.*

J21A One pound pattern. (England.) R. Millennium Bridge but dated 2003 with plain edge and hallmark.
— Proof in silver *FDC* (in 2003 set, see PSS1)* £25
— Proof in gold *FDC* (in 2003 set, see PPS2)* £900

J21B One pound pattern. (England.) R. Lion with the word 'PATTERN' below with plain edge and hallmark and dated 2004. (Reverse design: Timothy Noad.)
— Proof in silver *FDC* (in 2004 set, see PPS3)* £25
— Proof in gold *FDC* (in 2004 set, see PPS4)* £850

J21C 2008
— Proof in silver as J21 with selected gold plating on reverse *FDC* (in 2008 set, see PSS30)* £40

PSS25 - 2004/7 £1 (J18-J21) silver proofs (4) £115
PSS26 - 2004/7 £1 (J18-J21) silver proof piedforts (4) £200
PGCS05 - 2004/7 £1 (J18-J21) gold proofs (4) (Edition: 300 taken from individual coin limits) .. £3500

Pattern Proof sets
PPS1 - 2003 Silver proof set of £1 designs with plain edge and hallmark (Edition: 7,500) (4) £75
PPS2 - 2003 Gold proof set of £1 designs with plain edge and hallmark (Edition: 3,000) (4) £3500
PPS3 - 2004 Silver proof set of £1 designs with plain edge and hallmark (Edition: 5,000) (4) £75
PPS4 - 2004 Gold proof set of £1 designs with plain edge and hallmark (Edition: 2,250) (4) £3500

J22 One pound. (Scottish design.) Edge 'NEMO ME IMPUNE LACESSIT'. (Rev. as J2.) 2008
— Proof in gold *FDC* (in 2008 set, see PGCS08)* £900

J22A 2008
— Proof in silver with selected gold plating on reverse *FDC* (in 2008 set, see PSS30)* £40

J23 One pound. (Welsh design). Edge 'PLEIDOL WYF I'M GWLAD'. (Rev. see J3.) 2008
— Proof in gold *FDC* (in 2008 set, see PGCS08)* £900

J23A 2008
— Proof in silver with selected gold plating on reverse *FDC* (in 2008 set, see PSS30)* £40

J24 One pound. (Northern Irish design). Edge 'DECUS ET TUTAMEN'. (Rev. see J4.) 2008
— Proof in gold *FDC* (in 2008 set, see PGCS08)* £900

J24A 2008
— Proof in silver with selected gold plating on reverse *FDC* (in 2008 set, see PSS30)* £40

J25 One pound. (English design). Edge 'DECUS ET TUTAMEN'. (Rev. see J5.) 2008
— Proof in gold *FDC* (in 2008 set, see PGCS08)* £900

J25A 2008
— Proof in silver with selected gold plating on reverse *FDC* (in 2008 set, see PSS30)* £40

J26 One pound. (Royal Shield.) Edge 'DECUS ET TUTAMEN'. (Rev. as J6.) 2008
— Proof in gold *FDC* (in 2008 set, see PGCS08)* £900
2013. 30th Anniversary of the introduction of the £1 coin.
— Proof silver *FDC* (Issued: 1,311 in 3 coin sets, see after J27)* £60
— Proof in gold *FDC* (Issued: 17 in 3 coin sets, see after J27)* £1250

* Coins marked thus were originally issued in Royal Mint sets.

J26A 2008
—   Proof in silver with selected gold plating on reverse *FDC*
     (in 2008 set, see PSS30)* £40

2008 25th Anniversary of the introduction of the £1 coin.
PSS30 - 2008 £1 with reverse designs 1983-2007 and with selected gold plating
     silver proofs (14) (Issued: 2,005) £395
PSS31 - 2008 Set of 3 £1 Regional designs for Scotland with selected gold plating to
     the reverse designs (Edition: 750, taken from above) (3)....................£95
PSS32 - 2008 Set of 3 £1 Regional designs for Wales with selected gold plating to the
     reverse designs (Edition: 750, taken from above) (3)............................£95
PSS33 - 2008 Set of 3 £1 Regional designs for Northern Ireland with selected gold
     plating to the reverse designs (Edition: 750, taken from above) (3)..........£95
PSS34 - 2008 Set of 3 £1 Regional designs for England with selected gold plating to
     the reverse designs (Edition: 750, taken from above) (3)......................£95
PGCS08 - 2008 £1 with reverse designs 1983-2007 gold proofs (14) (Issued: 150)......£12,500

J27

J27   **One pound.** ℞. A shield of Our Royal Arms with the words 'ONE' to the left and
         'POUND' to the right. Edge inscription 'DECUS ET TUTAMEN'. (Reverse design:
         Matthew Dent.)
         2008...Unc £2; BU* £3
         —   Proof *FDC* (in 2008 set, see PS96)* £5
         —   Proof in silver *FDC* (Issued: 5,000) £30
         —   Proof piedfort in silver *FDC* (Issued: 2,456) £50
         —   Proof in gold *FDC* (Issued: 860)*..£900
         —   Proof in platinum *FDC* (in 2008 set, see PPLS2)* £800
         2009...Unc £2; BU* £3
         —   BU in presentation folder (Edition: 15,000)...£7
         —   Proof *FDC* (in 2009 set, see PS97)* £5
         —   BU in silver (Issued: 8,508) £30
         —   Proof in silver *FDC* (Edition: 20,000 including coins in sets)...........£35
         —   Proof in gold *FDC* (Issued: 540)..£900
         2010...Unc £2; BU* £3
         —   Proof *FDC* (in 2010 set, see PS101)* £5
         —   BU in silver (Issued: 1,551) £30
         —   Proof in silver *FDC* (Edition: 20,000 including coins in sets)...........£35
         2011 ....Unc £2; BU* £3
         —   Proof *FDC* (in 2011 set, see PS104) * £5
         —   BU in silver...£30
         —   Proof in silver *FDC* (Edition: 2,500) (in 2011 set, see PSS44)* £35
         2012...Unc £2; BU* £3
         —   Proof *FDC* (in 2012 set, see PS107)* £3
         —   BU in silver £25
         —   Proof in silver with selected gold plating *FDC* (Edition: 2,012) (see PSS48)*.....£40
         —   Proof in gold *FDC* (Edition: 150) (see PGCS11)*...............................£900

* *Coins marked thus were originally issued in Royal Mint sets.*

2013	Unc £2; BU* £3
— Proof *FDC* (in 2013 set, see PS109)*	£7
— BU in silver	£25
— Proof in silver *FDC* (Issued: 2296 including coins in sets)	£40
— Proof in gold *FDC* (Issued: 76 including coins in sets, see PGCS13)*	£1000
2014	Unc £2; BU* £3
— Proof *FDC* (in 2014 set, see PS112)*	£3
— BU in silver	£25
— Proof in silver *FDC* (Edition: 2,014) (see PSS56)*	£35
2015	Unc £2; BU* £3
— Proof *FDC* (in 2015 set, see PS115)*	£5
— Proof in silver *FDC* (Edition: 7,500) (see PSS61)*	£35
— Proof in gold *FDC* (Edition: 500) (see PGCS18)*	£900
— Proof in platinum *FDC* (Issued: 10) (see PPLS3)*	£1500

PSS56 - 2013 £1 (J13, J26, J27) silver proofs (3) (Issued: 1,311) £150
PGCS16 - 2013 £1 (J13, J26, J27) gold proofs (3) (Issued: 17) £3500
The above two sets commemorated the 30th Anniversary of the £1 coin.

J28   J29

J28 – One pound. (London.) R. A design which depicts the official badges of the capital
cities of the United Kingdom, with the badge of London being the principal focus,
accompanied by the name 'LONDON' and the denomination 'ONE POUND'. Edge
inscription 'DOMINE DIRIGE NOS'. (Reverse design: Stuart Devlin.)

2010	Unc £3; BU* £5
— BU on presentation card (Issued: 66,313)	£6
— Proof *FDC* (in 2010 set, see PS101)*	£6
— Proof in silver *FDC* (Issued: 7,693)	£35
— Proof piedfort in silver *FDC* (Issued: 3,682)	£55
— Proof in gold *FDC* (Issued: 950)	£950

J29 – One pound. (Belfast.) R. A design which depicts the official badges of the capital
cities of the United Kingdom, with the badge of Belfast being the principal focus,
accompanied by the name 'BELFAST' and the denomination 'ONE POUND'. Edge
inscription 'PRO TANTO QUID RETRIBUAMUS'. (Reverse design: Stuart Devlin.)

2010	Unc £3; BU* £5
— BU on presentation card (Issued: 64,461)	£6
— Proof *FDC* (in 2010 set, see PS101)*	£5
— Proof in silver *FDC* (Issued: 5,805)	£35
— Proof piedfort in silver *FDC* (Issued: 3,503)	£55
— Proof in gold *FDC* (Issued: 585)	£950

US44 - 2010 £1 (J28 and J29) BU in folder (2) (Edition: 10,000) £20

* *Coins marked thus were originally issued in Royal Mint sets.*

   J30   J31   J32   J33

J30 **One pound.** (Edinburgh.) R. A design which depicts the official badges of the capital cities of the United Kingdom, with the badge of Edinburgh being the principal focus, accompanied by the name 'EDINBURGH' and the denomination 'ONE POUND'. Edge inscription 'NISI DOMINUS'. (Reverse design: Stuart Devlin.)

2011 ....Unc £7; BU* £3
— Proof *FDC* (in 2011 set, see PS104)*...£12
— Proof in silver *FDC* (Issued: 4,973) £45
— Proof piedfort in silver *FDC* (Issued: 2,696)...£78
— Proof in gold *FDC* (Issued: 499) £1000

J31 **One pound.** (Cardiff.) R. A design which depicts the official badges of the capital cities of the United Kingdom, with the badge of Cardiff being the principal focus, accompanied by the name 'CARDIFF' and the denomination 'ONE POUND'. Edge inscription 'Y DDRAIG GOCH DDYRY CYCHWYN'. (Reverse design: Stuart Devlin.)

2011 ....Unc £3; BU* £5
— Proof *FDC* (in 2011 set, see PS104) *...£8
— Proof in silver *FDC* (Issued: 5,553) £45
— Proof piedfort in silver *FDC* (Issued: 1,615)...£78
— Proof in gold *FDC* (Issued: 524) £1000

US47 - 2011 £1 (J30 and J31) BU in folder (2) (Edition: 10,000) £30

J32 **One pound.** (England.) R. Depicts an oak branch paired with a Tudor-inspired rose with the denomination 'ONE POUND' below. Edge inscription 'DECUS ET TUTAMEN'. (Reverse design: Timothy Noad.)

2013 ....Unc £3; BU* £5
— Proof *FDC* (in 2013 set, see PS109) *..£7
— Proof in silver *FDC* (Issued: 1,858) £50
— Proof piedfort in silver *FDC* (Issued: 1,071)...£100
— Proof in gold *FDC* (Issued: 185) £1000

J33 **One pound.** (Wales.) R. Depicts a leek and a daffodil with their leaves entwined and the denomination 'ONE POUND' below. Edge inscription 'PLEIDIOL WYF I'M GWLAD'. (Reverse design: Timothy Noad.)

2013 ....Unc £3; BU* £5
— Proof *FDC* (in 2013 set, see PS109) *..£7
— Proof in silver *FDC* (Issued: 1,618) £50
— Proof piedfort in silver *FDC* (Issued: 860)...£100
— Proof in gold *FDC* (Issued: 175) £1000

US51A - 2013 £1 (J32 and J33) BU in folder (2)..£18
PSS52 - 2013 £1 (J32 and J33) silver proofs (2) £100

* Coins marked thus were originally issued in Royal Mint sets.

J34

J34 **One pound.** (Northern Ireland.) R. Depicts a flax and shamrock being the principle
focus for Northern Ireland accompanied by the denomination 'ONE POUND'. Edge
inscription 'DECUS ET TUTANEM' (Reverse design: Timothy Noad.)
2014 ....Unc £3; BU* £6
— Proof *FDC* (in 2014 set, see PS112)* £7
— Proof in silver *FDC* (Issued: 1,502 including coins in sets)...................................£50
— Proof piedfort in silver *FDC* (Issued: 788 including coins in sets) £100
— Proof in gold *FDC* (Edition: 166 including coins in sets) £1000

J35

J35 **One pound.** (Scotland.) R. Depicts the thistle and bluebell being the principle focus
for Scotland accompanied by the denomination 'ONE POUND'. Edge inscription
'NEMO ME IMPUNE LACESSIT'. (Reverse design: Timothy Noad.)
2014 ....Unc £3; BU* £6
— Proof *FDC* (in 2014 set, see PS112)* £7
— Proof in silver *FDC* (Issued: 1,540 including coins in sets)...................................£50
— Proof piedfort in silver *FDC* (Edition: 3,014 including coins in sets) £100
— Proof in gold *FDC* (Issued: 154 including coins in sets) £1000

US53A - 2014 £1 (J34 and J35) BU in folder (2)..£18

Obverse portrait by Jody Clark

J36 **One pound.** R. A shield of Our Royal Arms with the words 'ONE' to the left and
'POUND' to the right. Edge inscription 'DECUS ET TUTAMEN'. (Rev. as J27.)
(Reverse design: Matthew Dent.)
2015 BU*...£4
— Proof *FDC* (in 2015 set, see PS116)*...£5
— Proof in silver *FDC* (Edition: 7,500) (see PSS63)* £50
— Proof in gold *FDC* (Edition: 500) (see PGCS19)* £900
— Proof in platinum FDC (Issued: 10) (see PPLS3)* £1500
2016
— BU (in 2016 set, see US57)..£10
— Proof *FDC* (in 2016 set, see PS119)*..£35
— Proof in silver *FDC* (Edition: 1,500 in sets, see PSS68)* £40

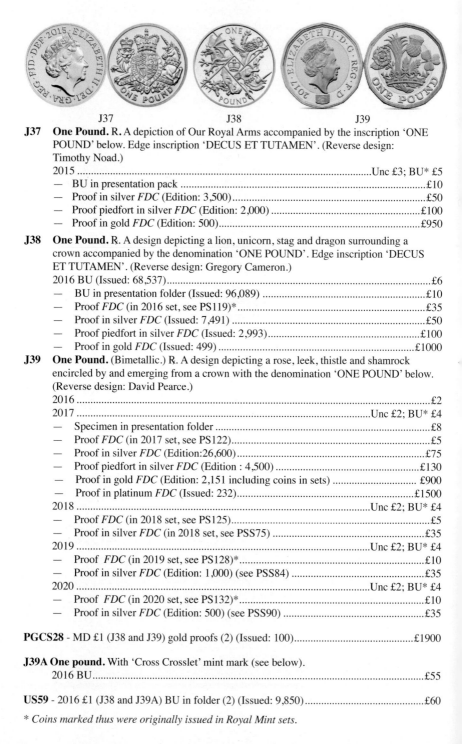

J37   J38   J39

J37   **One Pound.** R. A depiction of Our Royal Arms accompanied by the inscription 'ONE
POUND' below. Edge inscription 'DECUS ET TUTAMEN'. (Reverse design:
Timothy Noad.)
2015 ....Unc £3; BU* £5
— BU in presentation pack £10
— Proof in silver *FDC* (Edition: 3,500)..£50
— Proof piedfort in silver *FDC* (Edition: 2,000) £100
— Proof in gold *FDC* (Edition: 500)...£950

J38   **One Pound.** R. A design depicting a lion, unicorn, stag and dragon surrounding a
crown accompanied by the denomination 'ONE POUND'. Edge inscription 'DECUS
ET TUTAMEN'. (Reverse design: Gregory Cameron.)
2016 BU (Issued: 68,537)..£6
— BU in presentation folder (Issued: 96,089) £10
— Proof *FDC* (in 2016 set, see PS119)*...£35
— Proof in silver *FDC* (Issued: 7,491) £50
— Proof piedfort in silver *FDC* (Issued: 2,993)..£100
— Proof in gold *FDC* (Issued: 499) £1000

J39   **One Pound.** (Bimetallic.) R. A design depicting a rose, leek, thistle and shamrock
encircled by and emerging from a crown with the denomination 'ONE POUND' below.
(Reverse design: David Pearce.)
2016 ....£2
2017 ....Unc £2; BU* £4
— Specimen in presentation folder £8
— Proof *FDC* (in 2017 set, see PS122)..£5
— Proof in silver *FDC* (Edition:26,600)..£75
— Proof piedfort in silver *FDC* (Edition : 4,500) £130
— Proof in gold *FDC* (Edition: 2,151 including coins in sets) £900
— Proof in platinum *FDC* (Issued: 232)..£1500
2018 ....Unc £2; BU* £4
— Proof *FDC* (in 2018 set, see PS125)...£5
— Proof in silver *FDC* (in 2018 set, see PSS75) £35
2019 ....Unc £2; BU* £4
— Proof *FDC* (in 2019 set, see PS128)*...£10
— Proof in silver *FDC* (Edition: 1,000) (see PSS84) £35
2020 ....Unc £2; BU* £4
— Proof *FDC* (in 2020 set, see PS132)*...£10
— Proof in silver *FDC* (Edition: 500) (see PSS90) £35

PGCS28 - MD £1 (J38 and J39) gold proofs (2) (Issued: 100)...........................£1900

J39A One pound. With 'Cross Crosslet' mint mark (see below).
2016 BU...£55

US59 - 2016 £1 (J38 and J39A) BU in folder (2) (Issued: 9,850).........................£60

* Coins marked thus were originally issued in Royal Mint sets.

NICKEL-BRASS

TWO POUND COINS
Obverse portrait by Raphael Maklouf

K1

K1 **Two pounds.** R. St. Andrew's cross with a crown of laurel leaves and surmounted by a thistle of Scotland with date '1986' above. Edge inscription 'XIII COMMONWEALTH GAMES SCOTLAND'. (Reverse design: Norman Sillman.)

1986 ....Unc £4; BU* £5
— BU in presentation folder £8
— Proof *FDC* (in 1986 set, see PS37)* £10
— 0.500 silver (Issued: 58,881) £18
— Proof in silver *FDC* (Issued: 59,779) £35
— Proof in gold *FDC* (Issued: 3,277 plus 12,500 in sets) £800

K2

K2 **Two pounds.** 300th Anniversary of Bill of Rights. R. Cypher of W&M (King William and Queen Mary) interlaced surmounting a horizontal Parliamentary mace and a representation of the Royal Crown above and the dates '1689'and '1989' below, all within the inscription 'TERCENTENARY OF THE BILL OF RIGHTS'. .(Reverse design: John Lobban.)

1989 ....Unc £4; BU* £5
— BU in presentation folder £8
— Proof *FDC* (in 1989 set, see PS43)* £10
— Proof in silver *FDC* (Issued: 25,000) £35
— Proof piedfort in silver *FDC* (in 1989 set, seePSS01)* £60

* Coins marked thus were originally issued in Royal Mint sets.

K3   K4   K5

K3 **Two pounds.** (Scotland.) 300th Anniversary of Claim of Right. R. As K2, but with
Crown of Scotland and the inscription 'TERCENTENARY OF THE CLAIM OF
RIGHT'. (Reverse design: John Lobban.)
1989..Unc £25; BU* £30
— BU in presentation folder £35
— Proof *FDC* (in 1989 set, see PS43)* £30
— Proof in silver *FDC* (Issued: 24,852) £40
— Proof piedfort in silver *FDC* (in 1989 set, seePSS01)* £60

US09 - 1989 £2 (K2 and K3) BU in folder (2) £40
PSS02 - 1989 £2 (K2 and K3) silver proofs (2) £65
PSS01 - 1989 £2 (K2 and K3) silver piedfort proofs (2) (Issued: 10,000)..............£85

K4 **Two pounds.** 300th Anniversary of the Bank of England. R. Bank's original Corporate
Seal, with Crown & Cyphers of William III & Mary II and the dates '1694' and '1994'.
Edge inscription 'SIC VOS NON VOBIS'on the silver and base metal versions.
(Reverse design: Leslie Durbin.)
1994..Unc £5; BU* £8
— BU in presentation folder £10
— Proof *FDC* (in 1994 set, see PS53)* £12
— Proof in silver *FDC* (Issued: 27, 957) £35
— Proof piedfort in silver *FDC* (Issued: 9,569) £60
— Proof in gold *FDC* (Issued: 1,000)...£850
K4A **— Gold Error – known as a Mule coin.** £3000
The obverse of the 1994 Bank of England issue should have included the denomination
'TWO POUNDS' as this was not included in the design of the commemorative reverse.
An unknown number of coins were struck and issued in gold using the die that
was reserved for the Double Sovereign or Two Pound coins in the sovereign series.
The Royal Mint wrote to its retail customers inviting them to return the error coin
for replacement with the correct design. No details are known as to how many were
returned, nor how many exist in the market. The incorrect obverse can be seen at SD2 in
the section listing Gold Sovereigns; the correct obverse is at K1.

K5 **Two pounds.** 50th Anniversary of the End of World War II. R. A stylised representation
of a dove as the symbol of Peace. Edge inscription '1945 IN PEACE GOODWILL
1995'. (Reverse design: John Mills.)
1995..Unc £5; BU* £8
— BU in presentation folder £10
— Proof *FDC* (in 1995 set, see PS55)* £12
— Proof in silver *FDC* (Issued: 35,751) £35
— Proof piedfort in silver *FDC* (Edition: 10,000)................................£60
— Proof in gold *FDC* (Issued: 2,500)...£850

* *Coins marked thus were originally issued in Royal Mint sets.*

K6   K7

K6   **Two pounds.** 50th Anniversary of the Establishment of the United Nations. R. 50th
Anniversary symbol and a fanning pattern of flags with the inscription 'NATIONS
UNITED FOR PEACE' above and the dates '1945-1995'below. (Reverse design:
Michael Rizzello.)

1995.. Unc £5; BU* £8
  — BU in presentation folder £12
  — BU in card (issued as part of multi country United Nations Collection)..................£12
  — Proof in silver *FDC* (Edition: 175,000) £35
  — Proof piedfort in silver *FDC* (Edition: 10,000)...£60
  — Proof in gold *FDC* (Edition: 17,500) £850

K7   **Two pounds.** European Football Championships. R. A stylised representation of a
football with the date '1996' centrally placed and surrounded by sixteen small rings.
Edge inscription 'TENTH EUROPEAN CHAMPIONSHIP'. The gold versions have a
plain edge with no inscription. (Reverse design: John Mills.)

1996.. Unc £5; BU* £8
  — BU in presentation folder £10
  — Proof *FDC* (in 1996 set, see PS57)* £12
  — Proof in silver *FDC* (Issued: 25,163)...£35
  — Proof piedfort in silver *FDC* (Issued: 7,634) £60
  — Proof in gold *FDC* (Issued: 2,098)..£850

K7A **Incorrect blank.** When struck the coins have a dished appearance on both the obverse
and reverse but several pieces in gold have been reported where the surface of the coins
is flat. Enquiries at the Mint are continuing with a view to understanding how this could
have occurred...£1500

Bimetallic issues

K8

K8   **Two pounds.** Bimetallic currency issue. R. Four concentric circles representing the
Iron Age, 18th Century industrial development, silicon chip, and Internet. Edge inscription
'STANDING ON THE SHOULDERS OF GIANTS'. (Reverse design: Bruce Rushin.)

1997.. Unc £4; BU* £5
  — BU in presentation folder £8
  — Proof *FDC* (in 1997 set, see PS59)* £10
  — Proof in silver *FDC* (Issued: 29,910)...£32
  — Proof piedfort in silver *FDC* (Issued: 10,000) £60
  — Proof in gold *FDC* (Issued: 2,482)...£850

* Coins marked thus were originally issued in Royal Mint sets.

Obverse portrait by Ian Rank-Broadley

K9

K9   Two pounds. Bimetallic currency issue. ℞. Four concentric circles, representing the
Iron Age, 18th Century industrial development, silicon chip and Internet. Edge
inscription 'STANDING ON THE SHOULDERS OF GIANTS'.

1998	Unc £4; BU* £5
— Proof *FDC* (in 1998 set, see PS61)*	£10
— Proof in silver *FDC* (Issued: 19,978)	£32
— Proof piedfort in silver *FDC* (Issued: 7,646)	£60
1999	£8
2000	Unc £4; BU* £5
— Proof *FDC* (in 2000 set, see PS65)*	£10
— Proof in silver *FDC* (in 2000 set, see PSS10)*	£35
2001	Unc £4; BU* £5
— Proof *FDC* (see PS68)*	£10
2002	Unc £4; BU* £5
— Proof *FDC* (in 2002 set, see PS72)*	£10
— Proof in gold *FDC* (in 2002 set, see PGCS02)*	£850
2003	Unc £4; BU* £5
— Proof *FDC* (see PS78)*	£10
2004	Unc £4; BU* £5
— Proof *FDC* (in 2004 set, see PS81)*	£10
2005	Unc £4; BU* £5
— Proof *FDC* (see PS84)*	£10
2006	Unc £4; BU* £5
— Proof *FDC* (in 2006 set, see PS87)*	£10
— Proof in silver *FDC* (in 2006 set, see PSS17)*	£35
2007	Unc £4; BU* £5
— Proof *FDC* (in 2007 set, see PS90)*	£10
2008	Unc £4; BU* £5
— Proof *FDC* (in 2008 set, see PS93)*	£10
2009	Unc £4; BU* £5
— Proof *FDC* (in 2009 set, see PS97)*	£10
— Proof in silver *FDC* (in 2009 set, see PSS37)*	£35
2010	Unc £4; BU* £5
— Proof *FDC* (in 2010 set, see PS101)*	£10
— Proof in silver *FDC* (in 2010 set, see PSS41)*	£35
2011	Unc £4; BU* £5
— Proof *FDC* (in 2010 set, see PS104)*	£10
— Proof in silver *FDC* (in 2010 set, see PSS44)*	£35
2012	Unc £4; BU* £5
— Proof *FDC* (in 2012 set, see PS107)*	£10
— Proof in silver *FDC* (Edition: 2,012) (see PSS48)*	£30
— Proof in gold *FDC* (Edition: 1500 (see PGGCS11)*	£850

2013 ....Unc £4; BU* £5
— Proof *FDC* (in 2013 set, see PS109)* £10
— Proof in silver *FDC* (Edition: 2,013) (see PSS50)* £30
— Proof in gold *FDC* (Edition: 50) (see PGCS13)* £1000
2014 ....Unc £4; BU* £5
— Proof *FDC* (in 2014 set, see PS112)* £10
— Proof in silver *FDC* (Edition: 2,014) (see PSS56)* £30
2015 ....Unc £4; BU* £5
— Proof *FDC* (in 2015 set, see PS115)* £10
— Proof in silver *FDC* (Edition: 9,000) (see PSS62)* £30
— Proof in gold *FDC* (Edition: 500) (see PGCS18)* £850
— Proof in platinum *FDC* (Issued: 10) (see PPLS3* £2000

K10 **Two pounds.** Rugby World Cup. R. In the centre a rugby ball and goal posts surrounded by a stylised stadium with the denomination 'TWO POUNDS' and the date '1999'. Edge inscription 'RUGBY WORLD CUP 1999'. (Reverse design: Ron Dutton.)
1999 ....Unc £4; BU* £6
— BU in presentation folder £10
— Proof *FDC* (in 1999 set, see PS63)* £10
— Proof in silver *FDC* (Issued: 9,665) £40
— Proof in gold *FDC* (Issued: 311) £850

K10A   K11

K10A — Proof piedfort in silver with coloured hologram on reverse *FDC*
(Issued: 10,000) £150

K11 **Two pounds.** Marconi commemorative. R. Decorative radio waves emanating from a spark of electricity linking the zeros of the date to represent the generation of the signal that crossed the Atlantic with the date '2001' and the denomination 'TWO POUNDS'. Edge inscription 'WIRELESS BRIDGES THE ATLANTIC MARCONI 1901'. (Reverse design: Robert Evans.)
2001 ....Unc £4; BU* £5
— BU in presentation folder £9
— Proof *FDC* (in 2001 set, see PS68)* £10
— Proof in silver *FDC* (Issued: 11,488) £35
— Proof piedfort in silver *FDC* (Issued: 6,759) £60
— Proof in gold *FDC* (Issued: 1,658) £850

K11A — Proof in silver *FDC*, with reverse frosting.
(Issued: 4,803 in a 2-coin set with a Canadian $5 Marconi silver proof) £60

* Coins marked thus were originally issued in Royal Mint sets.

K12   K13   K14

K12 **Two pounds.** (England.) Commonwealth Games commemorative. Ŗ. A moving figure
of an athlete holding a banner, the top of which being divided into lines to symbolise
lanes of a running track or swimming pool with a cameo of the English flag and the
inscription 'XVII COMMONWEALTH GAMES 2002' and the denomination '£2'.
Edge inscription 'SPIRIT OF FRIENDSHIP. MANCHESTER 2002'. (Reverse design:
Matthew Bonaccorsi.)
2002 ....Unc £10; BU* £12
— BU (in Presentation set, see US25)* £15
— Proof *FDC* (in set, see PS76)* £20
— Proof in silver *FDC* (in set, see PSS9)* £50
— Proof in gold *FDC* (in set, see PCGS1)* £900

K12A As above but with colour added to the flag and parts of the banner, Proof Piedfort
in silver.
FDC (in set, see PSS10)* £100

K13 **Two pounds.** (Northern Ireland.) Commonwealth Games commemorative. Ŗ. As
above but with a cameo of the Northern Ireland flag. Edge inscription 'SPIRIT OF
FRIENDSHIP. MANCHESTER 2002'. (Reverse design: Matthew Bonaccorsi.)
2002 ....Unc £20.; BU* £25
— BU (in Presentation set, see US25)* £30
— Proof *FDC* (in set, see PS76)* £30
— Proof in silver *FDC* (in set, see PSS9)* £50
— Proof in gold *FDC* (in set, see PCGS1)* £900

K13A As above but with colour added to the flag and parts of the banner, Proof Piedfort
in silver.
FDC (in set, see PSS10)* £100

K14 **Two pounds.** (Scotland.) Commonwealth Games commemorative. Ŗ. As above
but with a cameo of the Scottish flag. Edge inscription 'SPIRIT OF FRIENDSHIP.
MANCHESTER 2002'. (Reverse design: Matthew Bonaccorsi.)
2002 ....Unc £10; BU* £12
— BU (in Presentation set, see US25)* £15
— Proof *FDC* (in set, see PS76)* £20
— Proof in silver *FDC* (in set, see PSS9)* £50
— Proof in gold *FDC* (in set, see PCGS1)* £900

K14A As above but with colour added to the flag and parts of the banner, Proof Piedfort
in silver.
FDC (in set, see PSS10)* £100

* *Coins marked thus were originally issued in Royal Mint sets.*

| K15 | K16 | K17 |

K15   **Two pounds.** (Wales.) Commonwealth Games commemorative. R. As above but with a
cameo of the Welsh flag. Edge inscription 'SPIRIT OF FRIENDSHIP. MANCHESTER
2002'. (Reverse design: Matthew Bonaccorsi.)

2002 .... Unc £10; BU* £12

    —   BU (in Presentation set, see US25)* £20

    —   Proof *FDC* (in set, see PS76)* £20

    —   Proof in silver *FDC* (in set, see PSS9)* £50

    —   Proof in gold *FDC* (in set, see PCGS1)* £900

K15A As above but with colour added to the flag and parts of the banner, Proof Piedfort
in silver.

   FDC (in set, see PSS10)* £100

US25 - 2002 £2 (K12-K15) BU in folder (4) £80

PS76 - 2002 £2 (K12-K15) proofs (4) (Issued: 3358) £150

PS77 - 2002 £2 (K12-K15) proofs in display type case (4) (Issued: 673) £150

PSS09 - 2002 £2 (K12-K15) silver proofs (4) (Issued: 2553) £180

PSS10 - 2002 £2 (K12A-K15A) silver proof piedfort (4) (Issued: 3497) £300

PGCS01 - 2002 £2 (K12-K15) gold proofs (4) (Issued: 315) £3500

K16   **Two pounds.** Discovery of the Structure of DNA. R. In the centre the spiralling double
helix structure of DNA with the inscription 'DNA DOUBLE HELIX' and the dates
'1953' and '2003' separated by the denomination 'TWO POUNDS'. Edge inscription
'DEOXYRIBONUCLEIC ACID'. (Reverse design: John Mills.)

2003 .... Unc £4; BU* £5

    —   BU in presentation folder (Issued: 41,568) £10

    —   Proof *FDC* (in set, see PS78)* £10

    —   Proof in Silver *FDC* (Issued: 11,204) £35

    —   Proof piedfort in silver *FDC* (Issued: 8,728) £60

    —   Proof in gold *FDC* (Issued: 1,500) £850

K17   **Two pounds.** 200th Anniversary of the First Steam Locomotive. R. In the centre a
depiction of Trevithick's Locomotive Penydarren and the denomination 'TWO POUNDS'
surrounded by a cog representing the Industrial Revolution and the inscription 'R.
TREVITHICK 1804 INVENTION INDUSTRY PROGRESS 2004'. Patterned edge.
(Reverse design: Robert Lowe.)

2004 .... Unc £4; BU* £5

    —   BU in presentation folder (Issued: 56,871) £10

    —   Brilliant uncirculated in silver (Issued: 1,923) £25

    —   Proof *FDC* (in 2004 set, see PS81)* £10

    —   Proof in Silver *FDC* (Issued: 10,233) £35

    —   Proof piedfort in silver *FDC* (Issued: 5,303) .... £ 65

    —   Proof in gold *FDC* (1,500) £850

* Coins marked thus were originally issued in Royal Mint sets.

K18   K19   K20

K18 **Two pounds.** 400th Anniversary of the Gunpowder Plot. ℞. An arrangement of
        crosiers, maces and swords, surrounded by stars, with the dates '1605' and '2005'
        above, and the denomination 'TWO POUNDS' below. Edge inscription 'REMEMBER
        REMEMBER THE FIFTH OF NOVEMBER'. (Reverse design: Peter Forster.)
        2005 ....Unc £4; BU* £5
        — BU in presentation folder (Issued: 12,044) £10
        — Proof *FDC* (in 2005 set, see PS84)* £10
        — Proof in Silver *FDC* (Issued: 4,394) £40
        — Proof piedfort in silver *FDC* (Issued: 4,585) £65
        — Proof in gold *FDC* (Issued: 914)...£850

K19 **Two pounds.** 60th Anniversary of the End of World War II. ℞. In the centre a
        depiction of the front of St. Paul's Cathedral in full floodlights with the denomination
        'TWO POUNDS' and the dates '1945 - 2005'. Edge inscription 'IN VICTORY
        MAGNANIMITY IN PEACE GOODWILL'. (Reverse design: Robert Elderton.)
        2005 ....Unc £4; BU* £5
        — BU in presentation folder with medal (Issued: 53,686) £10
        — Proof in Silver *FDC* (Issued: 21,734) £35
        — Proof piedfort in silver *FDC* (Issued: 4,798) £65
        — Proof in gold *FDC* (Issued: 1,578 single coins and 1,346 in sets)......................£850

K20 **Two pounds.** 200th Anniversary of the Birth of Isambard Brunel. ℞. In the centre
        a portrait of the engineer with segments of a wheel and bridge in the background
        surrounded by links of a heavy chain and the date '2006' and the denomination
        'TWO POUNDS'. Edge inscription '1806 - 1859 ISAMBARD KINGDOM BRUNEL
        ENGINEER'. (Reverse design: Rod Kelly.)
        2006 ....Unc £4; BU* £5
        — Proof *FDC* (in 2006 set, see PS87)* £10
        — Proof in silver *FDC* (Issued: 7,251) £35
        — Proof piedfort in silver *FDC* (Issued: 3,199) (see PSS19)* £65
        — Proof in gold *FDC* (Issued: 1,071)...£850

* Coins marked thus were originally issued in Royal Mint sets.

SPINK

COINS OF ENGLAND 2021
E-book available on Amazon, iBookstore,
Google, Kobo, OverDrive
and across most other platforms

For more information or enquiries please contact
Tel: +44 (0)20 7563 4119 | Email: books@spink.com
69 Southampton Row, Bloomsbury, London WC1B 4ET
WWW.SPINKBOOKS.COM

K21   K22

K21   Two pounds. 200th Anniversary of the Birth of Isambard Brunel. ℞. In the centre a
section of the roof of Paddington Station with 'BRUNEL' below and the date '2006'
and the denomination 'TWO POUNDS'. Edge inscription 'SO MANY IRONS IN
THE FIRE'. (Reverse design: Robert Evans.)

2006 ....Unc £4; BU* £5
—   Proof *FDC* (in 2006 set, see PS87)* £10
—   Proof in silver *FDC* (Issued: 5,375) £35
—   Proof piedfort in silver *FDC* (Issued: 3,018) (see PSS25)* £65
—   Proof in gold *FDC* (Issued: 746)..£850

US33 - 2006 £2 (K20 and K21) BU in folder..£15
PSS18 - 2006 £2 (K20 and K21) silver proofs (2) £70
PSS19 - 2006 £2 (K20 and K21) silver piedfort proofs (2)....................................130
PGCS03 - 2006 £2 (K20 and K21) gold proofs (2) £1700

K22   Two pounds. Tercentenary of the Act of Union between England and Scotland.
℞. A design dividing the coin into four quarters, with a rose and a thistle occupying two
of the quarters, and a portcullis in each of the other two quarters. The whole is overlaid
with a linking jigsaw motif and surrounded by the dates '1707' and '2007' and the
denomination 'TWO POUNDS'. Edge inscription 'UNITED INTO ONE KINGDOM'.
(Reverse design: Yvonne Holton.)

2007 ....Unc £4; BU* £5
—   BU in presentation folder £10
—   Proof *FDC* (in 2007 set, see PS90)* £10
—   Proof in Silver *FDC* (Issued: 8,310) £35
—   Proof piedfort in silver *FDC* (Issued: 4,000) £60
—   Proof in gold *FDC* (Issued: 750)..£850

K22A — Error edge. The obverse and reverse designs of the Act of Union silver proof
combined with the edge inscription of the Abolition of Slave Trade issue (K23 below).
The edge inscription is impressed on the blanks prior to the striking of the obverse and
reverse designs and whilst one example has been reported, and confirmed as genuine
by the Royal Mint, it seems possible that a small batch may have been produced and
other pieces have yet to be detected. £1000

* Coins marked thus were originally issued in Royal Mint sets.

K23   K24   K25

K23 **Two pounds.** Bicentenary of the Abolition of the Slave Trade in the British Empire.
℞. The date '1807' with the '0' depicted as a broken chain link, surrounded by the
inscription 'AN ACT FOR THE ABOLITION OF THE SLAVE TRADE', and the
date '2007'. Edge inscription 'AM I NOT A MAN, AND A BROTHER'. (Reverse
design: David Gentleman.) The designer's initials DG apppear below and to the right
of the 7 in 1807 on all coins except those issued for circulation.
2007 ....Unc £4; BU* £5
— BU in presentation folder £10
— Proof *FDC* (in 2007 set, see PS90)* £15
— Proof in Silver *FDC* (Issued: 7,095) £35
— Proof piedfort in silver *FDC* (Issued: 3,990)* £60
— Proof in gold *FDC* (Issued: 1,000) £850

2008 £2 Olympic Centenary. *See 4951 in London 2012 Olympic section.*

K24 **Two pounds.** 250th Anniversary of the Birth of Robert Burns. Obv. as K27.
℞. A design featuring a quote from the song *Auld Lang Syne* 'WE'LL TAK A CUP
A' KINDNESS YET, FOR AULD LANG SYNE', the calligraphy of which is based
on the handwriting of Robert Burns with the inscription '1759 ROBERT BURNS
1796' and the denomination 'TWO POUNDS'. Edge inscription 'SHOULD AULD
ACQUAINTANCE BE FORGOT'. (Reverse design: Royal Mint Engraving Team.)
2009 ....Unc £4; BU* £5
— BU in celebration card (Issued: 120,223)...£8
— BU in presentation folder (Edition: 50,000)...£10
— Proof *FDC* (in 2009 set, see PS97)* £10
— Proof in Silver *FDC* (Issued: 9,188)) £35
— Proof piedfort in silver *FDC* (Issued: 3,500) £60
— Proof in gold *FDC* (Issued: 1,000) £850

K25 **Two pounds.** 200th Anniversary of the Birth of Charles Darwin. ℞. A design showing
a portrait of Charles Darwin facing an ape surrounded by the inscription '1809
DARWIN 2009' and the denomination 'TWO POUNDS'. Edge inscription 'ON THE
ORIGIN OF SPECIES 1859'. (Reverse design: Suzie Zamit.)
2009 ....Unc £4; BU* £5
— BU in presentation folder (Issued: 119,713) £10
— Proof *FDC* (in 2009 set, see PS97)* £10
— Proof in Silver *FDC* (Issued: 9,357)) £35
— Proof piedfort in silver *FDC* (Issued: 3,282) £60
— Proof in gold *FDC* (Issued: 1,000) £850

2009 £2 Beijing Olympic Handover. *See 4952 in London 2012 Olympic section.*

* Coins marked thus were originally issued in Royal Mint sets.

K26

K26 **Two pounds.** The Centenary of the Death of Florence Nightingale and the 150th Anniversary of the Publication of *NOTES ON NURSING*. Obv. as K27. R. A design depicting the pulse of a patient being taken, surrounded by the inscription 'FLORENCE NIGHTINGALE – 1910' and the denomination 'TWO POUNDS'. The design being set against a background texture of lines symbolising rays of light from a lamp. Edge inscription '150 YEARS OF NURSING' on the precious metal versions. (Reverse design: Gordon Summers.)

2010 ....Unc £4; BU* £5
— BU on presentation card £8
— BU in presentation folder (Edition: 25,000)..£10
— Proof *FDC* (in 2010 set, see PS101)* £10
— Proof in silver *FDC* (Issued: 5,117) £35
— Proof piedfort in silver *FDC* (Issued: 2770) £60
— Proof in gold *FDC* (Issued: 472)...£1000

K27

K27 **Two pounds.** 500th Anniversary of the Launch of the Mary Rose. R. A depiction of the ship based on a contemporary painting, surrounded by a cartouche bearing the inscription 'THE MARY ROSE' above, the denomination 'TWO POUNDS' below, and a rose to the left and right. The lettering on the reverse is rendered in the Lombardic style employed on the coins of Henry VII. Edge inscription 'YOUR NOBLEST SHIPPE 1511'. (Reverse design: John Bergdahl.)

2011 ....Unc £8; BU* £10
— BU in presentation folder (Edition: 20,000) £20
— Proof *FDC* (in 2011 set, see PS104)* £20
— Proof in silver *FDC* (Issued: 6,618) £50
— Proof piedfort in silver *FDC* (Issued: 2,680)..£88
— Proof in gold *FDC* (Issued: 692) £900

* Coins marked thus were originally issued in Royal Mint sets.

K28   K29   K30

K28 **Two pounds.** The 400th Anniversary of the King James Bible. ℞. A design
focusing on the opening verse of St John's Gospel, 'IN THE BEGINNING WAS
THE WORD', showing the verse as printing blocks on the left and the printed
page on the right, with the inscription 'KING JAMES BIBLE' above and the dates
'1611-2011' below. Edge inscription 'THE AUTHORISED VERSION'.
(Reverse design: Paul Stafford and Benjamin Wright.)

2011 ....Unc £8; BU* £10
— BU in presentation folder (Edition: 20,000) £12
— Proof *FDC* (in 2011 set, see PS104)* £15
— Proof in silver *FDC* (Issued: 4,494) £50
— Proof piedfort in silver *FDC* (Issued: 2,394)..£88
— Proof in gold *FDC* (Issued: 355) £1000

K29 **Two pounds.** The 200th Anniversary of the Birth of Charles Dickens. ℞. A
silhouette profile of the writer through the titles of his works, greater prominence
being given to those that are more well known, with the inscription 'CHARLES
DICKENS 1870' to the left. Edge inscription 'SOMETHING WILL TURN UP'.
(Reverse design: Matthew Dent.)

2012...Unc £4; BU* £5
— BU in presentation folder (Issued: 15,035) £10
— Proof *FDC* (in 2012 set, see PS107)* £10
— Proof in silver *FDC* (Issued: 2,631) £50
— Proof piedfort in silver *FDC* (Issued: 1,279) £88
— Proof in gold *FDC* (Issued: 202)..£1000

2012 **£2 Rio Olympic Handover.** *See 4953 in London 2012 Olympic section.*

K30 **Two pounds.** 350th Anniversary of the Guinea. ℞. A depiction of the Royal
Arms based on that on the reverse of the 'SPADE GUINEA' of George III and
surrounded by the inscription 'ANNIVERSARY OF THE GOLDEN GUINEA'
and the date '2013' below. Edge inscription 'WHAT IS A GUINEA? 'TIS A
SPLENDID THING'. (Reverse design: Anthony Smith.)

2013...Unc £5; BU* £6
— BU in presentation folder £12
— Proof *FDC* (in 2013 set, see PS109)* £10
— Proof in silver *FDC* (Issued: 1,640) £50
— Proof piedfort in silver *FDC* (Issued: 969) £100
— Proof in gold *FDC* (Issued: 284)..£1200

* Coins marked thus were originally issued in Royal Mint sets.

K31   K32

K31 **Two pounds.** 150th Anniversary of the London Underground. R.The Roundel logo of
the London underground system with the dates '1863' above and '2013' below. Edge
inscription 'MIND THE GAP'. (Reverse design: Edwina Ellis.)
2013 ....Unc £5; BU* £6
— Proof *FDC* (in 2013 set, see PS109)* £10
— Proof in silver *FDC* (Issued: 1,185) £50
— Proof piedfort in silver *FDC* (Issued: 162) £100
— Proof in gold *FDC* (Issued: 132)..£1500

K32 **Two pounds.** 150th Anniversary of the London Underground. R. Depicts a train
emerging from a tunnel with the date '1863' to the left and the inscription 'LONDON
UNDERGROUND' and the date '2013' to the right. Patterned edge inspired by the
map of the underground network. (Reverse design: Edward Barber and Jay Osgerby.)
2013 ....Unc £5; BU* £6
— Proof *FDC* (in 2013 set, see PS109)* £10
— Proof in silver *FDC* (Edition: Issued: 2,042) £50
— Proof piedfort in silver *FDC* (Issued: 186) £100
— Proof in gold *FDC* (Issued: 140)..£1500

US518 - 2013 £2 (K31 and K32) BU in folder (2) £20
PSS53 - 2013 £2 (K31 and K32) silver proofs (2) (Issued: 2204) £100
PSS53A - 2013 £2 (K31 and K32) silver proof piedforts (2)................................£200
PGCS14 - 2013 £2 (K31 and K32) gold proofs (2) (Issued: 111).......................£3000

K33

K33 **Two pounds.** Trinity House. R. A depiction of a lighthouse lens, surrounded by the
inscription 'TRINITY HOUSE' and the dates '1514' and '2014' with the denomination
'TWO POUNDS'. Edge inscription 'SERVING THE MARINER'. (Reverse design:
Joe Whitlock Blundell with David Eccles.)
2014 ....£4
— BU in presentation folder £12
— Proof *FDC* (in 2014 set, see PS112)* £10
— Proof in silver *FDC* (Issued: 1,285 including coins in sets) £50
— Proof piedfort in silver *FDC* (Issued: 652 including coins in sets).....................£100
— Proof in gold *FDC* (Issued: 204 including coins in sets) £1000

* Coins marked thus were originally issued in Royal Mint sets.

K34

K34 Two pounds. World War I. ℞. A depiction of Lord Kitchener pointing, with
the inscription 'YOUR COUNTRY NEEDS YOU' below the effigy of Lord
Kitchener, and the inscription 'THE FIRST WORLD WAR 1914-1918' and the
date '2014'. Edge inscription 'THE LAMPS ARE GOING OUT ALL OVER
EUROPE'. (Reverse design: John Bergdahl.)

2014..£4
— BU in presentation folder £10
— Proof *FDC* (in 2014 set, see PS112)* £10
— Proof in silver *FDC* (Issued: 4,983 including coins in sets) £50
— Proof piedfort in silver *FDC* (Issued: 2,496 including coins in sets).................£100
— Proof in gold *FDC* (Issued: 734 including coins in sets) £900

K34A Obverse mule error. Obverse K33 used in error so no denomination shown.

One specimen reported in VF.. £650

K35

K35 Two pounds. World War 1, The Royal Navy. ℞. The designs shows a dreadnought
at sea with the inscription 'THE FIRST WORLD WAR 1914 – 1918' and the date
of the year below. Edge inscription 'THE SURE SHIELD OF BRITAIN'. (Reverse
design: David Rowlands.)

2015 BU* £8
— BU in presentation pack £15
— Proof *FDC* (in 2015 set, see PS117) * £15
— Proof in silver *FDC* (Edition: 3,000 from sets)*................................£50
— Proof piedfort in silver *FDC* (Edition: 1,500 from sets)* £100

Obverse portrait by Jody Clark

K35A Two pounds. World War 1, The Royal Navy. ℞. As K35

2015..£10
— Proof in silver *FDC* (Edition: 5,000) £50
— Proof piedfort in silver *FDC* (Edition: 2,500)...................................£100
— Proof in gold *FDC* (Edition: 750) £900

* Coins marked thus were originally issued in Royal Mint sets.

Obverse portrait by Ian Rank-Broadley

K36

K36 **Two pounds.** 800th Anniversary of the Signing of Magna Carta. R. The design shows King John flanked by figures representing the clergy on one side and the barons on the other with the inscription 'MAGNA CARTA' and '1215 – 2015'. Edge inscription 'FOUNDATION OF LIBERTY'. (Reverse design: John Bergdahl).

2015 BU* £8
— BU in presentation pack £15
— Proof *FDC* (in 2015 set, see PS117) * £15
— Proof in silver *FDC* (Edition: 3,000) (see PSS64)* £50
— Proof piedfort in silver *FDC* (Edition: 1,500)..£100
— Proof in gold *FDC* (Edition: 100) £1000

Obverse portrait by Jody Clark

K36A   K37

K36A Two pounds. 800th Anniversary of the Signing of Magna Carta. R. As K36.

2015 ....£8
— Proof in silver *FDC* (Edition: 7,500) £60
— Proof piedfort in silver *FDC* (Edition: 2,000)..£100
— Proof in gold *FDC* (Edition: 500) £1000

K37 **Two pounds.** R. A depiction of Britannia holding a shield and trident with the inscription 'TWO POUNDS'. Edge inscription 'QUATUOR MARIA VINDICO'. (Reverse design: Antony Dufort.) ....

2015 ....Unc £5; BU* £6
— Proof *FDC* (in 2015 set, see PS116)* £10
— Proof in silver *FDC* (Edition: 7,500) (see PSS63)* £50
— Proof in gold *FDC* (Edition: 500) (see PGCS19)* £900
— Proof in platinum *FDC* (Issued:10) (see PPLS3)* £2000
2016 ....Unc £5; BU* £6
— Proof *FDC* (in 2016 set, see PS119)* £10
— Proof in silver *FDC* (Edition: 7,500) (see PSS68)* £50
2017 BU* £15
— Proof *FDC* (in 2017 set, see PS122)..£15
— Proof in silver *FDC* (Edition: 1,500) (see PSS72) £50
— Proof in gold *FDC* (Issued: 24) (see PGCS25)* £900

2018 BU*..£15
  — Proof *FDC* (in 2018 set, see PS125)*..£15
  — Proof in silver *FDC* (Edition: 1,000) (see PSS78)* £50
2019 BU*..£15
  — Proof *FDC* (in 2019 set, see PS128)*..£15
  — Proof in silver *FDC* (Edition: 1,000) (see PSS84)* £50
2020 BU*..£15
  — Proof *FDC* (in 2020 set, see PS132)*..£15
  — Proof in silver *FDC* (Edition: 500) (see PSS90)* £50

The £2 Britannia K37 became the definitive £2 for circulation from 2015 but very few have been issued as banks have adequate stocks of other types.

K38   K39

K38 **Two pounds.** Honouring the Work of William Shakespeare. Comedy. ℞. A cap and bells with a Jester's stick accompanied by the inscription 'WILLIAM SHAKESPEARE 2016'. Edge inscription 'ALL THE WORLD'S A STAGE'.(Reverse design: John Bergdahl.)
2016..£4
  — BU (Issued: 3,500 plus coins in sets) £5
  — Proof *FDC* (in 2016 set, see PS119)* £15
  — Proof in silver *FDC* (Issued: 951)..£60
  — Proof piedfort in silver *FDC* (Issued: 533) £100
  — Proof in gold *FDC* (Issued: 152)..£900

K39 **Two pounds.** Honouring the Work of William Shakespeare. History. ℞. A dagger through a crown accompanied by the inscription 'WILLIAM SHAKESPEARE 2016'. Edge inscription 'THE HOLLOW CROWN'. (Reverse design: John Bergdahl.)
2016 ....£4
  — BU (Issued: 6,341 plus coins in sets) £5
  — Proof *FDC* (in 2016 set, see PS119)* £15
  — Proof in silver *FDC* (Issued: 965)..£60
  — Proof piedfort in silver *FDC* (Issued: 624) £100
  — Proof in gold *FDC* (Issued: 156)..£900

K40 **Two pounds.** Honouring the Work of William Shakespeare. Tragedy. ℞. A skull next to a rose accompanied by the inscription 'WILLIAM SHAKESPEARE 2016'. Edge inscription 'WHAT A PIECE OF WORK IS A MAN'. (Reverse design John Bergdahl.)
2016 ....£4
  — BU (Issued: 6,550 plus coins in sets) £5
  — Proof *FDC* (in 2016 set, see PS119)* £15
  — Proof in silver *FDC* (Issued 1,004) £60
  — Proof piedfort in silver *FDC* (Issued: 769) £100
  — Proof in gold *FDC* (Issued: 209)..£900

US59A - 2016 £2 (K38-K40) BU in folder (3) (Issued: 22,060)...............................£28

* Coins marked thus were originally issued in Royal Mint sets.

K41   K42   K44

K41 **Two pounds.** World War 1, The Army. R. A stylised silhouette of the heads of three
soldiers and references the English cubism movement prevalent around the time of the
First World War with the inscription 'THE FIRST WORLD WAR 1914 – 1918', and
the date of the year. Edge inscription 'FOR KING AND COUNTRY'. (Reverse design:
John Bergdahl.)

2016 ....Unc £4; BU* £5
— BU in presentation folder (Issued: 19,066) £12
— Proof *FDC* (in 2016 set, see PS119)* £15
— Proof in silver *FDC* (Issued: 2,744 including coins in sets) £60
— Proof piedfort in silver *FDC* (Issued: 1,387 including coins in sets)............... £100
— Proof in gold *FDC* (Issued: 361 including coins in sets) £900

K42 **Two pounds.** 350th Anniversary of the Great Fire of London. R. A view across the
River Thames of the City of London in flames with boats fleeing the burning city with
the inscription '1666 THE GREAT FIRE OF LONDON 2016'. Edge inscription 'THE
WHOLE CITY IN DREADFUL FLAMES'. (Reverse design: Aaron West.)

2016 BU £4
— BU (Issued: 4,857 plus coins in sets) £5
— BU in presentation folder (Issued: 23,215) £12
— Proof *FDC* (in 2016 set, see PS119)* £15
— Proof in silver *FDC* (Issued: 2,690 including coin sets)........................... £60
— Proof piedfort in silver *FDC* (Issued: 1,812 including coin sets) £100
— Proof in gold *FDC* (Issued: 341 including coin sets).............................. £1000

K43 is re-listed as **RMB1**

*No commemorative £2s have been issued into circulation since 2016. Base metal coins are only
available in BU packs or year sets.*

K44 **Two pounds.** World War 1, The Air Force. R. A First World War aircraft engaged in
reconnaissance with the inscription '1914 - 1918' and 'THE WAR IN THE AIR'. Edge
inscription 'THE SKY RAINED HEROES'. (Reverse design: Dan Flashman, Tangerine
Design Agency.)

2017 BU £6
— BU in presentation folder £10
— Proof *FDC* (in 2017 set, see PS122)* £15
— Proof in silver *FDC* (Edition: 7,000 including coins in sets)............................. £68
— Proof piedfort in silver *FDC* (Edition: 3,500).....................................£110
— Proof in gold *FDC* (Edition: 634) £900

* Coins marked thus were originally issued in Royal Mint sets

| K45 | K47 | K48 |

K45 Two pounds. Bicentenary of the Birth of Jane Austen. ℞. A depiction of a regency style silhouette of Jane Austen accompanied by her signature and the inscription 'JANE AUSTEN 1817 - 2017' with the denomination 'TWO POUNDS'. Edge inscription 'THERE IS NO DOING WITHOUT MONEY'. (Reverse design: Dominique Evans.)

2017 BU £6
—   BU in presentation folder..£12
—   Proof *FDC* (in 2017 set, see PS122)* £17
—   Proof in silver *FDC* (Edition: 8,000 including coins in sets)................................£68
—   Proof piedfort in silver *FDC* (Edition : 4,000)...£110
—   Proof in gold *FDC* (Edition: 884 including coins in sets) £900

K46   is re-listed as **RMB2**

K47 Two pounds. 200th Anniversary of Mary Shelley's Frankenstein. ℞. The inscription 'FRANKENSTEIN' accompanied with 'BICENTENARY OF MARY SHELLEYS' and '1818 – THE MODERN PROMETHEUS - 2018'. Edge inscription 'A SPARK OF BEING'. (Reverse design: Thomas Docherty.)

2018 BU* £10
—   BU in presentation folder..£12
—   Proof *FDC* (in 2018 set, see PS125)* £15
—   Proof in silver *FDC* (Edition: 7,000 including coins in sets)................................£68
—   Proof piedfort in silver *FDC* (Edition: 2,818 including coins in sets).................£110
—   Proof in gold *FDC* (Edition: 575 including coins in sets) £900

K48 Two pounds. 250th Anniversary of Captain Cook's Voyage of Discovery. ℞. The hull of the ship Endeavour over a map of Plymouth Sound, Captain Cook's signature and '250', accompanied with the inscription 'CAPTAIN JAMES COOK 1768 – 2018'. Edge inscription 'OCEANI INVESTIGATOR ACERRMVS'. (Reverse design: Garry Breeze.)

2018 BU £8
—   BU in presentation folder..£10
—   Proof in silver *FDC* (Edition: 5,000) £68
—   Proof in gold *FDC* (Edition: 350)..£1000

* *Coins marked thus were originally issued in Royal Mint sets.*

K49

K49 **Two pounds.** 100th Anniversary of 1918 Armistice. R. The inscription 'THE TRUTH UNTOLD THE PITY OF WAR' accompanied with 'THE FIRST WORLD WAR • ARMISTICE • 1918'. Edge inscription 'WILFRED OWEN KILLED IN ACTION 4 NOV 1918'. (Reverse design: Stephen Raw.)

2018 BU*..£10
— BU in presentation folder..£14
— Proof *FDC* (in 2018 set, see PS125)*..£15
— Proof in silver *FDC* (Edition: 7,000 including coins in sets)...................£68
— Proof piedfort in silver *FDC* (Edition: 3,500 including coins in sets).....................£110
— Proof in gold *FDC* (Edition: 1,000 including coins in sets)....................£900

K50   K51

K50 **Two pounds.** 100th Anniversary of the Royal Air Force – Centenary Badge. R. The badge of the Royal Air Force with the inscription 'THE ANNIVERSARY OF THE ROYAL AIR FORCE 1918-2018'. Edge inscription 'PER ARDUA AD ASTRA'. (Reverse design: Rhys Morgan.)

2018 BU*..£10
— BU in presentation folder..£12
— Proof *FDC* (in 2018 set, see PS125)*..£15
— Proof in silver *FDC* (Edition: 10,000 including coins in sets)...................£68
— Proof piedfort in silver *FDC* (Edition: 4,000 including coins in sets)....................£110
— Proof in gold *FDC* (Edition: 1,918 including coins in sets)....................£900

K51 **Two pounds.** 100th Anniversary of the Royal Air Force. R. A depiction of a Vulcan bomber with the inscription 'RAF 1918 – 2018 VULCAN'. Edge inscription 'PER ARDUA AD ASTRA'. (Reverse design: Richard and Neil Talbot.)

2018 BU*..£8
— BU in presentation folder..£10
— Proof in silver *FDC* (Edition: 10,000)..£68
— Proof piedfort in silver *FDC* (Edition: 4,000)....................................... £110
— Proof in gold *FDC* (Edition: 1,000)...£950

* Coins marked thus were originally issued in Royal Mint sets.

K52   K53

K52 Two pounds. 100th Anniversary of the Royal Air Force. ℞. A depiction of a Spitfire
   with the inscription 'RAF 1918 – 2018 SPITFIRE'. Edge inscription 'PER
   ARDUA AD ASTRA'. (Reverse design: Richard and Neil Talbot.)
   2018 BU £8
   — BU in presentation folder £10
   — Proof in silver *FDC* (Edition: 10,000) £68
   — Proof piedfort in silver *FDC* (Edition: 4,000).. £110
   — Proof in gold *FDC* (Edition: 1,000) £950

K53 Two pounds. 100th Anniversary of the Royal Air Force. ℞. A depiction of a Sea King
   helicopter with the inscription 'RAF 1918 – 2018 SEA KING'. Edge inscription 'PER
   ARDUA AD ASTRA'. (Reverse design: Richard and Neil Talbot.)
   2018 BU £8
   — BU in presentation folder £10
   — Proof in silver *FDC* (Edition: 10,000) £68
   — Proof piedfort in silver *FDC* (Edition: 4,000).. £110
   — Proof in gold *FDC* (Edition: 1,000) £950

K54   K55

K54 Two pounds. 100th Anniversary of the Royal Air Force. ℞. A depiction of a Lightning 11
   jet fighter with the inscription 'RAF 1918 – 2018 LIGHTNING 11'. Edge inscription
   'PER ARDUA AD ASTRA'. (Reverse design: Richard and Neil Talbot.)
   2018 BU £8
   — BU in presentation folder £12
   — Proof in silver *FDC* (Edition: 10,000) £68
   — Proof piedfort in silver *FDC* (Edition: 4,000)..£110
   — Proof in gold *FDC* (Edition: 1,000) £950

K55 **Two pounds.** D Day 75th Anniversary. Edge inscription 'THE LONGEST DAY'.
   (Reverse design: Stephen Taylor)
   2019 BU £9
   — BU in folder £10
   — Proof in silver *FDC* (Edition: 8,750 including coins in sets)..........................£68
   — Proof piedfort in silver (Edition: 3,010 including coins in sets)..............................£110
   — Proof in gold *FDC* (Edition: 750 including coins in sets) £1000

K56   K57

K56   **Two pounds**. Wedgwood. ℞. A design depicting a Wedgwood vase and the inscription 'WEDGWOOD 1759-2019'. Edge inscription 'EVERYTHING GIVES WAY TO EXPERIMENT'. (Reverse design: Wedgwood Design Team.)

2019 BU £9
—   BU in folder £10
—   Proof in silver *FDC* (Edition: 4,500 including coins in sets)....................................£65
—   Proof piedfort in silver (Edition: 2,250 including coins in sets) £110
—   Proof in gold *FDC* (Edition: 350 including coins in sets) £1000

K57   **Two pounds**. Samuel Pepys. ℞. A depiction of Samael Pepys's handwriting on the last page of his diary with the inscription 'SAMUEL PEPYS DIARIST'. Edge inscription 'THE GOOD GOD PREPARE ME'. (Reverse design: Gary Breeze.)

2019 BU £9
—   BU in folder £10
—   Proof *FDC*...£15
—   Proof in silver *FDC* (Edition: 3,500 including coins in sets)....................................£65
—   Proof piedfort in silver *FDC* (Edition: 2,019 including coins in sets) £110
—   Proof in gold *FDC* (Edition: 350 including coins in sets) £1000

K58

K58   **Two pounds**. Captain Cook. Edge inscription 'OCEANI INVESTIGATOR ACERRIMVS'.(Reverse design: Gary Breeze.)

2019 BU £9
—   BU in folder £10
—   Silver proof *FDC* (Edition: 5,000)...£65
—   Gold proof *FDC* (Edition: 350) £1000

K59

K59 **Two pounds.** 75th Anniversary of VE Day. R. Joyful people symbolising the first steps towards peace and recovery with dates '1945 2020' and inscription 'VICTORY IN EUROPE'. Edge inscription 'JUST TRIUMPH & PROUD SORROW'.
(Reverse design: Dominique Evans)
2020 BU* £8
—   BU in folder £10
—   Proof* £15
—   Proof in silver *FDC* (Edition: 4,750 plus coins in sets) £68
—   Proof piedfort in silver *FDC* (Edition: 1,635 plus coins in sets) £110
—   Proof in gold *FDC* (Edition: 475 plus coins in sets)...£1115

K60

K60 **Two pounds.** 400th Anniversary of 'The Mayflower' voyage to the New World. R. The Mayflower bursting out of the frame as it sails through the rough seas with inscription '1620 MAYFLOWER 2020'. Edge lettering 'UNDERTAKEN FOR THE GLORY OF GOD'. (Reverse design: Chris Costello.)
2020 BU* £8
—   BU in folder £10
—   Proof* £15
—   Proof in silver *FDC* (Edition: 4,000 plus coins in sets) £68
—   Proof piedfort in silver *FDC* (Edition: 2,000 plus coins in sets) £110
—   Proof in gold *FDC* (Edition: 400 plus coins in sets)...£1115

* Coins marked thus were originally issued in Royal Mint sets.

K61

K61 **Two pounds.** Centenary of Agatha Christie's publication of first novel. R. Agatha Christie signature and monogram logo with inscription '1920 100 YEARS OF MYSTERY 2020'. Edge inscription 'LITTLE GREY CELLS'. (Reverse design: David Lawrence.)

2020 BU*	£8
— BU in folder	£10
— Proof*	£15
— Proof in silver *FDC*(Edition: 2,250 plus coins in sets)	£68
— Proof piedfort in silver *FDC* (Edition: 800 plus coins in sets)	£110
— Proof in gold *FDC* (Edition: 250 plus coins in sets)	£1115

K61

K62 **Two pounds.** 250th Anniversary of Captain Cook's great voyage, III. R. A Maori canoe in close proximity to the bow of HM Bark 'Endeavour'. Edge inscription 'OCEANI INVESTIGATOR ACERRIMVS'. (Reverse design: Garry Breeze.)

2020 BU	£8
— BU in folder	£10
— Proof in silver *FDC* (Edition: 4,795)	£68
— Proof in gold *FDC* (Edition: 340)	£1115

* Coins marked thus were originally issued in Royal Mint sets.

COINS OF ENGLAND

SPINK
COINS OF ENGLAND 2021
E-book available on Amazon, iBookstore,
Google, Kobo, OverDrive
and across most other platforms

For more information or enquiries please contact
Tel: +44 (0)20 7563 4119 | Email: books@spink.com
69 Southampton Row, Bloomsbury, London WC1B 4ET

WWW.SPINKBOOKS.COM

MAUNDY COINS

The Maundy coins continue to be presented each year in the traditional ceremony on Maundy Thursday, with the old denominations being retained as 'new pence'. In the early years of the present reign the ceremony tended to alternate between Westminster Abbey and a cathedral, usually close to London. In more recent years the Queen has travelled to cathedrals right across the country thus bringing this ancient ceremony to the people and increasing the awareness of these coins steeped, as they are, in great British heritage. Latterly St. George's Chapel, Windsor Castle has hosted this event.

Maundy money is given to the same number of men and women as the Monarch's age and each person receives coins to a total value in pence of the Monarch's age. The tradition dates back at least to the thirteenth century, though the origins of the ceremony are to be found in the Last Supper when Jesus washed the feet of His disciples.

The Maundy coins issued from 1977 onwards are frosted proofs. In 2000 and 2006, a 13 coin set was issued from £5 to 1p which included that year's Maundy coins which resulted in the Maundy coins for those years having a higher mintage. The prices below for these two years are for the cased coins out of the 13 coin set. Coins in the traditional Maundy cases would be priced similarly to those of the adjoining period. In 2002 the first Elizabethan Maundy coins in gold were issued, again in a 13 coin set as part of the Golden Jubilee celebrations.

4211 Maundy Set. (4p, 3p, 2p and 1p) 0.925 silver. Uniform dates   £

1971 *Tewkesbury Abbey*	225
1972 *York Minster*	200
1973 *Westminster Abbey*	200
1974 *Salisbury Cathedral*	200
1975 *Peterborough Cathedral*	200
1976 *Hereford Cathedral*	200
1977 *Westminster Abbey*	200
1978 *Carlisle Cathedral*	200
1979 *Winchester Cathedral*	200
1980 *Worcester Cathedral*	200
1981 *Westminster Abbey*	225
1982 *St. Davids Cathedral*	200
1983 *Exeter Cathedral*	200
1984 *Southwell Minster*	200
1985 *Ripon Cathedral*	200
1986 *Chichester Cathedral*	200
1987 *Ely Cathedral*	200
1988 *Lichfield Cathedral*	200
1989 *Birmingham Cathedral*	200
1990 *Newcastle Cathedral*	200
1991 *Westminster Abbey*	225
1992 *Chester Cathedral*	200

	£
1993 *Wells Cathedral*	200
1994 *Truro Cathedral*	200
1995 *Coventry Cathedral*	200
1996 *Norwich Cathedral*	200
1997 *Bradford Cathedral*	200
1998 *Portsmouth Cathedral*	200
1999 *Bristol Cathedral*	200
2000 *Lincoln Cathedral (inc. in PSS08)*	160
2001 *Westminster Abbey*	225
2002 *Canterbury Cathedral*	200
2002 *Proof in gold from set* (see PCGS1)*	1850
2003 *Gloucester Cathedral*	200
2004 *Liverpool Cathedral*	200
2005 *Wakefield Cathedral*	200
2006 *Guildford Cathedral (inc. in PSS17)*	160
2007 *Manchester Cathedral*	200
2008 *St Patrick's Cathedral, Armagh*	350
2009 *Bury St Edmunds Cathedral*	350
2010 *Derby Cathedral*	350
2011 *Westminster Abbey*	350
2012 *York Minster*	350
2013 *Christ Church Cathedral Oxford*	350
2014 *Blackburn Cathedral*	350
2015 *Sheffield Cathedral*	400
2016 *St George's Chapel Windsor Castle*	400
2017 *Leicester Cathedral*	400
2018 *St George's Chapel Windsor Castle*	400
2019 *St George's Chapel Windsor Castle*	400
2020 *St George's Chapel Windsor Castle*	400

Owing to the effects of the Coronavirus the 2020 sets were mailed to the chosen recipients.

4212 — **fourpence,** 1971-2020 ....*from* 50
4213 — **threepence,** 1971-2020 ....*from* 50
4214 — **twopence,** 1971-2020 ....*from* 50
4215 — **penny,** 1971-2020 ....*from* 75

The place of distribution is shown after each date.

CUPRO-NICKEL

The collecting of crown size coins is one of the most popular pursuits among new and established coin collectors. Before decimalisation in 1971, crowns had a nominal denomination of five shillings and this was then changed to twenty five pence in 1972 when the Silver Wedding commemorative was issued. Over time with increasing metal, manufacturing and distribution costs, the production of coins with such a low face value was not economic and the decision was taken to change to a higher value that would last for many years. The first of the five pound crowns was issued in 1990 to mark the ninetieth birthday of The Queen Mother. It seems sensible to group all of the crown size coins together and therefore the earlier twenty five pence issues are not listed between the twenty pence and fifty pence denominations but appear below.

Obverse portrait by Arnold Machin

LL1

LL1 **Twenty-five pence.** (Crown.) Silver Wedding Commemorative. ℞. The initials E P on a background of foliage, figure of Eros above the Royal Crown with the inscription 'ELIZABETH AND PHILIP' above and the dates '20 NOVEMBER 1947 – 1972' below. (Reverse design: Arnold Machin.)

1972 ....£2
— Proof *FDC* (in 1972 Set, See PS22)* £6
— Silver proof *FDC* (Issued: 100,000) £35

LL2

LL2 **Twenty-five pence.** (Crown.) Silver Jubilee Commemorative. ℞. The Ampulla and Anointing Spoon encircled by a floral border and above a Royal Crown. (Obverse and reverse design: Arnold Machin.)

1977 ....Unc £1; BU £2
— BU in presentation folder £2
— Proof *FDC* (in 1977 Set, See PS27)* £5
— Silver proof *FDC* (Issued: 377,000) £30

* Coins marked thus were originally issued in Royal Mint sets.

LL3   LL4

LL3 Twenty-Five pence. (Crown.) Queen Mother's 80th Birthday Commemorative.
R. In the centre a portrait of The Queen Mother surrounded by bows and lions with
the inscription 'QUEEN ELIZABETH THE QUEEN MOTHER 4 AUGUST 1980'.
(Reverse design: Richard Guyatt.)
1980...Unc £2; BU £2
—   BU in presentation folder £3
—   Silver proof *FDC* (Issued: 83,672) £35

LL4 Twenty-five pence. (Crown.) Royal Wedding Commemorative. R. .Portrait of the Prince
of Wales and Lady Diana Spencer with the inscription 'HRH THE PRINCE OF WALES
AND LADY DIANA SPENCER 1981'. (Reverse design: Philip Nathan.)
1981...Unc £2; BU £3
—   BU in presentation folder £4
—   Silver proof *FDC* (Issued: 218,142) £35

Obverse portrait by Raphael Maklouf

L1

L1   Five pounds. (Crown.) Queen Mother's 90th Birthday Commemorative. R. A
Cypher in the letter E in duplicate above a Royal Crown flanked by a rose and a
thistle all within the inscription 'QUEEN ELIZABETH THE QUEEN MOTHER'
and the dates '1900 – 1990'. (Reverse design: Leslie Durbin.)
1990...Unc £7; BU £8
—   BU in presentation folder (Issued: 45,250) £10
—   Proof in silver *FDC* (Issued: 56,102)...£35
—   Proof in gold *FDC* (Issued: 2,500)..£2000

L2

L2   Five pounds. (Crown.) 40th Anniversary of the Coronation. R. St Edward's Crown encircled by forty trumpets all within the inscription 'FAITH AND TRUTH I WILL BEAR UNTO YOU' and the dates '1953 – 1993'. (Reverse design: Robert Elderton.)

1993...Unc £7; BU £8
—   BU in presentation folder...£9
—   Proof *FDC* (in 1993 set, see PS51)*...£12
—   Proof in silver *FDC* (Issued: 58,877)..£35
—   Proof in gold *FDC* (Issued: 2,500)..£2000

L3

L3   Five pounds. (Crown.) 70th Birthday of Queen Elizabeth II. R. A representation of Windsor Castle with five flag poles, two holding forked pennants with anniversary dates '1926' and '1996', the other flags are Royal Arms, the Union flag and Our Personal flag. Edge inscription: 'VIVAT REGINA ELIZABETHA'. (Reverse design: Avril Vaughan.)

1996...Unc £7; BU £8
—   BU in presentation folder (issued: 73,311) £10
—   Proof *FDC* (in 1996 set, See PS57)* £10
—   Proof in silver *FDC* (Issued: 39,336)...£35
—   Proof in gold *FDC* (Issued: 2,127)...£2000

* Coins marked thus were originally issued in Royal Mint sets.

L4

L4   **Five pounds.** (Crown.) Golden Wedding of Queen Elizabeth II and Prince Philip.
Conjoint portraits of The Queen and Prince Philip. ℞. A pair of shields, chevronwise,
on the left, Our Royal Arms, on the right, the shield of Prince Philip, above a Royal
Crown separating the dates '1947' and '1997' with the date '20 NOVEMBER', below
an anchor cabled with the denomination 'FIVE POUNDS'. (Obverse design:
Philip Nathan, reverse design: Leslie Durbin.)
1997...Unc £7; BU £8
— BU in presentation folder...£10
— Proof *FDC* (in 1997 set, See PS59)*...£10
— Proof in silver *FDC* (Issued: 33,689)...£35
— Proof in gold *FDC* (Issued: 2,574)..£2000

Obverse portrait by Ian Rank-Broadley

L5

L5   **Five pounds.** (Crown.) Prince Charles' 50th Birthday. ℞. A portrait of Prince
Charles and in the background words relating to the work of The Prince's Trust.
A circumscription of 'FIFIETH BIRTHDAY OF HRH PRINCE OF WALES'
and below 'FIVE POUNDS' flanked by the anniversary dates '1948' and '1998'.
(Reverse design: Michael Noakes/Robert Elderton.)
1998...Unc £8; BU £9
— BU in presentation folder...£10
— Proof *FDC* (in 1998 set, see PS61)*..£15
— Proof in silver *FDC* (Issued: 13,379)..£50
— Proof in gold *FDC* (Issued: 773)..£2200

* Coins marked thus were originally issued in Royal Mint sets.

L6

L6 **Five pounds.** (Crown.) Diana, Princess of Wales Memorial. R. A portrait of Diana, Princess of Wales with the dates '1961' and '1997', and the circumscription 'IN MEMORY OF DIANA, PRINCESS OF WALES' with the value 'FIVE POUNDS'. (Reverse design: David Cornell.)

1999...Unc £7; BU £9
— BU in presentation folder £12
— Proof *FDC* (in 1999 set, see PS63)* £15
— Proof in silver *FDC* (Issued: 49,545)...£40
— Proof in gold *FDC* (Issued: 7,500)..£3000

L7   L7A

L7 **Five pounds.** (Crown.) Millennium commemorative. R. A representation of the dial of a clock with hands set at 12 o'clock with a map of the British Isles and the dates '1999' and '2000' and the words 'ANNO DOMINI' and the value 'FIVE POUNDS'. Edge inscription 'WHAT'S PAST IS PROLOGUE' in serif or sans serif font. (Reverse design: Jeffrey Matthews.)

1999...Unc £6; BU £7
— BU in presentation folder £10
— Proof in silver *FDC* (Issued: 49,057)...£35
— Proof in gold *FDC* (Issued: 2,500)..£1900
2000 BU £12
— BU in presentation folder £20
— Proof *FDC* (in 2000 set, see PS65)* £15
— Proof in gold *FDC* (Issued: 1,487)..£1900
L7A 2000
— BU in presentation folder with Dome mint mark £20
    (See illustration above - the mintmark is located within the shaded area at 3 o'clock).
L7B 2000
— Proof in 0.999 silver *FDC* (Issued: 14,255)...£50
(The reverse design is the same as the 1999 issue but with the British Isles highlighted with 22 ct. gold.)

* *Coins marked thus were originally issued in Royal Mint sets.*

L8   L9

L8 **Five pounds.** (Crown.) Queen Mother's 100th Birthday. R. A portrait of the
Queen Mother flanked by groups of people with the circumscription 'QUEEN
ELIZABETH THE QUEEN MOTHER' the anniversary dates '1900' and '2000'
below, and the denomination 'FIVE POUNDS'. Below the portrait a representation
of her signature. (Reverse design: Ian Rank-Broadley.)

2000 ....Unc £6; BU £7
—   BU in presentation folder £10
—   Proof in silver *FDC* (Issued: 31,316) £40
—   Proof piedfort in silver *FDC* (Issued: 14,850) £80
—   Proof in gold *FDC* (Issued: 3,000)..£1900

L9 **Five pounds.** (Crown.) Victorian Anniversary. R. A classic portrait of the young
Queen Victoria based on the Penny Black postage stamp with a V representing
Victoria, and taking the form of railway lines and in the background the iron
framework of the Crystal Palace, and the denomination '5 POUNDS' and the dates
'1901' and '2001'. (Reverse design: Mary Milner-Dickens.)

2001 ....Unc £6; BU £7
—   BU in presentation folder £10
—   Proof *FDC* (in 2001 set, see PS68)* £12
—   Proof in silver *FDC* (Issued: 19,216) £45
—   Proof in gold *FDC* (Issued: 2,098)..£2000

L9A —   Proof in silver *FDC* with 'reverse frosting' giving matt appearance (Issued:596)
(Crown issued with sovereigns of 1901 and 2001)* £200

L9B —   Proof in gold *FDC* with 'reverse frosting' giving matt appearance.(Issued:733)
(Crown issued with four different type sovereigns of Queen Victoria, - Young
Head with shield, and Young Head with St.George reverse, Jubilee Head and
Old Head.)* £2200

* Coins marked thus were originally issued in Royal Mint sets.

L10

L10   Five pounds. (Crown.) Golden Jubilee commemorative 2002. O. Equestrian portrait
of The Queen with the inscription 'ELIZABETH II DEI GRA REGINA FID DEF'
around the circumference and 'AMOR POPULI PRAESIDIUM REG' within, and
the date '2002' below separated by the central element of the Royal Arms. R. New
portrait of The Queen with the denomination 'FIVE POUNDS'. (Obverse and
reverse designs: Ian Rank-Broadley.)

2002 ....Unc £6; BU £7
— BU in presentation folder £10
— Proof *FDC* (in 2002 set, see PS72)* £10
— Proof in silver *FDC* (Issued: 54,012) £40
— Proof in gold *FDC* (Issued: 3,500)...£2000

L11

L11   Five pounds. (Crown.) Queen Mother Memorial 2002. R. Three quarter portrait
of the Queen Mother within a wreath with the inscription 'QUEEN ELIZABETH
THE QUEEN MOTHER' and the dates '1900' and '2002'. Edge inscription
'STRENGTH, DIGNITY AND LAUGHTER'. (Reverse design: Avril Vaughan.)

2002 ....Unc £7; BU £8
— BU in presentation folder £10
— Proof in silver *FDC* (Issued: 16,117) £40
— Proof in gold *FDC* (Issued: 2,086)...£1900

* Coins marked thus were originally issued in Royal Mint sets.

L12

L12 **Five pounds.** (Crown.) 50th Anniversary of the Coronation. O. Profile portrait of
The Queen in linear form facing right with the inscription 'ELIZABETH II DEI
GRATIA REGINA F D'. Ꝟ. In the centre the inscription 'GOD SAVE THE QUEEN'
surrounded by the inscription 'CORONATION JUBILEE' the denomination 'FIVE
POUNDS' and the date '2003'. (Obverse and reverse designs: Tom Phillips.)
2003 ....Unc £7; BU £8
— BU in presentation folder (Issued: 100,481) £10
— Proof *FDC* (in 2003 set, see PS78)* £12
— Proof in silver *FDC* (Issued: 28,758) £45
— Proof in gold *FDC* (Issued: 1,896)...£2000

PSS11 - 2002/3 £5 (L10 and L12) silver proofs (2) £100

L13

L13 **Five pounds.** (Crown.) Centenary of Entente Cordiale 2004. Ꝟ. In the centre the
head and shoulders of Britannia and her French counterpart Marianne with the
inscription 'ENTENTE CORDIALE' separated by the dates '1904' and '2004'.
Obv. as L11. (Reverse design: David Gentleman)
2004 ....Unc 8; BU £10
— BU in presentation folder (Issued: 16,507) £20
— Proof *FDC* with reverse frosting (Issued: 6,065)...£20
— Proof in silver *FDC* (Issued: 11,295) £60
— Proof piedfort in silver *FDC* (Issued: 2,500) £150
— Proof in gold *FDC* (Issued: 926)...£2000
— Proof piedfort in platinum *FDC* (Issued: 501) £3000

* Coins marked thus were originally issued in Royal Mint sets.

L14   L15

L14 **Five pounds.** (Crown.) 200th Anniversary of the Battle of Trafalgar 2005. R. A
depiction of the two British ships, HMS Victory and Temeraine, in the midst of the
battle, the central design surrounded by the inscription 'TRAFALGAR' and the
dates '1805' and '2005'. Edge inscription 'ENGLAND EXPECTS THAT EVERY
MAN WILL DO HIS DUTY'. Obv. as L11. (Reverse design: Clive Duncan.)
*Note: Only the precious metal versions have edge inscriptions, the CuNi coins have a
milled edge.*
2005..Unc £8; BU £10
— BU in presentation folder (Issued: 79,868) £15
— Proof *FDC* (in 2005 set, see PS84)* £15
— Proof in silver *FDC* (Issued: 21,448) £40
— Proof piedfort in silver *FDC* (see PSS16)* £75
— Proof in gold *FDC* (Issued: 1,805)..£2000

L15 **Five pounds.** (Crown.) 200th Anniversary of the Death of Nelson 2005. R. A portrait
of Lord Nelson in the uniform of a Vice Admiral accompanied by the inscription
'HORATIO NELSON' and the dates '1805' and '2005'. Edge inscription 'ENGLAND
EXPECTS THAT EVERY MAN WILL DO HIS DUTY'. Obv. as L11.
(Reverse design: James Butler.)
*Note: Only the precious metal versions have edge inscriptions, the CuNi coins have a
milled edge.*
2005 ....Unc £8; BU £10
— BU in presentation folder (Issued: 72,498) £15
— Proof *FDC* (in 2005 set, see PS84)* £15
— Proof in silver *FDC* (Issued: 12,852) £40
— Proof piedfort in silver *FDC* (see PSS16)* £75
— Proof in gold *FDC* (Issued: 1,760) £2000
— Proof piedfort in platinum *FDC* (Edition: 200) £3000

US31 - 2005 £5 (L14 and L15) BU in folder (2) £25
PSS16 - 2005 £5 (L14 and L15) silver proof piedforts (2).....................................£150

* Coins marked thus were originally issued in Royal Mint sets.

L16

L16 **Five pounds.** (Crown.) 80th Birthday of Her Majesty Queen Elizabeth II. R. A fanfare of regal trumpets with the inscription 'VIVAT REGINA' and the dates '1926' and '2006'. Edge inscription 'DUTY SERVICE FAITH'. Obv. as L11. (Reverse design: Danuta Solowiej-Wedderburn.)

2006...Unc £6; BU £7
— BU in presentation folder...£10
— Proof *FDC* (in 2006 set, see PS87)*...£12
— Proof in silver *FDC* (Issued: 20,790)...£45
— Proof in gold *FDC* (Issued: 2,750)..£2000
— Proof piedfort in platinum *FDC* (Issued: 250)...£3000
L16A — Proof piedfort in silver with selected gold plating *FDC* (Issued: 5,000)..................£65

L17

L17 **Five pounds.** (Crown.) Diamond Wedding Anniversary of Her Majesty Queen Elizabeth II and The Duke of Edinburgh. O. Conjoint portrait of The Queen and Prince Philip. R. The Rose window of Westminster Abbey with the inscription 'TVEATVR VNITA DEVS', the dates '1947' and '2007', the denomination 'FIVE POUNDS'. Edge inscription 'MY STRENGTH AND STAY'. (Obverse design: Ian Rank-Broadley, reverse design: Emma Noble.)

2007...Unc £6; BU £7
— BU in presentation folder...£10
— Proof *FDC* (in 2007 set, see PS90)*...£15
— Proof in silver *FDC* (Issued: 15,186)..£45
— Proof piedfort in silver *FDC* (Issued: 2,000)...£65
— Proof in gold *FDC* (Issued: 2,380)...£2000
— Proof piedfort in platinum *FDC* (Issued: 250)...£3000

* Coins marked thus were originally issued in Royal Mint sets.

L18   L19

L18   Five pounds. (Crown.) 450th Anniversary of the Accession of Queen Elizabeth
I. ℞. A portrait of Queen Elizabeth I surrounded by four Tudor roses placed at the
centre points of connecting arches, with two side panels containing details taken
from carvings made by Robert Dudley, Earl of Leicester, found at the Tower of
London, the design being encircled by the inscription 'ELIZABETH REGINA' with
the dates 'MDLVIII' and 'MMVIII'. Edge inscription 'I HAVE REIGNED WITH
YOUR LOVES' on the precious metal versions. Obv. as L11. (Reverse design:
Rod Kelly.)

2008..Unc £8; BU £10
—   BU in presentation folder (Issued: 26,700)..£12
—   Proof *FDC* (in 2008 set, see PS93)*..£15
—   Proof in silver *FDC* (Issued: 9,216)..£50
—   Proof piedfort in silver *FDC* (Issued: 1,602)...£80
—   Proof in gold *FDC* (Issued: 1,500)...£2000
—   Proof piedfort in platinum *FDC* (Issued: 125)..£3250

L19   Five pounds. (Crown.) Prince of Wales 60th Birthday. ℞. A profile portrait of
His Royal Highness The Prince of Wales with the inscription 'THE PRINCE OF
WALES' above and '1948 ICH DIEN 2008' below. Edge inscription 'SIXTIETH
BIRTHDAY' on the precious metal versions. Obv. as L11. (Reverse design :
Ian Rank-Broadley.)

2008..Unc £8; BU £10
—   BU in presentation folder (Issued: 54,746)..£12
—   Proof *FDC* (in 2008 set, see PS93)*..£15
—   Proof in silver *FDC* (Issued: 6,264)..£50
—   Proof piedfort in silver *FDC* (Issued: 1,088)...£80
—   Proof in gold *FDC* (Issued: 867)...£2000
—   Proof in platinum *FDC* (Issued: 54)...£3250

* Coins marked thus were originally issued in Royal Mint sets.

L20   L20   L21

L20   **Five pounds.** (Crown.) 500th Anniversary of the Accession of Henry VIII. ℞. A design inspired by a Holbein painting of King Henry VIII, set within a tressure and surrounded by the inscription 'THE ACCESSION OF HENRY VIII 1509' and the denomination 'FIVE POUNDS'. Edge inscription 'ROSA SINE SPINA' on the precious metal versions. Obv. as L6. (Reverse design: John Bergdahl.)

2009 ....Unc £8; BU £10
—   BU in presentation folder (Issued: 67,119) £12
—   Proof *FDC* (in 2009 set, see PS97)* £15
—   Proof in silver *FDC* (Issued: 10,419))...£50
—   Proof piedfort in silver *FDC* (Issued: 3,580) £80
—   Proof in gold *FDC* (Issued: 1,130)..£2000
—   Proof piedfort in platinum *FDC* (Issued: 100) £3250

L21   **Five pounds.** (Crown.) 350th Anniversary of the Restoration of the Monarchy. ℞. A design featuring a crown, a spray of oak leaves, interlinked 'C's, the date '1660', the inscription 'RESTORATION OF THE MONARCHY' and the denomination 'FIVE POUNDS'. Edge inscription 'A QUIET AND PEACEFUL POSSESSION' on the precious metal versions. (Reverse design: David Cornell.)

2010 ....Unc £8; BU £10
—   BU on presentation card (Edition: 150,000) £12
—   BU in presentation folder (Edition: 50,000)..£12
—   Proof *FDC* (in 2010 set, see PS101)* £15
—   Proof in silver *FDC* (Issued: 6,518) £45
—   Proof piedfort in silver *FDC* (Issued: 4,435) £80
—   Proof in gold *FDC* (Issued: 1,182)..£2000
—   Proof piedfort in platinum *FDC* (Edition: 100) £3250

No £5 cupro-nickel crowns have been issued at face value by banks or post offices since 2010.

* Coins marked thus were originally issued in Royal Mint sets.

SPINK
COINS OF ENGLAND 2021
E-book available on Amazon, iBookstore,
Google, Kobo, OverDrive
and across most other platforms

For more information or enquiries please contact
Tel: +44 (0)20 7563 4119 | Email: books@spink.com
69 Southampton Row, Bloomsbury, London WC1B 4ET

WWW.SPINKBOOKS.COM

L22

L22   **Five pounds.** (Crown.) Royal Wedding commemorative. R.A design featuring facing portraits of His Royal Highness Prince William and Miss Catherine Middleton with the inscription 'WILLIAM AND CATHERINE' above and the date '29 APRIL 2011 below. (Reverse design: Mark Richards.)

2011
— BU in presentation folder (Issued: 250,000) £18
— Proof in silver *FDC* (Issued: 26,069) £60
— Proof in silver with gold plating *FDC* (Issued: 7,451) £75
— Proof piedfort in silver *FDC* (Issued: 2,991)..£120
— Proof in gold *FDC* (Issued: 2,066) £2000
— Proof piedfort in platinum *FDC* (Issued: 133) £3250

L23

L23   **Five pounds.** (Crown.) 90th Birthday of Prince Philip. R. A profile portrait of His Royal Highness The Duke of Edinburgh with the inscription 'PRINCE PHILIP 90TH BIRTHDAY' and the denomination 'FIVE POUNDS' and the date '2011'. (Reverse design: Mark Richards.)

2011
— BU in presentation folder (Issued: 18,370) £20
— Proof *FDC* (in 2011 set, see PS104)* £20
— Proof in silver *FDC* (Issued: 4,599)..£70
— Proof piedfort in silver *FDC* (Issued: 2,659) £90
— Proof in gold *FDC* (Issued: 636) £2000
— Proof piedfort in platinum *FDC* (Issued: 49)..£3250

* Coins marked thus were originally issued in Royal Mint sets.

L24

L24 Five pounds. (Crown.) Diamond Jubilee commemorative 2012. O. Our Effigy, inspired by the sculpture mounted in the entrance to the Supreme Court building on Parliament Square, with the inscription 'ELIZABETH. II. D. G. REG. F. D. FIVE POUNDS'. R. Our Effigy first used on United Kingdom coins from 1953, with an olive branch and ribbon below, the date '2012' to the left and the inscription 'DIRIGE DEVS GRESSVS MEOS' to the right. Edge inscription 'A VOW MADE GOOD' on the precious metal coins. (Obverse and reverse designs: Ian Rank-Broadley)
2012
— BU in presentation folder (Issued: 484,775) £10
— Proof *FDC* (in 2012 set, see PS107)* £10
— Proof in silver *FDC* (Issued: 16,370 including coins in sets) £50
— Proof in silver with gold plating *FDC* (Issued: 12,112)...................................... £60
— Proof piedfort in silver *FDC* (Issued: 3,187) £85
— Proof in gold *FDC* (Issued: 1,085).. £2200
— Proof piedfort in platinum *FDC* (Issued: 20) £3500

L25

L25 Five pounds. (Crown.) 60th Anniversary of the Coronation. R. In the centre The Imperial State Crown with the inscription 'TO REIGN AND SERVE' and 'A VOW MADE GOOD'. (Reverse design: Emma Noble.)
2013
— BU in presentation folder £13
— Proof *FDC* (in 2013 set, see PS109)* £10
— Proof in silver *FDC* (Issued: 4,050 including coins in sets) £60
— Proof in silver with gold plating *FDC* (Issued: 2,547)....................................... £80
— Proof piedfort in silver *FDC* (Issued: 2,686 including coins in sets)................... £95
— Proof in gold *FDC* (Issued: 418 including coins in sets) £2500
— Proof piedfort in platinum *FDC* (Issued: 106) £3250

* Coins marked thus were originally issued in Royal Mint sets.

L26

L26   **Five pounds.** (Crown.) Commemorative coin to mark the birth of a son to the
Duke and Duchess of Cambridge. R. A depiction of St. George armed, sitting on
horseback, attacking the dragon with a sword, and a broken spear upon the ground,
and the date of the year. (Reverse design: Benedetto Pistrucci.)
2013
— Proof in silver *FDC* (Issued: 7,460) £80

L27

L27   **Five pounds.** (Crown.) The Christening of Prince George of Cambridge. R. A
deconstructed silver lily font incorporating cherubs and roses, with a Baroque-style
cartouche with the inscription 'DIEU ET MON DROIT' and 'TO CELEBRATE
THE CHRISTENING OF PRINCE GEORGE OF CAMBRIDGE 2013' in the
centre of the coin. (Reverse design: John Bergdahl.)
2013
— BU in presentation folder £20
— Proof in silver *FDC* (Issued: 7,264) £80
— Proof piedfort in silver *FDC* (Issued: 2,251) £140
— Proof in gold *FDC* (Issued: 486) £2200
— Proof piedfort in platinum *FDC* (Issued: 38) £3500

* Coins marked thus were originally issued in Royal Mint sets.

L28   L29

L30   L31

L28-L31 Five pounds. (Crown.) The Queen's Portraits. Obverse design depicts the Royal
Arms with the date '2013' below. (Obverse design: James Butler.)

  2013

  L28 ℞. The portrait of The Queen by Mary Gillick with the inscription
  'ELIZABETH II DEI GRATIA REGINA F.D.' and the denomination 'FIVE
  POUNDS' below.

  L29 ℞. The portrait of The Queen by Arnold Machin with the inscription
  'ELIZABETH II D: G: REG: F:D: FIVE POUNDS'.

  L30 ℞. The portrait of The Queen by Raphael Maklouf with the inscription
  'ELIZABETH II DEI. GRATIA. REGINA. F.D.' and the denomination 'FIVE
  POUNDS' below.

  L31 ℞. The portrait of The Queen by Ian Rank-Broadley with the inscription
  'ELIZABETH II D. G. REG. F.D. and the denomination 'FIVE POUNDS' below.

PSS54 - 2013 £5 (L28-L31) silver proofs (4) (Issued: 1465)......................................£350
PSS55 - 2013 £5 (L28-L31) silver proofs piedforts (4) (Issued: 697) £600
PGCS15 - 2013 £5 (L28-L31) gold proofs (4) (Issued: 148)...................................£9000

L32

L32   Five pounds. (Crown.) Queen Anne commemorative. ℞. The effigy of Queen Anne enclosed by baroque decoration including the Royal Arms from the reign of Queen Anne and surrounded by the inscription 'QUEEN ANNE DEI GRATIA 1665-1714'. (Reverse design: Mark Edwards.)
2014
— BU in presentation folder £25
— Proof *FDC* (in 2014 set, see PS112)* £25
— Proof in silver *FDC* (Issued: 2212 including coins in sets) £80
— Proof in silver with gold plating *FDC* (Issued: 627).. £100
— Proof piedfort in silver *FDC* (Issued: 636 including coins in sets).................... £160
— Proof in gold *FDC* (Issued: 253 including coins in sets) £2500
— Proof piedfort in platinum *FDC* (Edition: 150) £3500

L33

L33   Five pounds. (Crown.) Commemorative coin to mark the first birthday of Prince George of Cambridge. ℞. The four Quarterings of Our Royal Arms each contained in a shield and arranged in saltire with, in the intervening spaces, a Rose, a Thistle, both slipped and leaved, a sprig of shamrock and a Leek, in the centre the Crown and in the base the date of the year. (Reverse design: Edgar Fuller.)
2014
— Proof in silver *FDC* (Issued: 7,451) £80

* Coins marked thus were originally issued in Royal Mint sets.

L34   L35

L36   L37

L34-L37 Five pounds. (Crown.) Celebrating British Landmarks I.
  2014

> **L34** ℞. The head of one of the lions in Trafalger Square with Nelson's column in the background and the inscription 'FIVE POUNDS'.
> **L35** ℞. A view of the Elizabeth Tower and the inscription 'FIVE POUNDS'.
> **L36** ℞. Tower Bridge and the inscription 'FIVE POUNDS'.
> **L37** ℞. The Victoria Memorial with Buckingham Palace in the background and the inscription 'FIVE POUNDS'.
> (All reverse designs: Glyn Davies and Laura Clancy)

PSS60 - 2014 £5 (L34-L37) silver proofs with colour (4) (Issued: 1,299) £325

L38

L38   **Five pounds.** (Crown.) 50th Anniversary of the Death of Winston Churchill.
℞. A portrait of Winston Churchill with the inscription 'CHURCHILL'. Edge
inscription on the precious metal versions 'NEVER FLINCH, NEVER WEARY,
NEVER DESPAIR'. (Reverse design: Mark Richards.)
2015
— BU in presentation pack £20
— Proof *FDC* (in 2015 set, see PS115)* £25
— Proof in silver *FDC* (Issued: 4,902 including coins in sets)...................£70
— Proof piedfort in silver *FDC* (Issued: 2,234 including coins in sets) £160
— Proof in gold *FDC* (Issued: 374) £2000
— Proof piedfort in platinum *FDC* (Issued: 90)..£3500

L39

L39   **Five pounds.** (Crown.) Bicentenary of the Battle of Waterloo. ℞. A depiction of the
Duke of Wellington greeting the Prussian General Gebhard Leberecht von Blucher
after the Battle of Waterloo with the inscription 'THE BATTLE OF WATERLOO
1815'with the edge inscription on the precious metal versions 'THE NEAREST RUN
THING YOU EVER SAW' (Reverse design: David Lawrence).
2015
— BU in presentation pack..£20
— Proof *FDC* (in 2015 set, see PS117)* £20
— Proof in silver *FDC* (Issued: 664, only in sets) £80
— Proof piedfort in silver *FDC* (Issued: 434, only in sets)........................£130
— Proof in gold *FDC* (Issued: 99, only in sets) £2500

Obverse portrait by Jody Clark

L39A

L39A Five pounds. (Crown.) Bicentenary of the Battle of Waterloo, R. As L39
2015
— Proof in silver *FDC* (Issued: 2,523)..£70
— Proof piedfort in silver *FDC* (Issued: 896) £120
— Proof in gold *FDC* (Issued: 273) £2000

L40

L40 Five pounds. (Crown.) The Second Child of The Duke and Duchess of Cambridge.
R. An ornamental cartouche in the centre featuring the inscription 'THE DUKE AND
DUCHESS OF CAMBRIDGE 2015' surrounded by the inscription 'TO CELEBRATE
THE BIRTH OF THE SECOND CHILD'. (Reverse design: John Bergdahl.)
2015
— Proof in silver *FDC* (Edition: 9,500) £80
— Proof in gold *FDC* (Edition: 350)..£2200

COINS OF ENGLAND

SPINK
COINS OF ENGLAND 2021
E-book available on Amazon, iBookstore,
Google, Kobo, OverDrive
and across most other platforms
For more information or enquiries please contact
Tel: +44 (0)20 7563 4119 | Email: books@spink.com
69 Southampton Row, Bloomsbury, London WC1B 4ET
WWW.SPINKBOOKS.COM

L41

L41 **Five pounds.** (Crown.) The Christening of Princess Charlotte of Cambridge. R. A design depicting a deconstructed silver lily font incorporating cherubs,with a Baroque - Style cartouche and 'DIEU ET – MON DROIT' below and in the centre the inscription 'TO CELEBRATE THE CHRISTENING OF PRINCESS CHARLOTTE ELIZABETH DIANA OF CAMBRIDGE 2015' (Reverse design: John Bergdahl).
2015
- — BU in presentation pack..£25
- — Proof in silver *FDC* (Issued: 4,842)..£80
- — Proof in gold *FDC* (Issued: 350) £2200

L42

L42 **Five pounds.** (Crown.) Prince George's Second Birthday. R. A design depicting St George slaying the dragon and the date '2015'. (Reverse design: Christopher Le Brun).
2015
- — Proof in silver *FDC* (Issued: 4,009)..£80

Obverse portrait by James Butler

L43

L43   **Five pounds.** (Crown.) The Longest Serving Monarch. R. St Edwards crown in
the centre and the date '1952'and '2015' above and 'ONE CROWN' below. Edge
inscription on the precious metal versions 'LONG TO REIGN OVER US'.
(Obverse and reverse designs: James Butler).
2015

— BU in presentation pack £13
— Proof in silver *FDC* (Issued:10,249)...£60
— Proof piedfort in silver *FDC* (Issued: 3,171) £90
— Proof in gold *FDC* (Issued: 899) £2200
— Proof piedfort in platinum *FDC* (Issued: 88)..£3500

Obverse portrait by Jody Clark

L44

L44   **Five pounds.** (Crown.) 90th Birthday of Her Majesty Queen Elizabeth II. R. A crowned
Royal Cypher above the number '90' encircled by roses. Edge inscription 'FULL OF
HONOUR AND YEARS' on the precious metal versions. (Reverse design:
Christopher Hobbs.)
2016 BU (Issued: 10,181) £10
— Specimen in presentation folder (Issued: 74,195)....................................£15
— Proof *FDC* (in 2016 set, see PS119)* £15
— Proof in silver *FDC* (Issued: 9,988)...£60
— Proof piedfort in silver *FDC* (Issued: 3,555) £90
— Proof in gold *FDC* ((Issued: 988) £2200
— Proof piedfort in platinum *FDC* (Issued: 87).......................................£3500

* Coins marked thus were originally issued in Royal Mint sets.

L45   L46

L47   L48

L45-L48 Five pounds. (Crown.) Celebrating British Landmarks II.
  2016
      L45 Ɽ. The White Cliffs of Dover.
      L46 Ɽ. The Giant's Causeway.
      L47 Ɽ. The Lake District.
      L48 Ɽ. Snowdonia.
      (All reverse designs: Glyn Davies and Laura Clancy.)
  PSS71 - 2016 £5 (L45-L48) silver proofs with colour (4) (Issued: 1,098) £325

COINS OF ENGLAND & THE UNITED KINGDOM
PRE-DECIMAL ISSUES

STANDARD CATALOGUE OF BRITISH COINS
SPINK
2021

SPINK

COINS OF ENGLAND 2021
E-book available on Amazon, iBookstore,
Google, Kobo, OverDrive and across
most other platforms

For more information or enquiries please contact
Tel: +44 (0)20 7563 4119 | Email: books@spink.com
69 Southampton Row, Bloomsbury, London WC1B 4ET

WWW.SPINKBOOKS.COM

L49

L49 **Five pounds.** (Crown.) 100th Anniversary of the House of Windsor. R. A depiction of the crowned badge of the House of Windsor surrounded by a garland of oak leaves accompanied by the inscription ' CENTENARY OF THE HOUSE OF WINDSOR', and the year of the date. Edge inscription 'THE CHRISTENING OF A DYNASTY' on the precious metal versions. (Reverse design: Timothy Noads.)
2017

— BU in presentation folder £13
— BU in presentation folder to mark the engagement of Prince Harry and
  Meghan Markle (Issued: 5,000) £20
— Proof *FDC* (in 2017 set, see PS122)* £15
— Proof in silver *FDC* (Edition: 13,000 including coins in sets)............................. £60
— Proof piedfort in silver *FDC* (Edition: 5,500).. £90
— Proof in gold *FDC* (Issued: 523 including coins in sets) £2000

L50

L50 **Five pounds.** (Crown.) 1000th Anniversary of the Coronation of King Canute.
R. Stylised portrait of Canute accompanied by the inscription '1017 CANUTE 2017'.
Edge inscription 'TIME AND TIDE WAIT FOR NO MAN' on the precious metal
versions. (Reverse design: Lee R. Jones.)
2017

— BU in presentation folder (Issued: 26,567) £13
— Proof *FDC* (in 2017 set, see PS122)* £15
— Proof in silver *FDC* (Issued: 3,873 including coins in sets) £60
— Proof piedfort in silver *FDC* (Issued: 1,432 including coins in sets)................... £95
— Proof in gold *FDC* (Issued: 239 including coins in sets) £2500

* Coins marked thus were originally issued in Royal Mint sets.

L51

L51 **Five pounds.** (Crown.) Sapphire Jubilee of Her Majesty Queen Elizabeth II.
R. A depiction of the Imperial State Crown accompanied by the inscription 'MY
WHOLE LIFE, WHETHER IT BE LONG OR SHORT, DEVOTED TO YOUR
SERVICE' and surrounded by the inscription 'SAPPHIRE JUBILEE' along with the
dates '1952-2017'. Edge inscription 'SHINE THROUGH THE AGES' on the precious
metal versions.
(Reverse design: Glyn Davies.)
2017
— BU in presentation folder £13
— Proof in silver *FDC* (Issued: 8,260) £83
— Proof piedfort in silver *FDC* (Issued: 2,471) £155
— Proof in gold *FDC* (Issued: 697) £2200

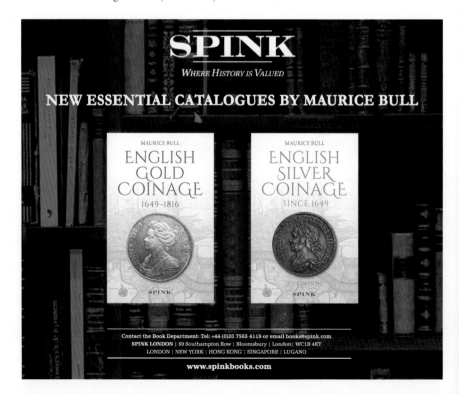

L52   L53

L54   L55

L52-L55 Five pounds. (Crown.) Celebrating British Landmarks III.
    2017

        L52 R. The door of 10 Downing Street.
        L53 R. Hampton Court Palace.
        L47 R. Edinburgh Castle.
        L48 R. Westminster Abbey.
        (All reverse designs: Glyn Davies and Laura Clancy.)
    PSS77 - 2017 £5 (L52-L55) silver proofs with colour (4) (Edition: 2017).................. £325

COINS OF ENGLAND

SPINK

COINS OF ENGLAND 2021
E-book available on Amazon, iBookstore,
Google, Kobo, OverDrive
and across most other platforms

For more information or enquiries please contact
Tel: +44 (0)20 7563 4119 | Email: books@spink.com
69 Southampton Row, Bloomsbury, London WC1B 4ET

WWW.SPINKBOOKS.COM

L56

L56 Five pounds. (Crown.) Prince Philip Celebrating a Life of Public Service. ℞. A portrait
of His Royal Highness Prince Philip, The Duke of Edinburgh accompanied by the
inscription 'HIS ROYAL HIGHNESS THE DUKE OF EDINBURGH' and 'NON SIBI
SED PATRIAE'. (Reverse design: Humphrey Paget.)
2017
—   BU in presentation folder (Issued: 29,097 .... £13
—   Proof in silver *FDC* (Issued: 2,524) £83
—   Proof piedfort in silver *FDC* £155
—   Proof in gold *FDC* (Issued: 299) £2200

L57

L57 Five pounds. (Crown.) Celebrating the Platinum Wedding Anniversary of HM The
Queen and HRH Prince Philip. O. Our effigy conjoined with His Royal Highness
Prince Philip, The Duke of Edinburgh with the inscription 'ELIZABETH II D G REG
F D – PHILIP PRINCEPS' and the denomination 'FIVE POUNDS'. ℞. A depiction
of Our effigy and that of His Royal Highness Prince Philip, The Duke of Edinburgh
on horseback with the inscription 'WEDDED LOVE HAS JOINED THEM IN
HAPPINESS' with the dates '1947-2017'. Edge inscription 'FELICES JUNXIT
CONUBIALIS AMOUR' on precious metal versions. (Obverse design: Etienne Milner,
reverse design: John Bergdahl.)
2017
—   BU in presentation folder £13
—   Proof in silver *FDC* (Edition: 15,950) £83
—   Proof piedfort in silver *FDC* (Issued: 2,268) £155
—   Proof in gold *FDC* (Edition: 1,250) £2000

L58

L58 **Five pounds.** (Platinum.) Celebrating the Platinum Wedding Anniversary of HM
The Queen and HRH Prince Philip. O. Our effigy conjoined with His Royal Highness
Prince Philip, The Duke of Edinburgh with the inscription 'ELIZABETH II D G REG
F D – PHILIP PRINCEPS' and the denomination 'FIVE POUNDS'. Ŗ. A depiction
of Our arms and those of His Royal Highness Prince Philip, The Duke of Edinburgh
above the inscription '70 YEARS OF MARRIAGE 2017'. Edge inscription 'FELICES
JUNXIT CONUBIALIS AMOUR'. (Obverse design: Etienne Milner, reverse design:
John Bergdahl.)

2017
— Proof Platinum Piedfort *FDC* (Edition: 125) £3500

L59

L59 **Five pounds**. (Crown.) Christmas 2017. Ŗ. A depiction of a decorated Christmas tree
accompanied by the inscription 'CHRISTMAS TREE 2017'. (Reverse design:
Edwina Ellis.)

2017 BU in presentation folder (Issued: 38,407) £13

L60   L61

L60 **Five pounds**. (Crown.) Remembrance Day. ℞. (Reverse design: Stephen Taylor).
2017
— BU in presentation folder £17
— Proof in silver *FDC* (Edition: 5,000) £83
— Proof piedfort in silver *FDC* (Edition: 1,500) £155

L61 Five pounds. (Crown.) Sapphire Coronation. ℞. A garlanded depiction of the Royal Arms
below a depiction of Our Royal Cypher, accompanied by the inscription 'SAPPHIRE
ANNIVERSARY 1953 - 2018. Edge inscription 'SHINE THROUGH THE AGES' on
the precious metal versions. (Reverse design: Stephen Taylor.)
2018
— BU in presentation folder £13
— Proof in silver *FDC* (Edition: 6,650) £83
— Proof piedfort in silver *FDC* (Edition: 2,000)...................................... £155
— Proof in gold *FDC* (Edition: 600) £2200

L62

L62 **Five pounds.** (Crown.) Prince Charles' 70th Birthday. ℞. A depiction of His Royal
Highness The Prince of Wales with the inscription 'H.R.H. THE PRINCE OF WALES'
and '70TH BIRTHDAY'. (Reverse design: Robert Elderton.)
2018
— BU in presentation folder £13
— Proof in silver *FDC* (Edition: 4,500) £83
— Proof piedfort in silver *FDC* (Edition: 1,000)...................................... £155
— Proof in gold *FDC* (Edition: 375) £2200
— Proof piedfort in platinum *FDC* (Edition: 70) £3500

L63   L64

L63 **Five pounds.** (Crown.) 5th Birthday of Prince George. R. A depiction of St George
slaying a dragon accompanied by the date'2018'. (Reverse design: Jody Clark.)
2018
— BU in presentation folder £13
— Proof *FDC* (in 2018 set) (see PS125)* £20
— Proof in silver *FDC* (Edition: 6,650) £83
— Proof piedfort in silver *FDC* (Edition: 1,000 in set PSS80) £155
— Proof in gold *FDC* (Edition: 175 in set PGCS28) £3000

L64 **Five pounds.** (Crown.) 250th Anniversary Royal Academy. R. A depiction of the
façade of Burlington House with the inscription 'A PLACE TO MAKE, EXHIBIT AND
DEBATE ART – ROYAL ACADEMY OF ARTS 1768 – 2018'. (Reverse Design:
Sir Christopher Chipperfield RA.)
2018
— Proof in silver *FDC* (Edition: 2,750) £83

C/N BU coins have been reported but there is yet no evidence of any Royal Mint sale of these.

L65

L65 **Five pounds.** (Crown.) Royal Wedding of Prince Harry and Meghan Markle. R. A
depiction of His Royal Highness Prince Henry of Wales and Rachel Meghan Markle
with the inscription 'ROYAL WEDDING – 19 MAY 2018' and 'HARRY AND
MEGHAN'. (Reverse design: Jody Clark).
2018
— Specimen in presentation folder.. £13
— Proof in silver *FDC* (Edition: 16,000) £83
— Proof piedfort in silver *FDC* (Edition: 2,220)...................................... £155
— Proof in gold *FDC* (Edition: 1,000) £1980

* Coins marked thus were originally issued in Royal Mint sets.

L66-L69 **Five pounds.** (Crown.) Celebrating British Landmarks IV.
2018
  L66 ℞. Tenby Harbour.
  L67 ℞. Blackpool Tower.
  L68 ℞. Brighton Pier.
  L69 ℞. Southwold Beach
  (All reverse designs: Glyn Davies and Laura Clancy.)
  PSS82 - 2018 £5 (L66-L69) silver proofs with colour (4) (Edition: 2018)................... £325

COINS OF
ENGLAND
& THE UNITED KINGDOM
PRE-DECIMAL ISSUES

STANDARD CATALOGUE OF BRITISH COINS
SPINK
2021

SPINK

COINS OF ENGLAND 2021
E-book available on Amazon, iBookstore,
Google, Kobo, OverDrive and across
most other platforms

For more information or enquiries please contact
Tel: +44 (0)20 7563 4119 | Email: books@spink.com
69 Southampton Row, Bloomsbury, London WC1B 4ET

WWW.SPINKBOOKS.COM

L70

L70 Five pounds. (Crown.) Celebrating Four Generations of the Royal Family. ℞. A depiction
of Our initial accompanied by those of His Royal Highness The Prince of Wales, His
Royal Highness The Duke of Cambridge and His Royal Highness Prince George
of Cambridge, royally crowned, above an oak garland with the inscription 'FOUR
GENERATIONS OF THE ROYAL FAMILY' and the date 2018. (Reverse design:
Timothy Noad.)

2018
— BU in presentation folder £13
— Proof in silver *FDC* (Edition: 5,000) £83
— Proof piedfort in silver *FDC* (Edition: 2,000).. £155
— Proof in gold *FDC* (Edition: 500) £2200

L71   L72

L71 Five pounds. (Crown.) Remembrance Day. ℞. A section of a poppy accompanied by
the inscription 'REMEMBRANCE'. (Reverse design: Laura Clancy.)

2018
— BU in folder... £17
— Proof in silver *FDC* (Edition: 2,500) £83
— Proof piedfort in silver *FDC* (Edition: 1,500).. £170

L72   **Five pounds.** (Crown.) Christmas 2018. The Nutcracker. (Reverse design:
Harry Brockway.)

2018
BU in folder... £13

L73

L73 **Five pounds.** (Crown.) Tower of London. R. A depiction of a raven and a section of a plan of Mint Street accompanied by the inscription 'TOWER OF LONDON'. Edge inscription 'ON INTO TWILIGHT WITHIN WALLS OF STONE'. (Reverse design: Glyn Davies.)

2019 BU £11
— BU in folder... £13
— Proof in silver *FDC* (Edition: 4000) £83
— Proof piedfort in silver *FDC* (Edition:1160)....................................... £155
— Proof in gold *FDC* (Edition: 385) £2200

L74

L74 **Five pounds.** (Crown.) Tower of London. R. A depiction of the crown of Mary of Modena and a section of a plan of Mint Street accompanied by the inscription 'TOWER OF LONDON'. Edge inscription 'ON INTO TWILIGHT WITHIN WALLS OF STONE'. (Reverse design: Glyn Davies.)

2019 BU £11
— BU in folder... £13
— Proof in silver *FDC* (Edition: 4000) £83
— Proof piedfort in silver *FDC* (Edition:1160)....................................... £155
— Proof in gold *FDC* (Edition: 385) £2200

L75

L75 **Five pounds.** (Crown.) Tower of London. R. A depiction of a Yeoman Warder and a section of a plan of Mint Street accompanied by the inscription 'TOWER OF LONDON'. Edge inscription 'ON INTO TWILIGHT WITHIN WALLS OF STONE'. (Reverse design: Glyn Davies.)

2019 BU £11
— BU in folder.. £13
— Proof in silver *FDC* (Edition: 4000) £83
— Proof piedfort in silver *FDC* (Edition:1160).................................... £155
— Proof in gold *FDC* (Edition: 385) £2200

L76

L76 **Five pounds.** (Crown.) Tower of London. R. A depiction of Queen Elizabeth's keys and a lamp and a section of a plan of Mint Street accompanied by the inscription 'TOWER OF LONDON'. Edge inscription 'ON INTO TWILIGHT WITHIN WALLS OF STONE'. (Reverse design: Glyn Davies.)

2019 BU £11
— BU in folder.. £13
— Proof in silver (Edition: 4000) £83
— Proof piedfort in silver *FDC* (Edition:1160).................................... £155
— Proof in gold *FDC* (Edition: 385) £2200

L77

L77   Five pounds. (Crown.) 200th Anniversary of the Birth of Queen Victoria. Ŗ. A depiction of Queen Victoria surrounded by gears enclosing scenes portraying achievements of the Victorian age and the inscription 'VICTORIA 1819 – 2019'. Edge inscription: WORKSHOP OF THE WORLD on the precious metal versions. (Reverse design: John Bergdahl.)

2019
— BU (also included in the 2019 BU Coin set)...£11
— BU in folder... £13
— Proof *FDC* (in 2019 set, see PS128)* £20
— Proof in silver *FDC* (Edition: 7,500) £83
— Proof piedfort in silver *FDC* (Edition: 2,750) £155
— Proof in gold *FDC* (Edition: 725) £2500

L78

L78   Five pounds. (Crown.) Centenary of Remembrance Day Ŗ. A depiction of a poppy with the inscription 'WE WILL REMEMBER THEM' and the dates, '1919' and '2019'. (Reverse design: Harry Brockway.)

2019
— BU in folder... £17
— Proof in silver *FDC* (Edition: 4,100) £90
— Proof piedfort in silver *FDC* (Edition: 785).. £170
— Proof in gold *FDC* (Edition: 240) £2500

L79

L79 **Five pounds.** (Crown.) 200th Anniversary of the death of King George III. R. Portrait of George III with symbols of his kingdom framed by his crown. Edge inscription 'I GLORY IN THE NAME OF BRITON' on the precious metal versions. (Reverse design: Dominique Evans.)

2020 BU* £10
—   BU in folder.. £13
—   Proof* £20
—   Proof in silver *FDC* (Edition: 2,500 plus coins in sets) £83
—   Proof piedfort in silver *FDC* (Edition: 550 plus coins in sets) £155
—   Proof in gold *FDC* (Edition: 250 plus coins in sets)... £2640

L80

L80 **Five pounds.** (Crown.) 250th Anniversary of the birth of William Wordsworth. R. A mountainous landscape and lakes as a backdrop to the words "Nature never did betray the heart that loved her" taken from the Wordsworth poem 'Lines Written a few miles above Tintern Abbey'. Edge inscription 'I WANDERED LONELY AS A CLOUD' on the precious metal versions. (Reverse design: David Lawrence.)

2020 BU* £10
—   BU in folder.. £13
—   Proof in silver *FDC* (Edition: 3,000) £83
—   Proof in gold *FDC* (Edition: 300) £2640

* Coins marked thus were originally issued in Royal Mint sets.

L81

L81   Five pounds. (Crown.) Tower of London II. The White Tower. R. The Iconic Mace
of Office carried by the Chief Yeoman Warder, with edge inscription 'THE WHITE
TOWER' on the precious metal versions. (Reverse design: Timothy Noad.)
2020 BU £10
— BU in folder... £13
— Proof in silver *FDC* (Edition: 2,510) £83
— Proof piedfort in silver *FDC* (Edition: 460)... £155
— Proof in gold *FDC* (Edition: 135) £2640

L82

L82   Five pounds. (Crown.) Tower of London II. The Royal Menagerie. R. Three lions
set against a Norman arched window from the White Tower. Edge inscription 'THE
ROYAL MENAGERIE'. (Reverse design: Timothy Noad.)
2020 BU £10
— BU in folder... £13
— Proof in silver *FDC* (Edition: 1,510) £83
— Proof piedfort in silver *FDC* (Edition: 410)... £155
— Proof in gold *FDC* (Edition: 135) £2640

L83

L83 **Five pounds.** (Crown.) Tower of London II. R. The Royal Mint. (Reverse design: Timothy Noad.)

2020 BU £10
—   BU in folder.. £13
—   Proof in silver *FDC* (Edition: 1,510) £83
—   Proof piedfort in silver *FDC* (Edition: 410).. £155
—   Proof in gold *FDC* (Edition: 135) £2640

L84

L84 **Five pounds.** (Crown.) Tower of London II. R. The Infamous Prison. (Reverse design: Timothy Noad.)

2020 BU £10
—   BU in folder.. £13
—   Proof in silver *FDC* (Edition: 1,510) £83
—   Proof piedfort in silver *FDC* (Edition: 410).. £155
—   Proof in gold *FDC* (Edition: 135) £2640

L85

L85   Five pounds. (Crown.) 150th Anniversary of the British Red Cross. ℞. Map of UK
with cross (in red on the c/n and silver versions) in the centre with inscription '1870
BRITISH RED CROSS 2020' and 'THE POWER OF KINDNESS'. Edge inscription
'PER HUMANITATEM AD PACEM' on the precious metal versions. (Reverse design:
Henry Gray.)

2020 BU £10
—   BU in folder.. £17
—   Proof in silver *FDC* (Edition: 4,000) £90
—   Proof piedfort in silver *FDC* (Edition: 1,150).................................. £170
—   Proof in gold FDC (Edition: 250) £2640

L86

L86   Five pounds. (Crown.) 75th Anniversary of the End of the Second World War. ℞. The
words "WAR" and "PEACE" typographically intersected to capture the sense of the
conflict abating and the dawn of a new era. Edge inscription 'THROUGH COURAGE
AND ENDURANCE' on the precious metal versions. (Reverse design: Matt Dent and
Christian Davies.)

2020 BU £10
—   BU in folder.. £13
—   Proof in silver FDC (Edition: 2,575)... £83
—   Proof piedfort in silver FDC (Edition: 565)...................................... £155
—   Proof in gold FDC (Edition: 225) £2640
Additional coins with this design may be struck for inclusion in sets.

L87 **Five pounds.** (Crown.) Remembrance Day, 2020.
 2020 BU £10
 — BU in folder.. £13
 — Proof in silver FDC £83
 — Proof piedfort in silver FDC £155
L88 **Five pounds.** (Crown.) 95th Birthday of Her Majesty Queen Elizabeth II.
 2021 BU* £10
 — BU in folder.. £13
 — Proof* £20
 — Proof in silver FDC £83
 — Proof piedfort in silver FDC £155
 — Proof in gold FDC £2640
L89 **Five pounds.** (Crown.) 150th Anniversary of the Royal Albert Hall.
 2021 BU £10
 — BU in folder.. £13
 — Proof in silver FDC £83
 — Proof piedfort in silver FDC £155
 — Proof in gold FDC £2640

* Coins marked thus were originally issued in Royal Mint sets.

Prior to decimalisation, the Royal Mint had issued proof sets mainly at the start of a new reign or for significant Royal events and details of these may be found in our companion volume *Coins of England & the United Kingdom Pre-Decimal Issues*. A final proof set of the £sd coinage was issued in 1970 and the proof sets listed in this catalogue follow on from the catalogue number of that set. To enable the public to be familiar with the new decimal coins, a blue wallet containing the 10p down to the ¹/2p was issued from June 1968 with the bronze coins dated 1971

In 1982 the Royal Mint issued its first uncirculated set and from 1984 onwards the coins in these sets had a superior finish to coins issued for circulation which the Mint called brilliant uncirculated. Loose coins from such sets are listed as BU.

Some coins previously listed here as sets but comprising usually just two coins of the same denomination have now been listed immediately following the corresponding single coins and we hope that users of this catalogue will find this more convenient.

In addition to the annual sets of proof and uncirculated coins sold by the Royal Mint to collectors and dealers, the Mint has produced specially packaged sets and single coins for companies. No details have been made available of these issues and therefore no attempt has been made to include them in the listings although the most well-known of such sets are the 1983 uncirculated sets produced for the Martini and Heinz companies some of which contained the 2p mule (see C2A). The Mint also sells 'Wedding' and 'Christening' sets in distinctive packaging but the numbers circulating in the market are relatively modest and of limited appeal after the year of issue.

In more recent years the Mint has offered sets of coins to collectors that include coins obtained from the secondary market. It is considered that these are beyond the scope of this catalogue.

The sets that immediately follow are sets containing currency type coins. Sets comprising gold sovereign coins, Britannia gold and silver and other special series are listed later after the relevant section

Uncirculated Sets

			£
US00–**MD**	10p,5p,2p,1p,¹/2p in blue wallet	(5)	1
US01–**1982**	Uncirculated (specimen) set in Royal Mint folder, 50p to ½p, new reverse type, including 20 pence (Issued: 205,000)	(7)	9
US02–**1983**	'U.K.' £1 to ½p (Issued: 637,100)	(8)	15
US03–**1984**	'Scottish' £1 to ½p (Issued: 158,820)	(8)	15
US04–**1985**	'Welsh' £1 to 1p, new portrait of The Queen (Issued: 102,015)	(7)	13
US05–**1986**	'Commonwealth Games' £2 plus 'Northern Irish' £1 to 1p, (Issued: 167,224)	(8)	18
US06–**1987**	'English' £1 to 1p, (Issued: 172,425)	(7)	14
US07–**1988**	'Arms' £1 to 1p, (Issued: 134,067)	(7)	15
US08–**1989**	'Scottish' £1 to 1p, (Issued: 77,569)	(7)	20
US09–**1989**	£2 (K2 and K3) BU in folder	(2)	40
US10–**1990**	'Welsh' £1 to 1p plus new smaller 5p, (Issued: 102,606)	(8)	16
US11–**1991**	'Northern Irish' £1 to 1p, (Issued: 74,975)	(7)	15
US12–**1992**	'English' £1, 'European Community' 50p and 'Britannia' 50p, 20p to 1p plus new smaller 10p (Issued: 78,421)	(9)	80
US13-**1992**	50p (H4 and H5) BU in folder	(2)	75
US14–**1993**	'UK' £1, 'European Community' 50p to 1p ((Issued: 56,945)	(8)	80
US15–**1994**	'Bank of England' £2, 'Scottish' £1 and 'D-Day' 50p to 1p, (Issued: 177,971)(8)		15
US16–**1995**	'Peace' £2 and 'Welsh' £1 to 1p (Issued: 105, 647)	(8)	18
US17–**1996**	'Football' £2 and 'Northern Irish' £1 to 1p (Issued: 86,501)	(8)	18
US18–**1997**	'Bimetallic' £2, 'English' £1 (4340) to 1p plus new smaller 50p (Issued: 109,557)	(9)	15
US19–**1998**	'Bimetallic' £2, 'UK' £1 and 'EU' 50 pence to1 pence (Issued: 96,192)	(9)	30
US20–**1998**	50p (H8 and H9) BU in folder	(2)	6
US21–**1999**	'Bimetallic' 'Rugby' £2, 'Scottish' £1 to 1p (Issued: 136,696)	(8)	30

US22

£

US45–**2011**	'Bimetallic' 'Mary Rose' £2, 'Bimetallic' King James Bible'£2,'Bimetallic' £2, 'Edinburgh' £1, 'Cardiff' £1, 'Royal Shield '£1, 50 pence,' WWF', 50 pence to 1 pence	(13)	80
US46–**2011**	'Bimetallic'£2, 'Royal Shield' £1, 50 pence to 1 pence	(8)	30
US47–**2011**	£1 (J30 and J31) BU in folder (Edition: 10,000)	(2)	30
US48–**2012**	Diamond Jubilee £5, struck in c/n, 'Bimetallic' 'Charles Dickens' £2, 'Bimetallic' £2 'Royal Shield' £1, 50 pence to 1 pence	(10)	39
US49–**2012**	'Bimetallic' £2 'Royal Shield '£1, 50 pence to 1 pence	(8)	21
US50–**2013**	Coronation £5, 'Bimetallic' 'Guinea' £2, 'Bimetallic' 'Roundel' £2, 'Bimetallic' 'Train' £2,'Bimetallic' £2, 'Royal Shield' £1, 'England' £1, 'Wales' £1, 50 pence 'Ironside', 50 pence to 1 pence	(15)	120
US51–**2013**	'Bimetallic' £2, 'Royal Shield '£1, 50 pence to 1 pence	(8)	40
US51A–**2013**	£1 (J32 and J33) BU in folder	(2)	£18
US51B–**2013**	£2 (K31 and K32) BU in folder	(2)	£20
US52–**2014**	Queen Anne £5, 'Bimetallic' 'Trinity House' £2, 'Bimetallic' 'World War I' £2, 'Bimetallic' £2 'Royal Shield' £1, 'Northern Ireland' £1, 'Scotland' £1, 50 pence 'Commonwealth Games', 50 pence to 1 pence	(14)	140
US53–**2014**	'Bimetallic' £2 'Royal Shield '£1, 50 pence to 1 pence	(8)	50
US53A–**2014**	£1 (J34 and J35) BU in folder	(2)	£18
US54–**2015**	Churchill £5, Waterloo £5, 'Bimetallic' 'Magna Carta' £2, 'Bimetallic' 'Royal Navy' £2, 'Bimetallic' £2 'Royal Shield' £1, 50 pence 'Battle of Britain', 50 pence to 1 pence	(13)	75
US55–**2015**	Fourth Portrait 'Bimetallic' £2 'Royal Shield' £1, 50 pence to 1 pence (Edition: 75,000)	(8)	25
US56–**2015**	Fifth Portrait 'Bimetallic' £2 'Royal Shield' £1, 50 pence to 1 pence (Edition: 75,000)	(8)	25
US57–**2016**	Queen's Birthday £5, 'Bimetallic' £2 'Comedy', 'Bimetallic' £2 'History', 'Bimetallic' £2 'Tragedy', 'Bimetallic' £2 'The Army', 'Bimetallic' £2 'Great Fire', 'Bimetallic' £2, 'Royal Shield' £1, Royal Arms £1, 50 pence 'Battle of Hastings', 50 pence to 1 pence (Issued: 22,786)	(16)	100
US58–**2016**	£2, 'Royal Shield' £1, 50 pence to 1 pence (Issued: 7,419)	(8)	25
US59–**2016**	£1 (J38 and J39A) BU in folder (Issued: 9,850)	(2)	60
US59A–**2016**	£2 (K38-K40) BU in folder (Issued: 22,060)	(3)	£28
US60–**2017**	House of Windsor £5, King Canute £5, 'Bimetallic' £2 'First World War Aviation', 'Bimetallic' £2 'Jane Austen', 'Bimetallic' £2 'Britannia', 'Bimetallic' £1, 50 pence 'Sir Isaac Newton', 50 pence to 1 pence (Issued: 27,551)	(13)	65
US61–**2017**	Bimetallic £2 'Britannia' 'Bimetallic' £1, 50 pence to 1 pence (Issued: 12,980)	(8)	30
US62–**2018**	5th Birthday Prince George £5, 'Bimetallic' £2 ' Royal Air Force Badge', 'Bimetallic' £2 'Frankenstein', 'Bimetallic' £2 ' Armistice' ...Bimetallic' £2 'Britannia', 'Bimetallic' £1, 50 pence 'Representation of People Act', 50 pence to 1 pence .	(13)	65
US63–**2018**	Bimetallic £2 'Britannia' 'Bimetallic' £1, 50 pence to 1 pence	(8)	30
US64–**2019**	200th Anniversary of the birth of Queen Victoria £5, 'Bimetallic' £2 '75th Anniversary of D-Day', 'Bimetallic' £2 'Wedgwood', 'Bimetallic' £2 'Samuel Pepys' Bimetallic' £2 'Britannia', 'Bimetallic' £1, 50 pence 'Sherlock Holmes', 50 pence to 1 pence	(13)	55
US65–**2019**	Bimetallic £2 'Britannia' 'Bimetallic' £1, 50 pence to 1 pence	(8)	30
US66–**2019**	British Culture Set of five different 50 pence designs of the past to mark the 50th Anniversary of the introduction of the 50 pence coin in 1969	(5)	45
US67–**2019**	Military Set of five different 50 pence designs of the past to mark the 50th Anniversary of the introduction of the 50 pence coin in 1969	(5)	45

£

| US68–**2020** | George III £5, 'Bimetallic' £2 'D-Day', 'Bimetallic' £2 'Mayflower', 'Bimetallic' £2 'Agatha Christie', 'Bimetallic' £2 'Britannia', 'Bimetallic' £1, 50 pence 'Team GB', 50 pence to 1 pence. ...... (13) | 55 |
| US69–**2020** | 'Bimetallic' £2 'Britannia', 'Bimetallic' £1, 50 pence 'Team GB', 50 pence to 1 pence. ...... (8) | 30 |

Proof Sets in Base Metal

PS21–**1971**	Decimal coinage set, 50 new pence 'Britannia' to $^1/2$ new pence, in sealed plastic case with card wrapper (Issued: 350,000) ...... (6)	18
PS22–**1972**	Proof 'Silver Wedding' Crown struck in c/n plus 50p to ½p (Issued: 150,000) ...... (7)	20
PS23–**1973**	'EEC' 50p plus 10p to ½p, (Issued: 100,000) ...... (6)	15
PS24–**1974**	'Britannia' 50p to ½p, as 1971 (Issued: 100,000) ...... (6)	15
PS25–**1975**	'Britannia'50p to ½p (as 1974), (Issued: 100,000) ...... (6)	12
PS26–**1976**	'Britannia' 50p to ½p, as 1975, (Issued: 100,000) ...... (6)	12
PS27–**1977**	Proof 'Silver Jubilee' Crown struck in c/n plus 50p to ½p (Issued: 193,000) ...... (7)	12
PS28–**1978**	'Britannia' 50p to ½p, as 1976, (Issued: 86,100) ...... (6)	12
PS29–**1979**	'Britannia' 50p to ½p, as 1978, (Issued: 81,000) ...... (6)	12
PS30–**1980**	'Britannia' 50p to ½p, as 1979, (Issued: 143,000) ...... (6)	15
PS31–**1981**	'Britannia' 50p to ½p, as 1980, (Issued: 100,300) ...... (6)	15
PS32–**1982**	'Britannia' 50p to ½p including 20 pence (Issued: 106,800) ...... (7)	15
PS33–**1983**	'U.K.' £1 to ½p in new packaging (Issued: 107,800) ...... (8)	15
PS34–**1984**	'Scottish' £1 to ½p, (Issued: 106,520) ...... (8)	20
PS35–**1985**	'Welsh' £1 to 1p, (Issued: 102,015) ...... (7)	20
PS36–**1985**	As last but packed in deluxe red leather case (Included above) ...... (7)	20
PS37–**1986**	'Commonwealth Games' £2 plus 'Northern Irish' £1 to 1p, (Issued: 104,597) ...... (8)	20
PS38–**1986**	As last but packed in deluxe red leather case (Included above) ...... (8)	23
PS39–**1987**	'English' £1 to 1p, (Issued: 88,659) ...... (7)	20
PS40–**1987**	As last but packed in deluxe leather case (Included above) ...... (7)	23
PS41–**1988**	'Arms' £1 to 1p, (Issued: 79,314) ...... (7)	25
PS42–**1988**	As last but packed in deluxe leather case (Included above) ...... (7)	29
PS43–**1989**	'Bill of Rights' and 'Claim of Right' £2s, 'Scottish' £1 to 1p (Issued: 85,704) ...... (9)	35
PS44–**1989**	As last but packed in red leather case, (Included above) ...... (9)	35
PS45–**1990**	'Welsh' £1 to 1p plus new smaller 5p, (Issued: 79,052) ...... (8)	27
PS46–**1990**	As last but packed in red leather case (Included above) ...... (8)	32
PS47–**1991**	'Northern Irish' £1 to 1p, (Issued: 55,144) ...... (7)	27
PS48–**1991**	As last but packed in red leather case (Included above) ...... (7)	33
PS49–**1992**	'English' £1 , 'European community' 50p and 'Britannia' 50p, 20p to 1p plus new smaller 10p, (Issued: 44,337) ...... (9)	75
PS50–**1992**	As last but packed in red leather case (Issued: 17,989) ...... (9)	75
PS51–**1993**	Proof 'Coronation Anniversary' £5 struck in c/n (4302), 'U.K.' £1, 50p to 1p, (Issued: 43,509) ...... (8)	30
PS52–**1993**	As last but packed in red leather case (Issued: 22,571) ...... (8)	35
PS53–**1994**	'Bank' £2, 'Scottish' £1, 'D-Day' 50p to 1p, (Issued: 44,643) ...... (8)	30
PS54–**1994**	As last but packed in red leather case (Issued: 22,078) ...... (8)	35
PS55–**1995**	'Peace' £2, 'Welsh' £1 to 1p, (Issued: 42,842) ...... (8)	32
PS56–**1995**	As last but packed in red leather case (Issued: 17,797) ...... (8)	35
PS57–**1996**	Proof '70th Birthday' £5 struck in c/n, 'Football' £2, 'Northern Irish' £1 to 1p, (Issued: 46,295) ...... (9)	32

PS62   PS65

			£
PS58–**1996**	As last but packed in red leather case (Issued: 21,286)................................... (9)		37
PS59–**1997**	Proof 'Golden Wedding' £5 struck in c/n, 'Bimetallic' £2, 'English' £1 to 1p plus new smaller 50p (Issued: 48,761)..(10)		33
PS60–**1997**	As last but packed in red leather case (Issued: 31,987)...................................(10)		40
PS61–**1998**	Proof 'Prince of Wales 50th Birthday'£5 struck in c/n, 'Bimetallic' £2 'UK' £1, 'EU' 50 pence to 1p. (Issued: 36,907)..(10)		40
PS62–**1998**	As last, but packed in red leather case. (Issued: 26,763)................................(10)		40
PS63–**1999**	Proof 'Diana, Princess of Wales' £5 struck in c/n, 'Bimetallic' 'Rugby' £2, 'Scottish' £1 to 1p. (Issued: 40,317)... (9)		40
PS64–**1999**	As last, but packed in red leather case. (Issued: 39,827)................................. (9)		40
PS65–**2000**	Proof 'Millennium' £5 struck in c/n, 'Bimetallic' £2, 'Welsh' £1 'Library' 50 pence and 'Britannia' 50 pence to 1p.Standard Set, (Issued: 41,379).........(10)		30
PS66–**2000**	As last, but Deluxe set (Issued: 21,573 above) ....(10)		40
PS67–**2000**	As last, but Executive set (Issued: 9,517) ....(10)		40
PS68–**2001**	Proof 'Victoria' £5 struck in c/n, 'Bimetallic' £2, 'Bimetallic' 'Marconi' £2, 'Irish' £1 to 1p. Standard Set. (Issued: 28,244)..(10)		34
PS69–**2001**	As last, but Gift Set (Issued: 1,351) ....(10)		30
PS70–**2001**	As last, but packed in red leather case (Issued: 16,022)..................................(10)		40
PS71–**2001**	As last, but Executive Set (Issued: 3,755)..(10)		40
PS72–**2002**	Proof 'Golden Jubilee' £5 struck in c/n, 'Bimetallic' £2, 'English' £1 to 1p. Standard set. (Issued: 30,884) .... (9)		32
PS73–**2002**	As last, but Gift Set (Issued: 1,544) .... (9)		30
PS74–**2002**	As last, but packed in red leather case (Issued: 23,342).................................. (9)		46
PS75–**2002**	As last, but Executive Set (Issued: 5,000).. (9)		50
PS76–**2002**	£2 (K12-K15) proofs (Issued: 3358) .... (4)		150
PS77–**2002**	£2 (K12-K15) proofs in display type case (Issued: 673).............................. (4)		150
PS78–**2003**	Proof 'Coronation'£5 struck in c/n, 'Bimetallic' 'DNA' £2, 'Bimetallic' £2, 'UK' £1, 'Suffragette' 50 pence and 'Britannia' 50 pence to 1p. Standard set. (Issued: 23,650) .... (11)		34
PS79–**2003**	As last, but packed in red leather case (Issued: 14,863)................................(11)		47
PS80–**2003**	As last, but Executive Set (Issued: 5,000)...(11)		50
PS81–**2004**	'Bimetallic' 'Penydarren engine' £2, 'Bimetallic' £2, 'Forth Rail Bridge' £1, 'Sub four-minute mile' 50 pence and 'Britannia' 50 pence to 1p. Standard set. (Issued: 17,951) ....(10)		35
PS82–**2004**	As last, but packed in red leather case (Issued: 12,968)................................(10)		45
PS83–**2004**	As last, but Executive Set (Issued: 4,101)...(10)		50
PS84–**2005**	Proof 'Trafalgar'£5 struck in c/n, Proof 'Nelson'£5 struck in c/n 'Bimetallic' 'Gunpowder Plot' £2, 'Bimetallic' £2, 'Menai Straits Bridge' £1, 'Samuel Johnson's Dictionary' 50 pence and 'Britannia' 50 pence to 1p. (Issued: 21,374). (12)		40

£

PS85–**2005**	As last, but packed in red leather case (Issued: 14,899)...................................(12)	50
PS86–**2005**	As last, but Executive Set (Issued: 4,290)..(12)	50
PS87–**2006**	Proof '80th Birthday' £5 struck in c/n, 'Bimetallic' 'Isambard Brunel' £2, 'Bimetallic' 'Paddington Station' £2, 'Bimetallic' £2, 'MacNeill's Egyptian Arch' £1, 'Victoria Cross' 50 pence, 'Wounded soldier' 50 pence and 'Britannia' 50 pence to 1p (Issued: 17,689)...(13)	42
PS88 –**2006**	As last, but packed in red leather case (Issued: 15,000)................................(13)	50
PS89 –**2006**	As last, but Executive Set (Issued: 5,000)..(13)	50
PS90 –**2007**	Proof 'Diamond Wedding' £5 struck in c/n, 'Bimetallic' 'Act of Union' £2, 'Bimetallic' 'Abolition of Slave Trade' £2, 'Gateshead Millennium Bridge' £1, 'Scouting Movement' 50 pence, and 'Britannia' 50p to 1p (Issued: 18,215)..(12)	40
PS91 –**2007**	As last, but packed in red leather case (Issued: 15,000)................................(12)	50
PS92 –**2007**	As last, but Executive Set (Issued: 5,000)..(12)	50
PS93 –**2008**	Proof 'Prince Charles 60th Birthday' £5 struck in c/n, Proof 'Elizabeth I Anniversary' struck in c/n, 'Bimetallic' 'London Olympics Centenary' £2, 'Bimetallic' £2 'UK' £1, and 'Britannia' 50p to 1p (Issued: 17,719)..............(11)	40
PS94 – **2008**	As last, but packed in black leather case (Issued: 13,614) ....(11)	50
PS95 – **2008**	As last, but Executive Set (Issued: 5,000)..(11)	50
PS96 – **2008**	'The Royal Shield of Arms', 'Royal Shield' £1 to 1p (Issued: 20,000) .... (7)	45
PS97 – **2009**	Proof 'Henry VIII' £5 struck in c/n, 'Bimetallic' 'Charles Darwin' £2 'Bimetallic' 'Robert Burns' £2 'Bimetallic' £2, 'Royal Shield' £1, 'Kew Gardens' 50p, 50 pence, 50 pence to 1 pence (Issued: 34,438 including PS98 and PS99)....(12)	200
PS98 – **2009**	As last, but packed in black leather case (Edition: 15,000) ....(12)	220
PS99 **2009**	As last, but Executive Set (Edition: 5,000) ....(12)	275
PS100–**2009**	50p set with reverse designs 1973-2009 c/n proofs (Issued: 1,039) ....(16)	240
PS101–**2010**	Proof 'Restoration of the Monarchy' £5 struck in c/n, 'Bimetallic' 'Florence Nightingale' £2, 'Bimetallic' 'London' £1, 'Belfast' £1, Royal Shield £1, 'Girl Guiding' 50 pence, and 50 pence to 1 pence (Issued: 30,844 including PS102 and PS103) ....(13)	40
PS102–**2010**	As last, but packed in black leather case ....(13)	50
PS103–**2010**	As last, but Executive Set..(13)	60
PS104–**2011**	Proof 'Prince Philip 90th Birthday' £5 struck in c/n, 'Bimetallic' 'Mary Rose' £2, 'Bimetallic' King James Bible' £2, 'Bimetallic' £2 'Edinburgh' £1, 'Cardiff' £1, 'Royal Shield' £1, 50 pence, 'WWF', 50 pence to 1 pence (Edition: 20,000) ....(14)	140
PS105–**2011**	As last, but packed in black leather case (Edition: 15,000) ....(14)	150
PS106–**2011**	As last, but Executive Set (Edition: 5,000)...……..(14)	150
PS107–**2012**	Diamond Jubilee £5, struck in c/n, 'Bimetallic' 'Charles Dickens' £2 'Bimetallic' £2 'Royal Shield '£1 50 pence to 1 pence (Issued: 21,614) ....(10)	55
PS108–**2012**	Premium Proof set, Proof Diamond Jubilee £5, struck in c/n, 'Bimetallic' 'Charles Dickens' £2, 'Bimetallic' £2 'Royal Shield '£1, 50 pence to 1 pence and Mint medal (Issued:.3,463) ....(10)	99
PS109–**2013**	Premium Proof set, Coronation £5, struck in c/n, 'Bimetallic' 'Guinea' £2 'Bimetallic' 'Roundel' £2, 'Bimetallic' 'Train' £2,'Bimetallic' £2 'Royal Shield' £1, 'England' £1, 'Wales' £1 50 pence 'Ironside', 50 pence to 1 pence (Issued:3,965) .... (15)	150
PS110–**2013**	Collector Proof set, Coronation £5, struck in c/n, 'Bimetallic' 'Guinea' £2 'Bimetallic' 'Roundel' £2, 'Bimetallic' 'Train' £2, 'Bimetallic' £2 'Royal Shield' £1, 'England' £1, 'Wales' £1, 50 pence 'Ironside', 50 pence to 1 pence (Issued:8,493)..(15)	140
PS111–**2013**	Commemorative Proof set, Coronation £5, struck in c/n, 'Bimetallic' 'Guinea' £2 'Bimetallic' 'Roundel' £2, 'Bimetallic' 'Train' £2, 'England' £1, 'Wales' £1 and 50 pence 'Ironside' (Issued: 6,121) .... (7)	130

£

PS112–**2014**   Premium Proof set, Queen Anne £5, struck in c/n, 'Bimetallic' 'Trinity House'
£2, 'Bimetallic' 'World War I' £2, 'Bimetallic' £2 'Royal Shield' £1,
'Northern Ireland' £1, 'Scotland' £1(.), 50 pence 'Commonwealth Games',
50 pence to 1 pence (Issued: 3,405) .... (14)   155

PS113–**2014**   Collector Proof set, Queen Anne £5, struck in c/n, 'Bimetallic' 'Trinity House' £2,
'Bimetallic' 'World War I' £2, 'Bimetallic' £2 'Royal Shield' £1, 'Northern
Ireland' £1, 'Scotland'£1, 50 pence 'Commonwealth Games', 50 pence to
1 pence (Issued: 6,956) .... (14)   140

PS114–**2014**   Commemorative Proof set, Queen Anne £5, struck in c/n, 'Bimetallic'
'Trinity House' £2, Bimetallic' 'World War I' £2, 'Northern Ireland' £1,
'Scotland' £1, and 50 pence 'Commonwealth Games', (Issued: 3,763)........ (6)   130

PS115–**2015**   Fourth Portrait 'Bimetallic' £2 'Royal Shield', £1, 50 pence to 1 pence
(Issued: 13,206)... (8)   60

PS116–**2015**   Fifth Portrait 'Bimetallic' £2 'Royal Shield', £1, 50 pence to 1 pence
(Issued: 22,080)... (8)   60

PS117–**2015**   Premium Proof set, Churchill £5, struck in c/n, Waterloo £5, struck in c/n 'Bimetallic'
'Magna Carta' £2, 'Bimetallic' 'Royal Navy' £2, 'Bimetallic' £2 'Royal
Shield' £1, 50 pence 'Battle of Britain' 50 pence to 1 pence (Issued: 3,559)...... (13)   155

PS118–**2015**   Collector Proof set, Churchill £5, struck in c/n, Waterloo £5, struck in c/n
'Bimetallic' 'Magna Carta' £2, 'Bimetallic' 'Royal Navy' £2, 'Bimetallic'
£2 'Royal Shield' £1, 50 pence 'Battle of Britain', 50 pence to 1 pence
(Issued: 7,895).. (13)   110

PS118–**2015**   Commemorative Proof set, Churchill £5, struck in c/n, Waterloo £5, struck in
c/n 'Bimetallic' 'Magna Carta' £2, 'Bimetallic' 'Royal Navy' £2, 50 pence
'Battle of Britain' (Issued: 4,467) .... (5)   65

PS119–**2016**   Premium Proof set, Queen's Birthday £5, struck in c/n, 'Bimetallic' £2
'Comedy', 'Bimetallic' £2 'History', 'Bimetallic' £2 'Tragedy', 'Bimetallic'
£2 'The Army', 'Bimetallic' £2 'Great Fire','Bimetallic' £2, Royal Shield' £1,
Royal Arms £1, 50 pence 'Battle of Hastings', 50 pence to 1 pence
(Issued: 3,409)... (16)   195

PS120–**2016**   Collector Proof set, Queen's Birthday £5, struck in c/n, 'Bimetallic' £2
'Comedy', 'Bimetallic' £2 'History', 'Bimetallic' £2 'Tragedy', 'Bimetallic'
£2 'The Army' 'Bimetallic' £2 'Great Fire' 'Bimetallic' £2, Royal Shield' £1,
Royal Arms £1, 50 pence 'Battle of Hastings', 50 pence to 1 pence
(Issued: 6,919)... (16)   145

PS121–**2016**   Commemorative Proof set, Queen's Birthday £5, struck in c/n, 'Bimetallic'
£2 'Comedy', 'Bimetallic' £2 'History', 'Bimetallic' £2 'Tragedy', 'Bimetallic'
£2 ' The Army' 'Bimetallic' £2 'Great Fire' Royal Arms £1, 50 pence 'Battle
of Hastings' (Issued: 3,161) .... (8)   95

PS122–**2017**   Premium Proof set, House of Windsor £5, struck in c/n , King Canute £5,
struck in c/n , 'Bimetallic' £2 'First World War Aviation', 'Bimetallic' £2
'Jane Austen', Bimetallic' £2 'Britannia', 'Bimetallic' £1, 50 pence 'Sir Isaac
Newton', 50 pence to 1 pence (Issued: 3,603)... (13)   195

PS123–**2017**   Collector Proof set, House of Windsor £5, struck in c/n , King Canute £5,
struck in c/n , 'Bimetallic' £2 'First World War Aviation', 'Bimetallic' £2
'Jane Austen', Bimetallic' £2 'Britannia', 'Bimetallic' £1, 50 pence 'Sir Isaac
Newton', 50 pence to 1 pence (Issued: 7,522) ....(13)   145

PS124–**2017**   Commemorative Proof set, House of Windsor £5, struck in c/n , King Canute
£5, struck in c/n , 'Bimetallic' £2 'First World War Aviation', 'Bimetallic' £2
'Jane Austen', 50 pence 'Sir Isaac Newton', (Issued: 2,724) .... (5)   95

PS125–**2018**   Premium Proof set, 5th Birthday Prince George £5, struck in c/n ,'Bimetallic'
£2 ' Royal Air Force Badge', 'Bimetallic' £2 'Frankenstein', 'Bimetallic'
£2 ' Armistice' Bimetallic' £2 'Britannia', 'Bimetallic' £1, 50 pence
'Representation of People Act', 50 pence to 1 pence (Edition: 5,000)........... (13)   210

£

PS126–**2018** Collector Proof set, 5th Birthday Prince George £5, struck in c/n , 'Bimetallic'
£2 ' Royal Air Force Badge', 'Bimetallic' £2 'Frankenstein', 'Bimetallic'
£2 ' Armistice' Bimetallic' £2 'Britannia', 'Bimetallic' £1, 50 pence
'Representation of People Act', 50 pence to 1 pence (Edition: 10,000 .... (13)   155

PS127–**2018** Commemorative Proof set, 5th Birthday Prince George £5, struck in c/n ,
'Bimetallic' £2 ' Royal Air Force Badge', 'Bimetallic' £2 'Frankenstein',
'Bimetallic' £2 ' Armistice' 50 pence 'Representation of People Act',
(Edition: 5,000 .... (5)   95

PS128–**2019** Premium Proof set, 200th Anniversary of the birth of Queen Victoria £5,
struck in c/n , 'Bimetallic' £2 '75th Anniversary of D-Day', 'Bimetallic' £2
'Wedgewood', 'Bimetallic' £2 'Samuel Pepys' Bimetallic' £2 'Britannia',
'Bimetallic' £1, 50 pence 'Sherlock Holmes', 50 pence to 1 pence
(Edition:5,000) .... (13)   210

PS129–**2019** Collector Proof set, 200th Anniversary of the birth of Queen Victoria £5,
struck in c/n , 'Bimetallic' £2 '75th Anniversary of D-Day', 'Bimetallic' £2
'Wedgewood', 'Bimetallic' £2 ' Samuel Pepys' Bimetallic' £2 'Britannia',
'Bimetallic' £1, 50 pence 'Sherlock Holmes', 50 pence to 1 pence
(Edition: 10,000) .... (13)   155

PS130–**2019** British Culture Set of five different 50 pence designs of the past to mark the
50th Anniversary of the introduction of the 50 pence coin in 1969.
(Edition: 3,500) .... (5)   90

PS131–**2019** Military Set of five different 50 pence designs of the past to mark the 50th
Anniversary of the introduction of the 50 pence coin in 1969, (Edition: 3,500) (5)   90

PS132–**2020** Premium proof set, George III £5, 'Bimetallic' £2 'D-Day', 'Bimetallic' £2
'Mayflower', 'Bimetallic' £2 'Agatha Christie', 'Bimetallic' £2 'Britannia',
'Bimetallic' £1, 50 pence 'Team GB', 50 pence to 1 pence. (Edition: 2,500) (13)   210

PS133–**2020** Collector Proof set. George III £5, 'Bimetallic' £2 'D-Day', 'Bimetallic' £2
'Mayflower', 'Bimetallic' £2 'Agatha Christie', 'Bimetallic' £2 'Britannia',
'Bimetallic' £1, 50 pence 'Team GB', 50 pence to 1 pence. (Edition: 7,000) (13)   155

Proofs Sets in Silver

PSS01–**1989** £2 (K2 and K3) silver piedfort proofs (Issued: 10,000) .... (2)   85
PSS02–**1989** £2 (K2 and K3) silver proofs.. (2)   65
PSS03–**1990** 5p (D3 and D4) silver proofs (Issued: 35,000)... (2)   25
PSS04–**1992** 10p (F3 and F4) silver proofs…... (2)   30
PSS05–**1996** 25th Anniversary of Decimal Currency £1 to 1p silver proof (Edition: 15,000) (7)   125
PSS06–**1997** 50p (H4 and H7) silver proofs (Issued: 10,304)... (2)   45
PSS07–**1998** 50p (H9 and H10) silver proofs... (2)   60
PSS08–**2000** 'Millennium' £5, 'Bimetallic' £2, 'Welsh' £1, 50p to 1p, and Maundy coins,
4p-1p, in silver proof (Issued: 13,180) .... (13) 275
PSS09–**2002** £2 (K12-K15) silver proofs (Issued: 2553) .... (4)   180
PSS10–**2002** £2 (K12A-K15A) silver proof piedfort (Issued: 3497) .... (4)   300
PSS11–**2002/3** £5 (L10 and L12) silver proofs.. (2)   100
PSS12–**2003** 'Coronation' £5, 'Britannia' £2, 'Bimetallic' 'DNA' £2, 'UK' £1 and
'Suffragette' 50 pence silver proofs (Edition:) .... (5)   165
PSS13–**2004** 'Entente Cordiale' £5, 'Britannia' £2, 'Bimetallic' 'Penydarren engine' £2
'Forth Rail Bridge' £1 and 'Sub four-minute mile' 50 pence silver proofs
(Edition:) .... (5)   165
PSS14–**2004** 'Bimetallic' 'Penydarren engine' £2, 'Forth Rail Bridge' £1, 'Sub four-minute
mile' 50 pence Silver piedfort proofs .... (3)   145
PSS15–**2005** 'Bimetallic' 'Gunpowder Plot' £2, Bimetallic 'World War II' £2, 'Menai Straits
Bridge' £1, 'Samuel Johnson's Dictionary' 50 pence Silver piedfort proofs ... (4)   190
PSS16–**2005** £5 (L14 and L15) silver proof piedforts... (2)   150

£

PSS17–**2006**   'H M The Queen's 80th Birthday' £5, 'Bimetallic' £2, 'Northern Ireland' £1,
                 50p to 1p and Maundy Coins, 4p – 1p, in silver proof (Edition: 8,000) .... (13)   275

PSS18–**2006**   £2 (K20 and K21) silver proofs.. (2)   70

PSS19–**2006**   £2 (K20 and K21) silver piedfort proofs .... (2)   130

PSS20–**2006**   50p (H15 and H16) silver proofs.. (2)   65

PSS21–**2006**   50p (H15 and H16) silver piedfort proofs .... (2)   115

PSS22–**2006**   '80th Birthday' £5, 'Bimetallic' 'Isambard Brunel' £2 and 'Bimetallic'
                 'Paddington Station' £2, 'MacNeill's Egyptian Arch' £1, 'Victoria Cross'
                 50 pence, 'Wounded soldier' 50 pence silver piedforts (Edition: taken from
                 individual coin limits) .... (6)   325

PSS23–**2007**   'Diamond Wedding' £5, Britannia £2, 'Bimetallic' 'Act of Union' £2, 'Bimetallic'
                 'Abolition of Slavery' £2, 'Millennium Bridge' £1 and 'Scout Movement' 50p
                 in silver proof (Edition: taken from individual coin limits) .... (6)   200

PSS24–**2007**   'Diamond Wedding' £5, 'Bimetallic' 'Act of Union' £2, 'Bimetallic' 'Abolition
                 of Slavery' £2, 'Millennium Bridge' £1 and 'Scout Movement' 50p in silver
                 piedfort (Edition: taken from individual coin limits .... (5)   250

PSS25–**2004/7** £1 (J18-J21) silver proofs... (4)   115

PSS26–**2004/7** £1 (J18-J21) silver proof piedforts .... (4)   200

PSS27–**2008**   'Emblems of Britain', 'UK' £1, 'Britannia' 50 pence , 20 pence to 1p silver
                 proofs (Issued: 8,168).. (7)   150

PSS28–**2008**   'The Royal Shield of Arms', 'Royal Shield' £1 to 1p silver proof
                 (Issued: 10,000)... (7)   160

PSS29–**2008**   As above but silver piedforts (Issued: 3,000)... (7)   295

PSS30–**2008**   £1 with reverse designs 1983-2007 and with selected gold plating silver proofs
                 (Issued: 2,005)... (14)   395

PSS31–**2008**   Set of 3 £1 Regional designs for Scotland with selected gold plating to the
                 reverse designs (Edition: 750, taken from above)... (3)   95

PSS32–**2008**   Set of 3 £1 Regional designs for Wales with selected gold plating to the reverse
                 designs (Edition: 750, taken from above) .... (3)   95

PSS33–**2008**   Set of 3 £1 Regional designs for Northern Ireland with selected gold plating
                 to the reverse designs (Edition: 750, taken from above)................................. (3)   95

PSS34–**2008**   Set of 3 £1 Regional designs for England with selected gold plating to the
                 reverse designs (Edition: 750, taken from above)... (3)   95

PSS35–**2008**   'Prince Charles 60th Birthday' £5, 'Elizabeth I Anniversary' £5, Britannia £2,
                 'London Olympic Centenary' £2 and 'UK' £1 silver proofs (Issued: 1,182)... (5)   180

PSS36–**2008**   'Prince Charles 60th Birthday' £5, 'Elizabeth I Anniversary' £5, 'London
                 Olympic Centenary' £2 and 'Royal Shield' £1 silver piedforts (Issued: 1,746) (4)   250

PSS37–**2009**   'Henry VIII' £5, 'Bimetallic' 'Charles Darwin' £2, Bimetallic 'Robert Burns' £2
                 'Bimetallic' £2, 'Royal Shield' £1, 'Kew Gardens' 50 pence, 50 pence, 20 pence,
                 10 pence, 5 pence, 2 pence and 1 pence silver proofs (Issued: 7,500) .... (12)   400

PSS38–**2009**   'Henry VIII' £5, Britannia £2, 'Charles Darwin' £2, 'Robert Burns' £2, 'Royal
                 Shield' £1 and 50 pence 'Kew Gardens' silver proofs (Edition; 1,500)............. (6)   275

PSS39–**2009**   'Henry VIII' £5, 'Charles Darwin' £2, 'Robert Burns' £2 and 50 pence 'Kew
                 Gardens' silver piedforts (Edition: 2,500) .... (4)   255

PSS40–**2009**   50p Set with reverse designs 1973-2009 silver proofs (Issued: 1,168)............ (16)   425

PSS41–**2010**   'Restoration of the Monarchy' £5, 'Bimetallic 'Florence Nightingale' £2,
                 'Bimetallic' £2, 'London' £1, 'Belfast' £1, Royal Shield £1, 'Girl Guiding'
                 50 pence, and 50 pence to 1p silver proofs (Edition: 3,500)........................... (13)   300

PSS42–**2010**   'Restoration of the Monarchy' £5, 'Bimetallic 'Florence Nightingale' £2,
                 'London' £1, 'Belfast' £1, and 'Girl Guiding' 50 pence silver proofs
                 (Edition: 2,500) .... (5)   180

PSS43–**2010**   'Restoration of the Monarchy' £5, 'Bimetallic 'Florence Nightingale' £2
                 'London' £1, 'Belfast' £1, and 'Girl Guiding' 50 pence () silver piedforts
                 (Edition: 2,500) .... (5)   300

£

PSS44-**2011**	Proof 'Prince Philip 90th Birthday' £5,'Bimetallic' 'Mary Rose' £2, 'Bimetallic' King James Bible'£2,'Bimetallic' £2 'Edinburgh' £1, 'Cardiff' £1, 'Royal Shield '£1, 50 pence,' WWF', 50 pence to 1 pence silver proofs (Edition: 2,500)	(14)	450

PSS44-**2011** Proof 'Prince Philip 90th Birthday' £5,'Bimetallic' 'Mary Rose' £2, 'Bimetallic' King James Bible'£2,'Bimetallic' £2 'Edinburgh' £1, 'Cardiff' £1, 'Royal Shield '£1, 50 pence,' WWF', 50 pence to 1 pence silver proofs (Edition: 2,500) .... (14) 450

PSS45-**2011** Proof 'Prince Philip 90th Birthday' £5 ,'Bimetallic' 'Mary Rose' £2, 'Bimetallic' King James Bible'£2, 'Edinburgh' £1, 'Cardiff' £1, 50 pence,' 'WWF', silver proofs (Edition: 1,500) .... (6) 285

PSS46-**2011** Proof 'Prince Philip 90th Birthday' £5,'Bimetallic' 'Mary Rose' £2, 'Bimetallic' King James Bible'£2, 'Edinburgh' £1, 'Cardiff' £1, 'WWF', silver piedforts (Edition: 2,000) .... (6) 455

PSS47–**2012** Proof Diamond Jubilee £5, 50 pence to 1 pence silver proofs (Edition: 995) (7) 395

PSS48–**2012** Proof Diamond Jubilee £5, 'Bimetallic' 'Charles Dickens' £2, 'Bimetallic' £2 'Royal Shield '£1 50 pence to 1 pence silver proofs, £1 to 1 pence with selected gold plating (Edition: 2,012) .... (10) 490

PSS50–**2013** Proof 'Coronation' £5, 'Bimetallic' 'Guinea' £2 'Bimetallic' 'Roundel', 'Bimetallic' 'Train' £2,'Bimetallic' £2 'Royal Shield' £1, 'England' £1, 'Wales' £1, 50 pence 'Ironside', 50 pence to 1 pence silver proofs (Issued: 985) ..... (15) 600

PSS51–**2013** Proof 'Coronation' £5, 'Bimetallic' 'Guinea' £2 'Bimetallic' 'Roundel' £2, 'Bimetallic' 'Train'£2, 'England' £1, 'Wales' £1 and 50 pence 'Ironside' silver piedfort (Issued: 486)........................... (7) 650

PSS52–**2013** £1 (J32 and J33) silver proofs .... (2) 100

PSS53–**2013** £2 (K31 and K32) silver proofs (Issued: 2204) .... (2) 100

PSS53A–**2013** £2 (K31 and K32) silver proof piedforts .... (2) 200

PSS54–**2013** £5 (L28-L31) silver proofs (Issued: 1465)........................... (4) 350

PSS55–**2013** £5 (L28-L31) silver proofs piedforts (Issued: 697) .... (4) 600

PSS56–**2013** £1 (J13, J26, J27) silver proofs (Issued: 1,311) .... (3) 150

PSS57–**2014** Proof 'Queen Anne' £5, 'Bimetallic' 'Trinity House' £2, 'Bimetallic' 'World War I' £2, 'Bimetallic' £2 'Royal Shield' £1, 'Northern Ireland' £1, 'Scotland' £1, 50 pence 'Commonwealth Games', 50 pence to 1 pence silver proofs (Issued: 368) .... (14) 560

PSS58–**2014** Proof 'Queen Anne' £5, 'Bimetallic' 'Trinity House' £2, 'Bimetallic' 'World War I' £2, 'Bimetallic' £2 'Royal Shield' £1, 'Northern Ireland' £1, 'Scotland' £1, and 50 pence 'Commonwealth Games', silver proofs (Issued: 283)....... (6) 295

PSS59–**2014** Proof 'Queen Anne' £5, 'Bimetallic' 'Trinity House' £2, 'Bimetallic' 'World War I' £2, 'Bimetallic' £2 'Royal Shield'£1, 'Northern Ireland' £1, 'Scotland' £1, and 50 pence 'Commonwealth Games', silver piedforts (Issued: 487).... (6) 570

PSS60–**2014** £5 (L34-L37) silver proofs with colour (Issued: 1,299) .... (4) 325

PSS61–**2014** See after 4885 in World War I section

PSS62–**2015** Fourth Portrait 'Bimetallic' £2 'Royal Shield', £1, 50 pence to 1 pence, silver proofs, (Issued: 1,241) .... (8) 240

PSS63–**2015** Fifth Portrait 'Bimetallic' £2 'Royal Shield', £1, 50 pence to 1 pence, silver proofs, (Issued: 1,876) .... (8) 240

PSS64–**2015** Churchill £5, Waterloo £5, 'Bimetallic' 'Magna Carta' £2, 'Bimetallic' 'Royal Navy' £2, 'Bimetallic' £2 'Royal Shield' £1, 50 pence 'Battle of Britain' 50 pence to 1 pence silver proofs (Issued: 298) ....(13) 560

PSS65–**2015** Churchill £5, Waterloo £5, 'Bimetallic' 'Magna Carta' £2, 'Bimetallic' 'Royal Navy' £2, 50 pence 'Battle of Britain' , silver proofs (Issued: 366)... (5) 295

PSS66–**2015** Churchill £5, Waterloo £5, 'Bimetallic' 'Magna Carta' £2, 'Bimetallic' 'Royal Navy' £2, 50 pence 'Battle of Britain', silver piedforts (Issued: 434)....... (5) 570

PSS67–**2015** See after 4861 in World War I section

PSS68–**2016** Collector Proof set, Queen's Birthday £5, 'Bimetallic' £2 'Comedy''Bimetallic' £2 'History', 'Bimetallic' £2 'Tragedy', 'Bimetallic' £2 'The Army' 'Bimetallic' £2 'Great Fire' 'Bimetallic' £2, Royal Shield' £1, Royal Arms £1, 50 pence 'Battle of Hastings' 50 pence to 1 pence silver proofs (Issued: 383) .... (16) 595

£

PSS69–**2016** Commemorative Proof set, Queen's Birthday £5, 'Bimetallic' £2 'Comedy',
'Bimetallic' £2 'History', 'Bimetallic' £2 'Tragedy', 'Bimetallic' £2 'The
Army' 'Bimetallic' £2 'Great Fire' Royal Arms £1, 50 pence 'Battle of
Hastings' silver proofs (Issued: 658) .... (8)   395

PSS70–**2016** Commemorative Proof set, Queen's Birthday £5, 'Bimetallic' £2 'Comedy',
'Bimetallic' £2 'History', 'Bimetallic' £2 'Tragedy', 'Bimetallic' £2 'The
Army', 'Bimetallic' £2 'Great Fire', Royal Arms £1, 50 pence 'Battle of
Hastings' silver piedforts (Issued: 456) .... (8)   595

PSS71–**2016** £5 (L45-L48) silver proofs with colour (Issued: 1,098) .... (4)   325

PSS72–**2016** See after 4867 in World War I section

PSS73–**2017** Collector Proof set, House of Windsor £5, King Canute £5, 'Bimetallic' £2
'First World War Aviation', 'Bimetallic' £2 'Jane Austen', Bimetallic' £2
'Britannia', 'Bimetallic' £1, 50 pence 'Sir Isaac Newton', 50 pence to 1 pence
silver proofs (Issued: 609) .... (13)   625

PSS74–**2017** Commemorative Proof set, House of Windsor £5, King Canute £5,
'Bimetallic' £2 'First World War Aviation', 'Bimetallic' £2 'Jane Austen',
50 pence 'Sir Isaac Newton', silver proofs (Issued:335) .... (5)   350

PSS75–**2017** Commemorative Proof set, House of Windsor £5, King Canute £5,
'Bimetallic' £2 'First World War Aviation', 'Bimetallic' £2 'Jane Austen',
50 pence 'Sir Isaac Newton', silver piedforts (Issued:363) .... (5)   595

PSS76–**2017** See after 4873 in World War I section .... (6)   465

PSS77–**2017** £5 (L52-L55) silver proofs with colour (Edition: 2017) .... (4)   325

PSS78–**2018** Collector Proof set, 5th Birthday Prince George £5, 'Bimetallic' £2 'Royal
Air Force Badge', 'Bimetallic' £2 'Frankenstein', 'Bimetallic' £2 'Armistice'
Bimetallic' £2 'Britannia', 'Bimetallic' £1, 50 pence 'Representation of
People Act', 50 pence to 1 pence Silver proofs (Edition: 1,000) .... (13)   610

PSS79–**2018** Commemorative Proof set, 5th Birthday Prince George £5, 'Bimetallic' £2
'Royal Air Force Badge', 'Bimetallic' £2 'Frankenstein', 'Bimetallic' £2
'Armistice' 50 pence 'Representation of People Act' (Edition: 1,000)
silver proofs .... (5)   310

PSS80–**2018** Commemorative Proof set, 5th Birthday Prince George £5, 'Bimetallic' £2
'Royal Air Force Badge', 'Bimetallic' £2 'Frankenstein', 'Bimetallic' £2
'Armistice' 50 pence 'Representation of People Act' (Edition: 1,000)
silver piedforts .... (5)   550

PSS81–**2018** See after 4879 in World War I section

PSS82–**2018** £5 (L66-L69) silver proofs with colour (Edition: 2018) .... (4)   325

PSS83–**2018** See after 4885 in World War I section .... (6)   465

PSS84–**2019** Collector Proof set, 200th Anniversary of the birth of Queen Victoria £5,
'Bimetallic' £2 '75th Anniversary of D-Day', 'Bimetallic' '£2 'Wedgewood',
'Bimetallic' £2 'Samuel Pepys' Bimetallic' £2 'Britannia', 'Bimetallic' £1,
50 pence 'Sherlock Holmes', 50 pence to 1 pence. silver proofs
(Edition: 1,000) ....(13)   610

PSS85–**2019** Commemorative Proof set, 200th Anniversary of the birth of Queen Victoria
£5, 'Bimetallic' £2 '75th Anniversary of D-Day', 'Bimetallic' '£2 'Wedgewood',
'Bimetallic' £2 'Samuel Pepys' 50 pence 'Sherlock Holmes' silver piedforts
(Edition: 1,000) .... (5)   550

PSS86–**2019** 50p (H53-H57) silver proofs (Edition 1,969) .... (5)   250

PSS87–**2019** 50p (H53-H57) silver piedfort proofs (Edition 1,220) .... (5)   350

PSS88–**2019** 50p (H61-H65) silver proofs (Edition 1,969) .... (5)   250

PSS89–**2019** 50p (H61-H65) silver piedfort proofs (Edition 1,220) .... (5)   350

£

PSS90–**2020**   Collector proof set, George III £5, 'Bimetallic' £2 'D-Day', 'Bimetallic' £2
                'Mayflower', 'Bimetallic' £2 'Agatha Christie', 'Bimetallic' £2 'Britannia',
                'Bimetallic' £1, 50 pence 'Team GB', 50 pence to 1 pence silver proofs.
                (Edition: 500) .... (13)   610
PSS91–**2020**   Commemorative Proof set. George III £5, 'Bimetallic' £2 'D-Day',
                'Bimetallic' £2 'Mayflower', 'Bimetallic' £2 'Agatha Christie', 50 pence
                'Team GB' silver piedfort proofs. (Edition: 300) .... (5)   550

Proof Sets in Gold

PGCS01–**2002**   £2 (K12-K15) gold proofs (Issued: 315) .... (4) 3500
PGCS02–**2002**   'Golden Jubilee' £5, 'Bimetallic' £2, 'English' £1, 50p to 1p and Maundy
                coins, 4p-1p, in gold proof (Issued: 2,002)... (13) 8000
PGCS03–**2006**   £2 (K20 and K21) gold proofs... (2) 1700
PGCS04–**2006**   50p (H15 and H16) gold proofs.. (2) 1500
PGCS05–**2004/7** £1 (J18-J21) gold proofs (Edition: 300 taken from individual coin limits)   (4) 3500

£

PGCS06–**2008**   'Emblems of Britain', 'UK' £1, 'Britannia' 50 pence, 20 pence to 1p gold
                proofs (Issued: 780) .... (7) 4000
PGCS07–**2008**   'The Royal Shield of Arms', 'Royal Shield' £1 to 1p gold proof
                (Issued: 886) .... (7) 4000
PGCS08–**2008**   £1 with reverse designs 1983-2007 gold proofs (Issued: 150) .... (14)12500
PGCS09–**2009**   50p Set with reverse designs 1973-2009 gold proofs (Issued: 70)........... (16)12000
PGCS10–**2009**   50p Set with reverse designs 1973-2009 gold proofs piedfort
                (Issued: 40) .... (16)26000
PGCS11–**2012**   Diamond Jubilee £5, 'Bimetallic' 'Charles Dickens' £2, 'Bimetallic' £2
                'Royal Shield '£1, 50 pence to 1 pence gold proofs (Edition: 150) .... (10) 6000
PGCS12–**2012**   Diamond Jubilee £5, and £2 (Sovereign design) set of two (Edition: 60,
                taken from individual coins limits)... (2) 2600
PGCS13–**2013**   'Coronation' £5, 'Bimetallic' 'Guinea' £2 'Bimetallic' 'Roundel' £2,
                'Bimetallic' 'Train' £2, 'Bimetallic' £2, 'Royal Shield' £1, 'England' £1,
                'Wales' £1, 50 pence 'Ironside', 50 pence to 1 pence gold proofs
                (Issued: 59) .... (15)10000
PGCS14–**2013**   £2 (K31 and K32) gold proofs (Issued: 111) .... (2) 3000
PGCS15–**2013**   £5 (L28-L31) gold proofs (Issued: 148) .... (4) 8000
PGCS16–**2013**   £1 (J13, J26, J27) gold proofs (Issued: 17)... (3) 3500
PGCS17–**2014**   'Queen Anne' £5, 'Bimetallic' 'Trinity House' £2, 'Bimetallic' 'World
                War I' £2, 'Bimetallic' £2 'Royal Shield' £1, 'Northern Ireland' £1,
                'Scotland' £1, and 50 pence 'Commonwealth Games', gold proofs
                (Issued: 75)... (6) 7500
PGCS18–**2015**   Fourth Portrait 'Bimetallic' £2 'Royal Shield', £1, 50 pence to 1 pence
                gold proofs (Issued: 209)... (8) 3800
PGCS19–**2015**   Fifth Portrait 'Bimetallic' £2 'Royal Shield', £1 50 pence to 1 pence
                gold proofs (Issued: 245)... (8) 3800
PGCS20–**2015**   Churchill £5, Waterloo £5, 'Bimetallic' 'Magna Carta' £2, 'Bimetallic'
                'Royal Navy' £2, 50 pence 'Battle of Britain', gold proofs (Issued: 99) .. (5) 5800
PGCS21–**2014**   See after 4855 in World War I section
PGCS22–**2015**   See after 4861 in World War I section
PGCS23–**2016**   Commemorative Proof set, Queen's Birthday £5, 'Bimetallic' £2 'Comedy',
                'Bimetallic' £2 'History', 'Bimetallic' £2 'Tragedy', 'Bimetallic' £2 'The
                Army', 'Bimetallic' £2 'Great Fire', Royal Arms £1, 50 pence 'Battle of
                Hastings' gold proofs (Issued: 82)... (8) 6500

£

PGCS24–**2016**   See after 4867 in World War I section
PGCS25–**2017**   Collector Proof set. House of Windsor £5, King Canute £5, 'Bimetallic'
                  £2 'First World War Aviation', 'Bimetallic' £2 'Jane Austen', 'Bimetallic'
                  £2 'Britannia', 'Bimetallic' £1, 50 pence 'Sir Isaac Newton', 50 pence to
                  1 pence gold proofs (Issued: 24)..(13) 11000
PGCS26–**2017**   Commemorative Proof set, House of Windsor £5,,King Canute £5,
                  'Bimetallic' £2 'First World War Aviation', 'Bimetallic' £2 'Jane Austen',
                  50 pence 'Sir Isaac Newton', gold proofs (Edition: 100)........................... (5)   7000
PGCS27–**2017**   See after 4873 in World War I section
PGCS28–**MD**   £1 (J38 and J39) gold proofs (Issued: 100) .... (2)   1900
PGCS29–**2018**   Commemorative Proof set, 5th Birthday Prince George £5, 'Bimetallic'
                  £2 'Royal Air Force Badge', 'Bimetallic' £2 'Frankenstein', 'Bimetallic'
                  £2 'Armistice' 50 pence 'Representation of People Act', gold proofs
                  (Edition: 175)... (5)   5100
PGCS30–**2018**   See after 4879 in World War I section .... (6) 11100
PGCS31–**2018**   See after 4885 in World War I section
PGCS32–**2019**   50p (H53-H57) gold proofs (Edition: 75)... (5)   5000
PGCS33–**2019**   50p (H53-H57) gold piedfort proofs (Edition: 50).................................... (5)   8000
PGCS34–**2019**   50p (H61-H65) gold proofs (Edition: 75)... (5)   4500
PGCS35–**2019**   50p (H61-H65) gold piedfort proofs (Edition: 50)................................... (5)   7500
PGCS36–**2019**   Commemorative Proof set, 200th Anniversary of the birth of Queen
                  Victoria £5, 'Bimetallic' £2 '75th Anniversary of D-Day', 'Bimetallic' '£2
                  'Wedgewood', 'Bimetallic' £2 'Samuel Pepys' 50 pence 'Sherlock Holmes'
                  gold proofs (Edition: 125)... .(5)   5000
PGCS37-**2020**   Commemorative Proof set. George III £5, 'Bimetallic' £2 'D-Day',
                  'Bimetallic' £2 'Mayflower', 'Bimetallic' £2 'Agatha Christie', 50 pence
                  'Team GB' gold proofs. (Edition: 75) .... (5)   6650

Proof Sets in Platinum
PPLS1–**2008**   'Emblems of Britain', 'UK' £1, 'Britannia' 50 pence and 20 pence to 1p
                 (Issued: 250).. (7)   3000
PPLS2–**2008**   'The Royal Shield of Arms', 'Royal Shield' £1 to 1p (Issued: 184)............ (7)   3000
PPLS3–**2015**   Two portraits set, 2 x £2-1p (Issued: 10) .... (14) 12000

2012 saw two major events in the UK – the Diamond Jubilee of the reign of Queen Elizabeth II and the Olympic Games, the first in the UK since 1948. The Royal Mint decided this was the time to introduce new denominations and sizes and therefore 5 ounce and 1 kilo coins were issued in both silver and gold – two sizes which had become popular with collectors all over the world following similar issues from other countries. The new UK coins also proved popular and so the range has grown in the years since with other sizes and denominations added including some coins struck in platinum. Other higher denomination coins not listed in this section may be found in later sections where coins issued for a specific event or topic are grouped together which we hope catologue users will find convenient.

Denomination	Metal	Weight		Diameter
£10	0.999 Silver	5 ounce	156.30 g	65 mm
£10	0.9999 Gold	5 ounce	156.30 g	M1, M2, M18-65 mm, others-50 mm
£20	0.999 Silver	$^1/_2$ ounce	15.71 g	27 mm
£25	0.9995 Platinum	$^1/_4$ ounce	7.8 g	22 mm
£25	0.9999 Gold	$^1/_4$ ounce	7.8 g	20 mm
£50	0.999 Silver	1 ounce	31.43 g	34 mm
£100	0.999 Silver	2 ounce	62.86 g	40 mm
£500	0.999 Silver	1 kilo	1005 g	100 mm
£500	0.9999 Gold	5 ounce	156.295 g	50 mm
£1000	0.9999 Gold	1 kilo	1005 g	100 mm

Obverse portrait by Ian Rank Broadley

M1

M1   **Ten pounds.** (Five ounce.) Diamond Jubilee commemorative 2012. O. Our Effigy, inspired by the sculpture mounted in the entrance to the Supreme Court building on Parliament Square, with the inscription 'ELIZABETH. II. D. G. REG. F. D. TEN POUNDS'. R. An enthroned representation of Ourself surrounded by the inscription 'DILECTA REGNO MCMLII – MMXII'. (Obverse and reverse design: Ian Rank-Broadley)

2012

— Proof in silver *FDC* (Issued: 1,933) £350

— Proof in gold *FDC* (Issued: 140) £9000

M2

M2   **Ten pounds.** (Five ounce.) 60th Anniversary of the Coronation. R. In the foreground
the Orb and Sceptre resting upon the Coronation Robe with the arches of Westminster
Abbey in the background with the inscription 'HER MAJESTY QUEEN ELIZABETH II
CORONATION ANNIVERSARY'. (Reverse design: Jonathan Olliffe.)
2013
— Proof in silver *FDC* (Issued: 1,604) £450
— Proof in gold *FDC* (Issued: 74) £10000

M3

M3   **Ten pounds.** (Five ounce.) The Christening of Prince George of Cambridge. R. A
deconstructed silver lily font incorporating cherubs and roses, with a Baroque-style
cartouche with the inscription 'DIEU ET MON DROIT' and 'TO CELEBRATE THE
CHRISTENING OF PRINCE GEORGE OF CAMBRIDGE 2013' in the centre of the
coin. (Reverse design: John Bergdahl.)
2013
— Proof in silver *FDC* (Issued: 912) £450
— Proof in gold *FDC* (Issued: 48) £10000

For coin specifications please see table at the beginning of this section.

M4

M4   **Ten pounds.** (Five ounce.) 50th Anniversary of the Death of Winston Churchill.
R. A depiction of Sir Winston Churchill with the inscription 'CHURCHILL' at the base
of the coin. (Reverse design: Etienne Millner.)
2015
— Proof on silver *FDC* (Issued: 855) £425
— Proof in gold *FDC* (Issued: 58)..£10000

Obverse portrait by Jody Clark

M5

M5   **Ten pounds.** (Five ounce.) The Christening of Princess Charlotte of Cambridge.
R. A design depicting a deconstructed silver lily font incorporating cherubs, with a
Baroque-Style cartouche and 'DIEU ET – MON DROIT' below and in the centre the
inscription 'TO CELEBRATE THE CHRISTENING OF PRINCESS CHARLOTTE
ELIZABETH DIANA OF CAMBRIDGE 2015'. (Reverse design: John Bergdahl.)
2015
— Proof in silver *FDC* (Edition: 500) £400

For coin specifications please see table at the beginning of this section

Obverse portrait by James Butler

M6

M6 **Ten pounds.** (Five ounce.) The Longest Serving Monarch. ℞. A design depicting Our Royal Cypher below Our five definitive coinage portraits and the inscription 'THE LONGEST REIGN'. (Reverse design: Stephen Taylor.)
2015
— Proof in silver *FDC* (Issued: 1,499)...£395
— Proof in gold *FDC* (Issued: 180)...£9000

Obverse portrait by Jody Clark

M7

M7 **Ten pounds.** (Five ounce.) ℞. In the centre a depiction of William Shakespeare accompanied with the inscription 'OTHELLO ACT 1 SC 3' surrounded by the inscription 'PUT MONEY IN THY PURSE' 2016'. (Reverse design: Tom Phillips.)
2016
— Proof in silver *FDC* (Issued: 343)...£450
— Proof in gold *FDC* (Issued: 50)...£9000

For coin specifications please see table at the beginning of this section

M8

M8   **Ten pounds.** (Five ounce.) 90th Birthday of Her Majesty Queen Elizabeth II.
R. A crowned Royal Cypher above the number '90' encircled by roses.
(Reverse design: Christopher Hobbs.)
2016
—   Proof in silver *FDC* (Issued: 1,727) £395
—   Proof in gold *FDC* (Issued: 170) £9000

M9

M9   **Ten pounds.** (Five ounce.) Sapphire Jubilee of Her Majesty Queen Elizabeth II.
R. A crowned depiction of the Royal Arms above the number '65' surrounded by
sprigs of oak and olive leaves, accompanied by the inscription 'HER MAJESTY
THE QUEEN'S SAPPHIRE JUBILEE 1952-2017'. (Reverse design: Gregory Cameron.)
2017
—   Proof in silver *FDC* (Issued: 1,445) £415
—   Proof in gold *FDC* (Issued: 110) £9000

For coin specifications please see table at the beginning of this section

M10

M10 Ten pounds. (Five ounce.) Celebrating the Platinum Wedding Anniversary of HM The Queen and HRH Prince Philip. O. Our effigy conjoined with His Royal Highness Prince Philip, The Duke of Edinburgh with the inscription 'ELIZABETH 11 D G REG F D – PHILIP PRINCEPS' and the denomination 'TEN POUNDS'. ℞. A depiction of Our arms and those of His Royal Highness Prince Philip, The Duke of Edinburgh above the inscription '70 YEARS OF MARRIAGE 2017'. (Obverse design: Etienne Milner; reverse: John Bergdahl.)

2017
— Proof in silver *FDC* (Edition: 2,147) £415
— Proof in gold *FDC* (Issued: 86)..£9000

M11

M11 Ten pounds. (Five ounce.) Sapphire Coronation. ℞. Our portrait taken from Our Coronation and accompanied by the dates '1953' and '2018'. (Reverse design: Dominique Evans.)

2018
— Proof in silver *FDC* (Edition: 1,050) £420
— Proof in gold *FDC* (Edition: 85) £10000

M12 Ten pounds. (Five ounce.) Celebrating Four Generations of the Royal Family. ℞. As L70

2019
— Proof in silver *FDC* (Edition: 1000) £420
— Proof in gold *FDC* (Edition: 100) £9000

For coin specifications please see table at the beginning of this section

M13 **Ten pounds.** (Five ounce.) Tower of London - A Raven. R. as L73
2019
— Proof in silver *FDC* (Edition: 585) £420
— Proof in gold *FDC* (Edition 45) £9500
M14 **Ten pounds.** (Five ounce.) Tower of London - Crown of Mary of Modena. R. as L74
2019
— Proof in silver *FDC* (Edition: 585) £420
— Proof in gold *FDC* (Edition 45) £9500

M15 **Ten pounds.** (Five ounce.) Tower of London - A Yeoman Warder. R. as L75
2019
— Proof in silver *FDC* (Edition: 585) £420
— Proof in gold *FDC* (Edition 45) £9500
M16 **Ten pounds.** (Five ounce.) Tower of London - Queen Elizabeth's Keys. R. as L76
2019
— Proof in silver *FDC* (Edition: 585) £420
— Proof in gold *FDC* (Edition 45) £9500

M17

M17 **Ten pounds.** (Five ounce.) Queen Victorian Bi-centenary. R. A conjoined portrait
of Queen Victoria and Prince Albert with the inscription 'VICTORIA REGINA +
ALBERTUS PRINCEPS CONJUX' and the date 'MDCCCXIX'. (Reverse design:
William Wyon.)
2019
— Proof in silver *FDC* (Edition: 800) £420
— Proof in gold *FDC* (Edition 70) £10500
M18 **Ten pounds.** (Five ounce.) 75th Anniversary of the End of the Second World War.
R. As L86.
2020
— Proof in silver *FDC* (Edition: 285) £420
M19 **Ten pounds.** (Five ounce) 95th Birthday of Her Majesty Queen Elizabeth II.
R. As L88.
2021
— Proof in silver *FDC* £420
— Proof in gold *FDC*...£10605

For coin specifications please see table at the beginning of this section

Obverse portrait by Ian Rank-Broadley

N1   N2

N1   **Twenty pounds.** R. A depiction of St. George armed, sitting on horseback, attacking
the dragon with a sword, and a broken spear upon the ground and the date of the year.
(Reverse design: Benedetto Pistrucci.)
2013
— Silver BU (Issued: 250,000) £20

N2   **Twenty pounds.** R. A depiction of a lion behind the figure of Britannia holding a
shield and a trident, watching over departing ships from a cliff top, with the inscription
'THE FIRST WORLD WAR 1914 1918' and the date at the base of the coin. (Reverse
design: John Bergdahl.)
2014
— Silver BU (Issued: 141,751) £20

Obverse portrait by Jody Clark

N3   N4

N3   **Twenty pounds.** Churchill R. A depiction of Sir Winston Churchill with the inscription
'CHURCHILL' at the base of the coin. (Reverse design: Etienne Millner.)
2015
— Silver BU (Issued: 132,142) £20

N4   **Twenty pounds.** The Longest Serving Monarch. R. A design depicting Our Royal
Cypher below Our five definitive coinage portraits and the inscription 'THE LONGEST
REIGN'. (Reverse design: Stephen Taylor.)
2015
— Silver BU (Issued: 149,408) £20

For coin specifications please see table at the beginning of this section

N5

N5   **Twenty pounds.** 90th Birthday of Her Majesty Queen Elizabeth II. R. A crowned
Royal Cypher above the number '90' encircled by roses. (Reverse design:
Christopher Hobbs.)
2016 —   Silver BU (Issued: 116,354) £20

N6

N6   **Twenty pounds.** R. A dragon with the inscription 'TWENTY POUNDS'. (Reverse
design: Norman Sillman.)
2016
—   Silver BU (Edition: 150,000) £20

N7

N7   **Twenty pounds.** R. A depiction of Mary and the baby Jesus receiving gifts from
the Magi, with the inscription 'THE NATIVITY: CHRISTMAS 2016'. (Reverse design:
Gregory Cameron.)
2016
—   Silver BU (Issued: 29,929) £20

For coin specifications please see table at the beginning of this section

N8

N8   **Twenty pounds.** Celebrating the Platinum Wedding Anniversary of HM The Queen
and HRH Prince Philip. O. Our effigy conjoined with his Royal Highness Prince
Philip, The Duke of Edinburgh with the inscription 'ELIZABETH 11 D G REG F D –
PHILIP PRINCEPS' and the denomination. R. A depiction of Our effigy and that of his
Royal Highness Prince Philip, The Duke of Edinburgh on horseback with the
inscription 'WEDDED LOVE HAS JOINED THEM IN HAPPINESS' with the dates
'1947-2017'. (Obverse design: Etienne Milne, reverse: John Bergdahl.)
2017
— Silver BU (issued: 24,223) £20

*£20, £50 and £100 silver coins containing respectively $^1/2$ oz 1 oz and 2 oz fine silver were
issued by the Royal Mint at face value but it soon became apparent that these could not be
spent nor redeemed at any bank so they had no effective legal tender status with the result that
pieces are often traded at below their alleged face value.*

O1

O1   **Twenty five pounds.** (¼ oz of fine gold.) 150th Anniversary of the Birth of Beatrix
Potter. R. A portrait of Peter Rabbit with the incription 'PETER RABBIT'.
(Reverse design: Emma Noble.)
2016
— Proof in gold *FDC* (Issued: 500) £1000
O2   **Twenty five pounds.** (¼ oz of fine gold.) William Shakespeare. R. As M7.
2016
— Proof in gold *FDC* (Edition: 350) £500
O3   **Twenty five pounds**. (¼ oz platinum.) Celebrating the Platinum Wedding Anniversary
of HM The Queen and HRH Prince Philip. O. Our effigy conjoined with His Royal
Highness Prince Philip, The Duke of Edinburgh with the inscription 'ELIZABETH 11
D G REG F D – PHILIP PRINCEPS' and the denomination 'TWENTY FIVE
POUNDS' R. A depiction of Our arms and those of His Royal Highness Prince Philip,
The Duke of Edinburgh above the inscription '70 YEARS OF MARRIAGE 2017'.
(Obverse design: Etienne Milner, reverse: John Bergdahl.)
2017
— Proof in platinum (Edition:1,500) £450

For coin specifications please see table at the beginning of this section.

O3

O4   **Twenty five pounds**. (¼ oz platinum.) The 70th Birthday of HRH the Prince of
Wales. (Reverse design: Robert Elderton.)
2018
— Proof in platinum *FDC* (Edition: 650) £500

O5   **Twenty five pounds**. (¼ oz of fine gold.) Celebrating Four Generations of the
Royal Family. R̨. as L70.
2018
— Proof in gold *FDC* (Edition: 1000) £500

O6   **Twenty five pounds**. (¼ oz of fine gold.) Tower of London - A Raven. R̨. as L73.
2019
— Proof in gold *FDC* (Edition: 960) £500

O7   **Twenty five pounds**. (¼ oz of fine gold.) Tower of London - Crown of Mary of
Modena. R̨. as L74.
2019
— Proof in gold *FDC* (Edition: 960) £500

O8   **Twenty five pounds**. (¼ oz fine gold.) Tower of London - A Yeoman Warder.
R̨. as L75.
2019
— Proof in gold *FDC* (Edition: 960) £500

O9   **Twenty five pounds**. (¼ oz fine gold.) Tower of London - Queen Elizabeth's Keys.
R̨. as L76.
2019
— Proof in gold *FDC* (Edition: 960) £500

For coin specifications please see table at the beginning of this section

P1

P1   **Fifty pounds.** (1 oz of fine silver.) Britannia. R. A design of the standing figure of
Britannia bearing a trident and a shield, with a lion at her feet, set against the
backdrop of a globe, and the inscription 'BRITANNIA 50 POUNDS' and the date'
2015' below. (Reverse design: Jody Clark.)

2015 — Silver BU (Issued: 78,644)..£50

P2

P2   **Fifty pounds.** (1 oz of fine silver.) R. A design depicting a mask of tragedy and
comedy with inscription 'WILLIAM SHAKESPEARE 2016' (Reverse design:
John Bergdahl.)

2016

—   BU (Issued: 14,948) £50

For coin specifications please see table at the beginning of this section.

Obverse portrait by Ian Rank-Broadley

Q1

Q1   One hundred pounds. (2 oz of fine silver.) Elizabeth Tower. (Reverse design:
Glyn Davies and Laura Clancy.)
2015
— Silver BU (Edition: 50,000) £100

Obverse portrait by Jody Clark

Q2

Q2   One hundred pounds. (2 oz of fine silver.) R. A design of the Victoria Memorial with
Buckingham Palace in the background. (Reverse design: Glyn Davies and Laura Clancy.)
2015
— Silver BU (Issued: 50,000)..£100

For coin specifications please see table at the beginning of this section.

Q3

Q3 **One hundred pounds.** (2 oz of fine silver.) ℞. A view of Trafalgar Square with the head of a lion in the foreground and Nelson Column in the background. (Reverse design: Laura Clancy and Glyn Davies.)
2016
— Silver BU (Issued: 14,878) £100

See note below N8.

Obverse portrait by Ian Rank-Broadley

R1

R1 **Five hundred pounds.** (1 kilo of fine silver.) Diamond Jubilee commemorative 2012. O. Our Effigy, inspired by the sculpture mounted in the entrance to the Supreme Court building on Parliament Square, with the inscription 'ELIZABETH. II. D. G. REG. F. D. 500 POUNDS'. ℞. A full achievement of the Royal Arms based on those mounted on the front gates of Buckingham Palace with the date '2012' below. (Obverse and reverse design: Ian Rank-Broadley.)
2012
— Proof in silver *FDC* (Issued: 206) £1500

R2 **Five hundred pounds.** (1 kilo of fine silver.) ℞. Coronation commemorative 2013. ℞. In the foreground the Orb and Sceptre with the St. Edward's Crown behind surrounded by flowers representing the constituent parts of the United Kingdom and in the background a ribbon showing the '2nd JUNE 1953' with the inscription 'QUEEN ELIZABETH II' and 'THE 60TH ANNIVERSARY OF THE CORONATION'. (Reverse design: John Bergdahl.)
2013
— Proof in silver *FDC* (Issued: 301)) £1500

For coin specifications please see table at the beginning of this section.

R3

R3   **Five hundred pounds.** (1 kilo of fine silver.) Commemorative coin to mark the
christening of Prince George of Cambridge. R. A deconstructed silver lily font
incorporating cherubs and roses, with a Baroque-style cartouche with the inscription
'DIEU ET MON DROIT' and 'TO CELEBRATE THE CHRISTENING OF PRINCE
GEORGE OF CAMBRIDGE 2013' in the centre of the coin. (Reverse design:
John Bergdahl.)
2013
— Proof in silver *FDC* (Issued: 194) £1500

Obverse portrait by James Butler

R4

R4   **Five hundred pounds.** (1 kilo of fine silver.) The Longest Serving Monarch.
R. A design depicting Our Royal Cypher below Our five definitive coinage portraits
and the inscription 'THE LONGEST REIGN'. (Reverse design: Stephen Taylor.)
2015
— Proof in silver *FDC* (Issued: 278) £1500

Obverse portrait by Jody Clark

R5   **Five hundred pounds.** (1 kilo of fine silver.) Churchill. R. A depiction of Sir Winston
Churchill with the inscription 'CHURCHILL' at the base of the coin. (Reverse design:
Etienne Millner.) See N3.
2015
— Proof in silver *FDC* (Issued: 117) £1500

For coin specifications please see table at the beginning of this section.

R6

R6   Five hundred pounds. (5 oz of fine gold.) Commemorating the Christening of
Princess Charlotte of Cambridge. ℞. A design depicting a deconstructed silver lily font
incorporating cherubs, with a Baroque Style cartouche and 'DIEU ET – MON DROIT'
below and in the centre the inscription 'TO CELEBRATE THE CHRISTENING OF
PRINCESS CHARLOTTE ELIZABETH DIANA OF CAMBRIDGE 2015'.
(Reverse design: John Bergdahl.)
2015
—   Proof in gold *FDC* £10000

R7

R7   Five hundred pounds. (1 kilo of fine silver.) 90th Birthday of Her Majesty Queen
Elizabeth II. ℞. A crowned Royal Cypher above the number '90' encircled by
roses with the inscription 'FULL OF HONOUR AND YEARS'. (Reverse design:
Christopher Hobbs.)
2016
—   Proof in silver *FDC* (Issued: 447)..£1500

For coin specifications please see table at the beginning of this section.

R8   R10   R11

R8 **Five hundred pounds.** (1 kilo of fine silver.) Sapphire Jubilee of Her Majesty Queen
Elizabeth II. R. A crowned depiction of the Royal Arms above the number '65' surrounded
by sprigs of oak and olive leaves, accompanied by the inscription 'HER MAJESTY THE
QUEEN'S SAPPHIRE JUBILEE 1952-2017'. (Reverse design: Gregory Cameron.)
2017
— Proof in silver *FDC* (issued: 225) £1500

R9 **Five hundred pounds.** (1 kilo of fine silver.) Celebrating the Platinum Wedding
Anniversary of HM The Queen and HRH Prince Philip. O. Our effigy conjoined with
His Royal Highness Prince Philip, The Duke of Edinburgh with the inscription
'ELIZABETH 11 D G REG F D – PHILIP PRINCEPS' and the denomination 'FIVE
HUNDRED POUNDS'. R. A depiction of Our arms and those of His Royal Highness
Prince Philip, The Duke of Edinburgh above the inscription '70 YEARS OF
MARRIAGE 2017'. (Obverse design: Etienne Milner; reverse: John Bergdahl.) See S8.
2017
— Proof in silver *FDC* (Edition: 550) £1500

R10 **Five hundred pounds.** (1 kilo of fine silver.) Sapphire Coronation. R. Our
portrait taken from Our Coronation and accompanied by the dates '1953' and '2018'.
(Reverse design: Dominique Evans.)
2018
— Proof in silver *FDC* (Edition: 150) £2025

R11 **Five hundred pounds.** (1 kilo of fine silver.) Queen Victorian Bi-centenary. R. A
conjoined portrait of Queen Victoria and Prince Albert with the inscription 'VICTORIA
REGINA + ALBERTUS PRINCEPS CONJUX' and the date 'MDCCCXIX'.
(Reverse design: William Wyon.)
2019
— Proof in silver *FDC* (Edition: 125) £2025

R12 **Five hundred pounds.** (Five ounce.) 75th Anniversary of the End of the Second
World War. R. As L86.
2020
— Proof in gold *FDC* (Edition: 85) £10605

R13 **Five hundred pounds.** (1 kilo of fine silver.) 95th Birthday of Her Majesty Queen
Elizabeth II. R. As L88.
2021
— Proof in silver *FDC* £2050

For coin specifications please see table at the beginning of this section.

Obverse portrait by Ian Rank-Broadley

S1   S3

S1   **One thousand pounds.** (1 kilo of fine gold.) Diamond Jubilee commemorative 2012.
O. Our Effigy, inspired by the sculpture mounted in the entrance to the Supreme
Court building on Parliament Square, with the inscription 'ELIZABETH. II. D. G.
REG. F. D. 1000 POUNDS'. R. A full achievement of the Royal Arms based on those
mounted on the front gates of Buckingham Palace with the date '2012' below.
(Obverse and reverse design: Ian Rank Broadley.)
2012 —   Proof in gold *FDC* (Issued: 21)... £60000

S2   **One thousand pounds.** (1 kilo of fine gold.) Coronation commemorative 2013.
R. In the foreground the Orb and Sceptre with the St. Edward's Crown behind
surrounding by flowers representing the constituent parts of the United Kingdom
and in the background a ribbon showing the '2nd JUNE 1953' with the inscription
'QUEEN ELIZABETH II' and 'THE 60TH ANNIVERSARY OF THE CORONATION'.
(Reverse design: John Bergdahl.)
2013 —   Proof in gold *FDC* (Issued: 13)..£60000

S3   **One thousand pounds.** (1 kilo of fine gold.) Commemorative coin to mark the
christening of Prince George of Cambridge. R. A deconstructed silver lily font
incorporating cherubs and roses, with a Baroque-style cartouche with the inscription
'DIEU ET MON DROIT' and 'TO CELEBRATE THE CHRISTENING OF PRINCE
GEORGE OF CAMBRIDGE 2013'in the centre of the coin. (Reverse design:
John Bergdahl.)
2013 —   Proof in gold *FDC* (Issued: 19)..£60000

Obverse portrait by Jody Clark

S4   **One thousand pounds.** (1 kilo of fine gold.) Churchill. R. A depiction of Sir Winston
Churchill with the inscription 'CHURCHILL' at the base of the coin. (Reverse design:
Etienne Millner.) See N3.
2015—   Proof in gold *FDC* (Edition: 15) £60000

For coin specifications please see table at the beginning of this section.

Obverse portrait by James Butler

S5

S5   One thousand pounds. (1 kilo of fine gold.) The Longest Serving Monarch.
R. A design depicting Our Royal Cypher below Our five definitive coinage portraits
and the inscription 'THE LONGEST REIGN'. (Reverse design: Stephen Taylor.)
2015
— Proof in gold *FDC* (Issued: 15)...£60000

Obverse portrait by Jody Clark

S6

S6   One thousand pounds. (1 kilo of fine gold.) 90th Birthday of Her Majesty Queen
Elizabeth II. R. A crowned Royal Cypher above the number '90' encircled by roses
with the inscription 'FULL OF HONOUR AND YEARS'. (Reverse design:
Christopher Hobbs.)
2016
— Proof in gold *FDC* (Issued: 15) £60000

For coin specifications please see table at the beginning of this section.

S7

S7 **One thousand pounds.** (1 kilo of fine gold.) Sapphire Jubilee of Her Majesty Queen Elizabeth II. Ṙ. A crowned depiction of the Royal Arms above the number '65' surrounded by sprigs of oak and olive leaves, accompanied by the inscription 'HER MAJESTY THE QUEEN'S SAPPHIRE JUBILEE 1952-2017'. (Reverse design: Gregory Cameron.)
2017
— Proof in gold *FDC* (Issued: 18)...£60000

S8

S8 **One thousand pounds.** (1 kilo of fine gold.) Celebrating the Platinum Wedding Anniversary of HM The Queen and HRH Prince Philip. O. Our effigy conjoined with His Royal Highness Prince Philip, The Duke of Edinburgh with the inscription 'ELIZABETH 11 D G REG F D – PHILIP PRINCEPS' and the denomination 'FIVE HUNDRED POUNDS'. Ṙ. A depiction of Our arms and those of His Royal Highness Prince Philip, The Duke of Edinburgh above the inscription '70 YEARS OF MARRIAGE 2017'. (Obverse design: Etienne Milner; reverse: John Bergdahl.)
2017
— Proof in gold *FDC* (Issued: 15)...£55000

For coin specifications please see table at the beginning of this section.

S9

S9   **One thousand pounds.** (1 kilo of fine gold.) Sapphire Coronation. R. Our portrait
taken from Our Coronation and accompanied by the dates '1953' and '2018'.
(Reverse design: Dominique Evans.)
2018
—   Proof in gold *FDC* (Edition: 15) £60000

S10   **One thousand pounds.** (1 kilo of fine gold.) Queen Victorian Bi-centenary.
R. A conjoined portrait of Queen Victoria and Prince Albert with the inscription
'VICTORIA REGINA + ALBERTUS PRINCEPS CONJUX' and the date
'MDCCCXIX'. (Reverse design: William Wyon.)
2019
—   Proof in gold *FDC* (Edition: 12) £70000

S11   **One thousand pounds.** (1 kilo of fine gold.) 95th Birthday of Her Majesty Queen
Elizabeth II. R. As L88.
2021
—   Proof in gold *FDC* £63865

For coin specifications please see table at the beginning of this section.

COINS OF ENGLAND
& THE UNITED KINGDOM
PRE-DECIMAL ISSUES

SPINK

COINS OF ENGLAND 2021
E-book available on Amazon, iBookstore,
Google, Kobo, OverDrive and across
most other platforms

For more information or enquiries please contact
Tel: +44 (0)20 7563 4119 | Email: books@spink.com
69 Southampton Row, Bloomsbury, London WC1B 4ET

WWW.SPINKBOOKS.COM

The gold sovereign with a denomination of £1 in its present specification dates back to 1817 and so is the oldest UK coin still being issued with a heritage dating back to 1489. The outbreak of WWI in 1914 saw the sovereign and the half sovereign disappear from daily use, being replaced by banknotes. Since then these coins have become mainly bullion pieces trading at small premiums over their gold content although there are some interesting variations and some scarcer dates. Benedetto Pistrucci's famous St. George slaying the dragon reverse design first introduced in 1817 has been continued on almost all coins in this series although there are some modern interpretations of this design on the 2005 and 2012 issues. The 500th anniversary of the sovereign was commemorated in 1989 with designs reminiscent of the 1489 originals.

Following decimalisation, sovereigns for bullion use were issued between 1974 and 1982 with a half sovereign appearing in 1982. The first proof in the decimal series was issued in 1979 and half sovereigns were added to the range in 1980, the same year as the first four coin proof set containing a £5, £2, £1 and £1/2 sovereign. In 2000 the Royal Mint recommenced annual issues of bullion sovereigns and halves with the first ever quarter sovereign released in 2009. Prices for cased sets can now be found immediately after the £5 (five sovereign) listings.

In more recent years limited issues of BU sovereigns have been struck on the day of a particular event or anniversary and some of these have added mint marks or other notable differences from the basic type thus making the gold sovereign issues a much more interesting and collectable series. For clarity we have provided full details of the Struck-on-the-Day sovereigns with SSD numbers following the listing of the cased sets. There were also half sovereigns and £2 pieces "struck on the day" in 2012 & 2013 in sets and these appear at the end of the sets listing.

The earlier non-proof coins issued as bullion coins are UNC standard but in 2013 following the opening by the Royal Mint of a separate bullion department which continued to issue UNC coins, the mint also issued some coins in brilliant uncirculated condition referred to as BU and some of these coins have quite low mintages.

Prices for single proof coins relate to coins in original case with Royal Mint certificate. Single coins just in capsules from split up sets can usually be found in the market at lower prices.

Mintages: Numbers issued for coins sold individually are shown alongside each coin. Many coins were also sold within sets, some of which will have subsequently been broken up. A table showing details of these may be found at the end of this section. There are some gaps in these figures which we hope to update as more information becomes available from the Royal Mint. There are a few instances where the sales figures announced by the Royal Mint slightly exceed the authorised mintage! We will endeavour to check the accuracy of these numbers. There are also a number of instances in recent years where the Royal Mint has announced a sell-out and yet later published sales figures have fallen slightly short of the maximum mintage.

Gold Sovereign Series Specifications

Denomination	Metal	Weight	Diameter
¼ Sovereign	0.9166 Gold	1.997 g	13.50 mm
½ Sovereign	0.9166 Gold	3.99 g	19.30 mm
Sovereign	0.9166 Gold	7.98 g	22.05 mm
£2	0.9166 Gold	15.976 g	28.40 mm
£5	0.9166 Gold	39.94 g	36.02 mm

Obverse portrait by Ian Rank-Broadley

SA1   SA2

SA1 **Quarter sovereign.** R. The image of St George armed, sitting on horseback, attacking
the dragon with a sword, and a broken spear upon the ground, and the date of the year in
the exergue. (Reverse design: Benedetto Pistrucci.)
2009 Unc (Edition: 50,000) £120
— Proof in gold *FDC* (Issued: 11,745 plus coins in sets) £150
2010 Unc (Issued: 8,985)..£120
— Proof in gold *FDC* (Issued: 4,546 plus coins in sets) £150
2011 Unc (Edition: 50,000) £120
— Proof in gold *FDC* (Issued: 6,736 plus coins in sets) £150
2013 BU (Issued:1,729)...£130
— Proof in gold *FDC* (Issued: 1,696 plus coins in sets) £150
2014
— Proof in gold *FDC* (Issued: 1,886 plus coins in sets) £150
2015
— Proof in gold *FDC* (Issued: 1,808 plus coins in sets) £150
SA2 **Quarter sovereign.** R. The image of St George on horseback, attacking the dragon with
a lance, with date of the year to the left. (Reverse design: Paul Day.)
2012 Unc £130
— BU (Issued: 137) £150
— Proof in gold *FDC* (Issued: 7,579 plus coins in sets)....................................£180

Obverse portrait by Jody Clark

SA3

SA3 **Quarter sovereign.** R. St George and dragon as SA1.
2015 Proof in gold *FDC* (Issued: 550 plus coins in sets) ....£ 180
2019 Proof in gold *FDC* (Edition: 2,500 plus coins in sets)..........................£ 180
SA3A **Quarter sovereign.** R. As SA3 but with commemorative privy mark '65'.
2018 Proof in gold *FDC* (Edition: 2,500 plus coins in sets).....................£ 180
SA3B **Quarter sovereign.** R. As SA3 but with George III Royal Cypher on the reverse.
2020 Proof in gold *FDC* *..£ 180

Obverse portrait by James Butler

SA4

SA4 **Quarter sovereign.** R. St George and Dragon.
2016 Proof in gold *FDC* (Issued: 1,727 plus coins in sets)............................£200

* Coins marked thus were originally issued in Royal Mint sets.

Obverse portrait by Jody Clark

SA5

SA5   Quarter sovereign. ℞. The image of St George armed, sitting on horseback, attacking
the dragon with a broken spear surrounded by the inscription 'HONI SOIT QUI MAL Y
PENSE'.
2017 Proof in gold *FDC* (Issued: 2,442 plus coins in sets)...£200

Obverse portrait by Arnold Machin

SB1

SB1   Half sovereign. ℞. The image of St George armed, sitting on horseback, attacking the
dragon with a sword, and a broken spear upon the ground, and the date of the year.
(Reverse design: Benedetto Pistrucci.)
1980 Proof in gold *FDC* (Issued: 76,700 plus coins in sets) £250
1982 Unc £220
—   Proof in gold *FDC* (Issued: 19,090 plus coins in sets) £250
1983 Proof in gold *FDC* (Issued: 19,710)**..£260
1984 Proof in gold *FDC* (Issued: 12,410 plus coins in sets) £260

Obverse portrait by Raphael Maklouf

SB2

SB2   Half sovereign. ℞. St. George (as SB1)
1985 Proof in gold *FDC* (Issued: 9,951 plus coins in sets) £260
1986 Proof in gold *FDC* (Issued: 4,575 plus coins in sets) £260
1987 Proof in gold *FDC* (Issued: 8,187 plus coins in sets) £260
1988 Proof in gold *FDC* (Issued: 7,074 plus coins in sets) £260
1990 Proof in gold *FDC* (Issued: 4,231 plus coins in sets) £300
1991 Proof in gold *FDC* (Issued: 3,588 plus coins in sets) £300
1992 Proof in gold *FDC* (Issued: 3,783 plus coins in sets) £350
1993 Proof in gold *FDC* (Issued: 2,910 plus coins in sets) £350
1994 Proof in gold *FDC* (Issued: 5,000 plus coins in sets) £300
1995 Proof in gold *FDC* (Issued: 4,900 plus coins in sets) £300
1996 Proof in gold *FDC* (Issued: 5,730 plus coins in sets) £300
1997 Proof in gold *FDC* (Issued: 7,500 plus coins in sets) £300

** Numbers include coins sold in sets.

SB3

SB3 **Half sovereign.** 500th Anniversary of Sovereign. O. A representation Of Ourself as at Our Coronation, seated in King Edward's Chair and having received the Sceptre with the Cross and the Rod with the Dove, all within the circumscription 'ELIZABETH. II.DEI.GRA. REG.FID.DEF'. ℞. A Shield of Our Royal Arms ensigned by an open Royal Crown, the whole superimposed upon a double Rose, with the circumscription 'ANNIVERSARY OF THE GOLD SOVEREIGN 1489-1989'. (Designs: Bernald Sindall.)
1989 Proof in gold *FDC (*Issued: 8,888 plus coins in sets) £500

Obverse portrait by Ian Rank-Broadley

SB4   SB5   SB6

SB4 **Half sovereign.** ℞. St.George
1998 Proof in gold *FDC* (Issued: 6,147 plus coins in sets) £300
1999 Proof in gold *FDC* (Issued: 7,500 plus coins in sets) £300
2000 Unc (Issued: 146,822) £220
— Proof in gold *FDC* (Issued: 7,458 plus coins in sets) £260
2001 Unc (Issued: 94,763)..£220
— Proof in gold *FDC* (Issued: 4,596 plus coins in sets) £260
2003 Unc (Issued: 47,818) £220
— Proof in gold *FDC* (Issued: 4,868 plus coins in sets) £260
2004 Unc (Issued: 34,924) £220
— Proof in gold *FDC* (Issued: 4,446 plus coins in sets) £260
2006 Unc £220
— Proof in gold *FDC* (Issued: 4,173 plus coins in sets) £260
2007 Unc (Edition: 75,000)..£220
— Proof in gold *FDC* (Issued: 2,442 plus coins in sets) £260
2008 Unc (Edition: 75,000)..£220
— Proof in gold *FDC* (Issued: 2,465 plus coins in sets) £260

SB5 **Half sovereign** ℞. The Shield of Arms of Our United Kingdom of Great Britain and Northern Ireland within an open wreath of laurel and ensigned by Our Royal Crown and beneath the date of the year. (Reverse design: Timothy Noad.)
2002 Unc (Issued: 61,347) £250
— Proof in gold *FDC* (Issued: 10,000 plus coins in sets) £350

SB6 **Half sovereign.** ℞. A depiction of St George, carrying a shield and a sword, slaying the dragon, with the date '2005' beneath the wing of the dragon. (Reverse design: Timothy Noad.)
2005 Unc (Issued: 30,299) £250
— Proof in gold *FDC* (Issued: 5,011 plus coins in sets) £350

SB7

SB7 **Half sovereign.** R. St George. Based on the original design of 1893 with reduced
ground below design and larger exergue with no BP initials

2009 Unc (Edition: 50,000)..£220

— Proof in gold *FDC* (Issued: 2,996 plus coins in sets)............................£260

2010 Unc (Issued: 16,485) £220

— Proof in gold *FDC* (Issued: 3,351 plus coins in sets)............................£260

SB7A Half sovereign. R. As SB7 but with BP initials.

2011 Unc (Edition: 50,000)..£220

— Proof in gold *FDC* (Issued 3,138 plus coins in sets)............................£260

2013 BU (Issued: 1,051 plus coins in sets) £250

— Proof in gold *FDC* (Issued: 1,863 plus coins in sets)............................£350

2014 BU (Issued: 672) £250

— Proof in gold *FDC* (Issued: 1,367 plus coins in sets)............................£350

2015 BU (Issued: 500) £250

— Proof in gold *FDC* (Issued: 1,704 plus coins in sets)............................£350

SB7B Half sovereign. R. St George as SB7A above but with 'I' mint mark on reverse for coins
struck in India.

2014 BU £400

SB8

SB8 **Half sovereign.** R. The image of St George on horseback, attacking the dragon with
a lance, with date of the year to the left. (Reverse design: Paul Day.)

2012 Unc £250

— BU (Issued: 2,137 plus coins in sets) £250

— Proof in gold *FDC* (Issued: 2,303 plus coins in sets)............................£350

Obverse portrait by Jody Clark

SB9 **Half Sovereign.** R. St George and dragon as SB7A.

2015 Proof in gold *FDC** £330

2016 Unc £220

— BU (Issued: 472) £250

2018 Unc £220

2019 Unc £220

— Proof in gold *FDC* (Edition: 2,500 plus coins in sets)............................£270

2020 Unc £220

SB9A Half Sovereign. As SB9 but with 200th Anniversary privy mark on the reverse.

2017 Unc £220

SB9B Half sovereign. R. As SB9 but with commemorative privy mark '65'.

2018 Proof in gold *FDC* (Edition: 2,500 plus coins in sets) £270

SB9C Half sovereign. R. As SB9 but with George III Royal Cypher on the reverse.

2020 Proof in gold *FDC* (Edition: 2,500 plus coins in sets) £300

* Coins marked thus were originally issued in Royal Mint sets.

Obverse portrait by James Butler

SB10

SB10 Half sovereign. ℞. St George and Dragon.
2016
— Proof in gold *FDC* (Issued: 1,995 plus coins in sets)..£450

Obverse portrait by Jody Clark

SB11

SB11 Half sovereign. ℞. The image of St George armed, sitting on horseback, attacking the
dragon with a broken spear surrounded by the inscription 'HONI SOIT QUI MAL Y PENSE'.
2017
— Proof in gold *FDC* (Edition: 5,150 including coins in sets)....................................£450

Obverse portrait by Arnold Machin

SC1

SC1 Sovereign. ℞. The image of St George armed, sitting on horseback, attacking the
dragon with a sword, and a broken spear upon the ground, and the date of the year.
(Reverse design: Benedetto Pistrucci.)
1974 Unc £380
1976 Unc £380
1976 VIP Proof in gold *FDC* ....*Extremely rare*
1978 Unc £380
1979 Unc £380
— Proof in gold *FDC* (Issued: 50,000)..£450
1980 Unc £380
— Proof in gold *FDC* (Issued: 81,200 plus coins in sets) £450
1981 Unc £380
— Proof in gold *FDC* (Issued: 32,960 plus coins in sets) £450
1982 Unc £380
— Proof in gold *FDC* (Issued: 20,000 plus coins in sets) £450
1983 Proof in gold *FDC* (Issued: 21,250)**..£500
1984 Proof in gold *FDC* (Issued: 12,880 plus coins in sets) £500

** *Numbers include coins sold in sets.*

Obverse portrait by Raphael Maklouf

SC2   SC3

SC2 Sovereign. R. St. George (as SC1)
  1985 Proof in gold *FDC* (Issued: 11,393 plus coins in sets)..£500
  1986 Proof in gold *FDC* (Issued: 5,079 plus coins in sets)..£500
  1987 Proof in gold *FDC* (Issued: 9,979 plus coins in sets)..£500
  1988 Proof in gold *FDC* (Issued: 7,670 plus coins in sets)..£500
  1990 Proof in gold *FDC* (Issued: 4,767 plus coins in sets)..£550
  1991 Proof in gold *FDC* (Issued: 4,713 plus coins in sets)..£550
  1992 Proof in gold *FDC* (Issued: 4,772 plus coins in sets)..£650
  1993 Proof in gold *FDC* (Issued: 4,349 plus coins in sets)..£650
  1994 Proof in gold *FDC* (Issued: 4,998 plus coins in sets)..£550
  1995 Proof in gold *FDC* (Issued: 7,500 plus coins in sets)..£550
  1996 Proof in gold *FDC* (Issued: 7,500 plus coins in sets)..£550
  1997 Proof in gold *FDC* (Issued: 7,500 plus coins in sets)..£550

SC3 Sovereign. 500th Anniversary of Sovereign. O. A representation Of Ourself as at
  Our Coronation, seated in King Edward's Chair and having received the Sceptre with
  the Cross and the Rod with the Dove, all within the circumscription 'ELIZABETH.II.
  DEI.GRA.REG.FID.DEF'. R. A Shield of Our Royal Arms ensigned by an open Royal
  Crown, the whole superimposed upon a double Rose, with the circumscription
  'ANNIVERSARY OF THE GOLD SOVEREIGN 1489-1989'. (Designs: Bernald Sindall.)
  1989 Proof in gold *FDC* (Issued: 10,535 plus coins in sets) £1600

Obverse portrait by Ian Rank-Broadley

SC4

SC4 Sovereign. R. St.George
  1998 Proof in gold *FDC* (Issued: 10,000 plus coins in sets)......................................£500
  1999 Proof in gold *FDC* (Issued: 10,000 plus coins in sets)......................................£500
  2000 Unc (Issued: 129,069) £400
  — Proof in gold *FDC* (Issued: 9,909 plus coins in sets)..£500
  2001 Unc (Issued: 49,462) £400
  — Proof in gold *FDC* (Issued: 8,915 plus coins in sets)..£480
  2003 Unc (Issued: 43,230) £400
  — Proof in gold *FDC* (Issued: 12,433 plus coins in sets)..£480
  2004 Unc (Issued: 30,688) £400
  — Proof in gold *FDC* (Issued: 10,175 plus coins in sets)..£480
  2006 Unc £400
  — Proof in gold *FDC* (Issued: 9,195 plus coins in sets)..£480

2007 Unc (Edition: 75,000)..£400
— Proof in gold *FDC* (Issued: 8,199 plus coins in sets)..................................£480
2008 Unc (Edition: 75,000)..£400
— Proof in gold *FDC* (Issued: 7,735 plus coins in sets)..................................£480

SC5   SC6

SC5 **Sovereign** R. The Shield of Arms of Our United Kingdom of Great Britain and Northern Ireland within an open wreath of laurel and ensigned by Our Royal Crown and beneath the date of the year. (Reverse design: Timothy Noad.)
2002 Unc (Issued: 75,264) £425
— Proof in gold *FDC* (Issued: 12,500 plus coins in sets)................................£600

SC6 **Sovereign** R. A depiction of St George, carrying a shield and a sword, slaying the dragon, with the date '2005' beneath the wing of the dragon. (Reverse design: Timothy Noad.)
2005 Unc (Issued: 45,542) £425
— Proof in gold *FDC* (Issued: 12,500 plus coins in sets)................................£550

SC7

SC7 **Sovereign.** R. St George, based on the original design of 1820 with the plumed helmet without its streamer.
2009 Unc (Edition: 75,000)..£400
— Proof in gold *FDC* (Issued: 7,354 plus coins in sets)..................................£480
2010 Unc (Issued: 243,986) £400
— Proof in gold *FDC* (Issued: 5,809 plus coins in sets)..................................£480
2011 Unc (Edition: 250,000)..£400
— Proof in gold *FDC* (Issued: 6,060 plus coins in sets)..................................£480
2013 Unc £400
— BU (Issued: 2,695 plus coins in sets & SSD2 & 3)......................................£400
— Proof in gold *FDC* (Issued: 8,243 plus coins in sets)..................................£500
2014 Unc £400
— BU (Issued: 1,000 plus SSD4) £450
— Proof in gold *FDC* (Issued: 3,263 plus coins in sets)..................................£600
2015 Unc £400
— BU (Issued: 890 plus SSD5 & 6) £450
— Proof in gold *FDC* (Issued: 4,546 plus coins in sets)..................................£550

SC7A **Sovereign.** As SC7 but with 'I' mint mark on reverse for coins struck in India.
2013 BU £550
2014 BU £550
2015 BU £600

SC8

SC8   Sovereign. Ɍ. The image of St George on horseback attacking the dragon with a lance, with date of the year to the left. (Reverse design: Paul Day.)

2012 Unc £425

—   BU (Issued: 4,559 plus coins in sets & SSD1) £425

—   Proof in gold *FDC* (Issued: 5,501 plus coins in sets) £1200

Obverse portrait by Jody Clark

SC9

SC9   Sovereign. Ɍ. As SC7.

2015 Proof in gold *FDC* (Issued: 7,494 plus coins in sets)...£550

2016 Unc £400

—   BU (Issued: 1,251 plus SSD7) £425

2017 BU (See SSD8 & 10) £425

2018 Unc £400

2019 Unc £400

—   BU matt £450

—   Proof in gold *FDC* (Edition: 10,500 plus coins in sets) £550

—   Proof in gold piedfort *FDC* (Edition: 1,800)..£1000

2020 Unc £400

SC9A Sovereign. As SC9 but with 200th Anniversary privy mark on the reverse.

2017 Unc £425

SC9B Sovereign. As SC9 but with 'I' mint mark on reverse for coins struck in India.

2017 BU £550

2018 BU £550

2019 BU £550

SC9C Sovereign. As SC9 but with plain edge.

2017 BU (See SSD9)..£850

2018 BU (See SSD12)..£750

SC9D Sovereign. As SC9 but with commemorative privy mark 65 on the reverse.

2018 Proof in gold *FDC* (Edition: 10,500 plus coins in sets)....................................£550

—   Proof in gold piedfort *FDC* (Edition: 2,750)...£1000

SC9E Sovereign. As SC9 but with commemorative privy mark 65 on the reverse and plain edge.

2018 BU (See SSD 11)..£750

SC9F Sovereign. As SC9 but with commemorative privy mark VA on the reverse and plain edge.

2019 BU Matt (See SSD 13 & 14)..£750

SC9G Sovereign. As SC9 but with George III Royal Cypher on reverse.
    2020 BU matt (Edition: 12,000)..£450
    —   Proof in gold *FDC* (Edition 10,500 plus coins in sets) £550
SC9H Sovereign. As SC9 but with Crowned Portcullis privy mark 65 on the reverse
    and plain edge.
    2020 BU matt (See SSD 15) £900
SC9J Sovereign. As SC9 but with commemorative privy mark VE75 on the reverse
    and plain edge.
    2020 BU matt (See SSD 16) £800
SC9K Sovereign. As SC9 but with commemorative privy mark VJ75 on the reverse
    and plain edge.
    2020 BU matt (See SSD 17) £800

Obverse portrait by James Butler

SC10

SC10 Sovereign. Ŗ. As SC7.
    2016 Proof in gold *FDC* (Issued: 7,995 plus coins in sets) £750

Obverse portrait by Jody Clark

SC11

SC11 Sovereign. Ŗ. The image of St George armed, sitting on horseback, attacking the
    dragon with a broken spear surrounded by the inscription 'HONI SOIT QUI MAL Y
    PENSE'.
    2017 Proof in gold *FDC* (Issued: 10,486 plus coins in sets).......................................£850
    —   Proof in gold piedfort *FDC* (Issued: 3,484) £1250

For further details of SSD 'Struck on the Day' coins, see after the listing of the sets.

Obverse portrait by Arnold Machin

SD1

SD1 Two pounds R. The image of St George armed, sitting on horseback, attacking the dragon with a sword, and a broken spear upon the ground, and the date of the year. (Reverse design: Benedetto Pistrucci.)

1980 Proof in gold *FDC** £750

1982 Proof in gold *FDC**...£800

1983 Proof in gold *FDC* (Issued: 12,500) ** £750

Obverse portrait by Raphael Maklouf

SD2   SD3

SD2 Two pounds. R. St. George as SD1.

1985 Proof in gold *FDC**...£600

1987 Proof in gold *FDC* (Issued: 1,801 plus coins in sets).......................................£750

1988 Proof in gold *FDC* (Issued: 1,551 plus coins in sets).......................................£750

1990 Proof in gold *FDC* (Issued: 716 plus coins in sets)...£750

1991 Proof in gold *FDC* (Issued: 620 plus coins in sets)...£750

1992 Proof in gold *FDC* (Issued: 476 plus coins in sets)...£750

1993 Proof in gold *FDC* (Issued: 414 plus coins in sets)...£750

1996 Proof in gold *FDC**...£750

SD3 Two pounds. 500th Anniversary of Sovereign. O. A representation Of Ourself as at Our Coronation, seated in King Edward's Chair and having received the Sceptre with the Cross and the Rod with the Dove, all within the circumscription 'ELIZABETH. II.DEI.GRA.REG.FID.DEF'. R. A Shield of Our Royal Arms ensigned by an open Royal Crown, the whole superimposed upon a double Rose, with the circumscription 'ANNIVERSARY OF THE GOLD SOVEREIGN 1489-1989' (Designs: Bernald Sindall.)

1989 Proof in gold *FDC* (Issued: 2,000 plus coins in sets).....................................£1400

* *Coins marked thus were originally issued in Royal Mint sets.*

** *Numbers include coins sold in sets*

Obverse portrait by Ian Rank-Broadley

SD4

SD4 Two pounds. ℞. St. George

1998 Proof in gold *FDC** £750

2000 Proof in gold *FDC** £750

2003 Proof in gold *FDC** £750

2006 Proof in gold *FDC** £750

2007 Proof in gold *FDC** £750

2008 Proof in gold *FDC** £750

SD5   SD6   SD7

SD5 Two pounds. ℞. The Shield of Arms of Our United Kingdom of Great Britain and Northern Ireland within an open wreath of laurel and ensigned by Our Royal Crown and beneath the date of the year. (Reverse design: Timothy Noad.)

2002 Proof in gold *FDC** £850

— thin milling (*reported in a number of 3 coin sets*) £1250

SD6 Two pounds. ℞. A depiction of St George, carrying a shield and a sword, slaying the dragon, with the date '2005' beneath the wing of the dragon. (Reverse design: Timothy Noad).

2005 Proof in gold *FDC** £850

SD7 Two pounds. ℞. St George. Based on the original design of 1820 with greater detail on the dragon.

2009 Proof in gold *FDC** £750

2010 Proof in gold *FDC** £750

2011 Proof in gold *FDC** £750

2013 BU* £800

— Proof in gold *FDC** £850

2014 BU (Issued: 835) £800

— Proof in gold *FDC** £850

2015 Proof in gold *FDC** £850

The 2014 £2 BU was issued to celebrate the 1st Birthday of Prince George.

* *Coins marked thus were originally issued in Royal Mint sets.*

SD8

SD8 **Two pounds.** R. The image of St George on horseback, attacking the dragon with a
lance, with date of the year to the left. (Reverse design: Paul Day.)
2012 BU*...£1000
— Proof in gold *FDC*...£1300

Obverse portrait by Jody Clark

SD9 **Two pounds.** R. St George and dragon as SD7.
2015 Proof in gold *FDC*...£1000
2019 Proof in gold *FDC*..£900
2020 Unc £850
SD9A Two pounds. R. As SD9 but with commemorative privy mark '65'.
2018 Proof in gold *FDC*...£1000
SD9B Two pounds. R. As SD9 but with George III Royal Cypher on the reverse.
2020 Proof in gold *FDC*...£1000

Obverse portrait by James Butler

SD10

SD10 Two pounds. R. St George and Dragon.
2016 Proof in gold *FDC*...£1300

* Coins marked thus were originally issued in Royal Mint sets.

Obverse portrait by Jody Clark

SD11

SD11 Two pounds. R. The image of St George armed, sitting on horseback, attacking the dragon with a broken spear surrounded by the inscription 'HONI SOIT QUI MAL Y PENSE'.

2017 Proof in gold *FDC** £1500

Obverse portrait by Arnold Machin

SE1   SE2

SE1 Five pounds. R. The image of St George armed, sitting on horseback, attacking the dragon with a sword, and a broken spear upon the ground, and the date of the year. (Reverse design: Benedetto Pistrucci.)

1980 Proof in gold *FDC** £2000

1981 Proof in gold *FDC* (Issued: 5,400)** £2000

1982 Proof in gold *FDC** £3000

1984 Proof in gold *FDC* (Issued: 7,095)** £2000

SE2 As SE1 but, 'U' in a circle to left of date

1984 BU (Issued: 15,104) £1900

* Coins marked thus were originally issued in Royal Mint sets.

** Numbers include coins sold in sets

Obverse portrait by Raphael Maklouf

SE3

SE3 **Five pounds.** R. St. George.
1985 Proof in gold *FDC* (Issued: 281 plus coins in sets)* £2000
1990 Proof in gold *FDC*...£2000
1991 Proof in gold *FDC*...£2000
1992 Proof in gold *FDC*...£2200
1993 Proof in gold *FDC*...£2200
1994 Proof in gold *FDC*...£2200
1995 Proof in gold *FDC*...£2200
1996 Proof in gold *FDC*...£2200
1997 Proof in gold *FDC*...£2200

SE4 **Five pounds** R. St George, 'U' in a circle to left of date.
1985 BU (Issued: 13,626) £1900
1986 BU (Issued: 7,723) £1900
1990 BU (Issued: 1,226) £1900
1991 BU (Issued: 976) £2000
1992 BU (Issued: 797) £2000
1993 BU (Issued: 906) £2000
1994 BU (Issued: 1,000) £2000
1995 BU (Issued: 1,000) £2000
1996 BU (Issued: 901) £2000
1997 BU (Issued: 802) £2000

SE5

SE5 **Five pounds** Uncouped portrait of Queen Elizabeth II. As illustration. R. St. George,
'U' in a circle to left of date.
1987 BU (Issued: 5,694) £1900
1988 BU (Issued: 3,315) £1900

* Coins marked thus were originally issued in Royal Mint sets.

SE6

SE6 **Five pounds** 500th Anniversary of Sovereign. O. A representation Of Ourself as at Our Coronation, seated in King Edward's Chair and having received the Sceptre with the Cross and the Rod with the Dove, all within the circumscription 'ELIZABETH.II.DEI.GRA. REG.FID.DEF'. R. A Shield of Our Royal Arms ensigned by an open Royal Crown, the whole superimposed upon a double Rose, and with the circumscription 'ANNIVERSARY OF THE GOLD SOVEREIGN 1489-1989' (Designs: Bernald Sindall.)
1989 Proof in gold *FDC** £3000
SE6A Five pounds. As SE6, but with 'U' under the throne on the obverse.
1989 BU (Issued: 2,937) £2250

Obverse portrait by Ian Rank-Broadley

SE7

SE7 Five pounds. R. St.George
1998 Proof in gold *FDC** £2000
1999 Proof in gold *FDC** £2000
2000 Unc (Issued: 4,177) £1850
— Proof in gold *FDC** £2000
2001 Proof in gold *FDC** £2000
2003 BU (Issued: 812) £1900
— Proof in gold *FDC** £2000
2004 BU (Issued: 1,000) £1900
— Proof in gold *FDC** £2000
2006 BU (Issued: 731) £1900
— Proof in gold *FDC** £2000
2007 BU (Issued: 768) £1900
— Proof in gold *FDC** £2000
2008 BU (Issued: 750) £1900
— Proof in gold *FDC** £2000

* Coins marked thus were originally issued in Royal Mint sets.

SE8 **Five pounds. ℞.** St. George, 'U' in a circle to left of date
1998 BU (Issued: 825) £2000
1999 BU (Issued: 970) £2000
2000 BU (Issued: 994) £1900
2001 BU (Issued: 1,000) £1900

SE9   SE10   SE11

SE9 **Five pounds. ℞.** The Shield of Arms of Our United Kingdom of Great Britain and
Northern Ireland within an open wreath of laurel and ensigned by Our Royal Crown
and beneath the date of the year. (Reverse design: Timothy Noad.)
2002 BU (Issued: 1,370) £2100
—   Proof in gold *FDC** £2400

SE10 **Five pounds. ℞.** A depiction of St George, carrying a shield and a sword, slaying
the dragon, with the date '2005' beneath the wing of the dragon.(Reverse design:
Timothy Noad.)
2005 BU (Issued: 936) £2100
—   Proof in gold *FDC** £2400

SE11 **Five pounds. ℞.** St George. Based on the original pattern piece of 1820 with the
designer's name, 'PISTRUCCI', shown in full in the exergue, and with a broader rim.
2009 BU (Issued: 1,000)...£2000
—   Proof in gold *FDC** £2000
2010 BU (Issued: 1,000)...£2000
—   Proof in gold *FDC** £2000
2011 BU (Issued: 657)..£2000
—   Proof in gold *FDC** £2000
2013 BU (Issued: 262)..£2250
—   Proof in gold *FDC** £2400
2014 BU (Issued 605)...£2100
—   Proof in gold *FDC** £2400
2015 Proof in gold *FDC** £2400

* Coins marked thus were originally issued in Royal Mint sets.

SE12

SE12 Five pounds. R. The image of St George on horseback, attacking the dragon with a lance, with date of the year to the left. (Reverse design: Paul Day.)

2012 BU (Issued: 496) £2300
—   Proof in gold *FDC** £3500

Obverse portrait by Jody Clark

SE13 Five pounds. R. St George and dragon as SE11

2015 BU (Issued: 609) £2100
—   Proof in gold *FDC** £3000
2016 BU (Issued: 498) £2200
2019 BU Matt (Edition: 505) £2000
—   Proof in gold *FDC** £2200

SE13A Five pounds. R. As SE13 but with commemorative privy mark '65'.

2018 BU (Edition: 1,000)..£2200
—   Proof in gold *FDC* * £2400

SE13B Five pounds. R. As SE13 but with George III Royal Cypher on the reverse.

2020 BU Matt (Edition: 355) £2400
—   Proof in gold *FDC** £2500

Obverse portrait by James Butler

SE14

SE14 Five pounds. R. St George and Dragon.

2016 Proof in gold *FDC** £3500

* Coins marked thus were originally issued in Royal Mint sets.

Obverse portrait by Jody Clark

SE15

SE15 Five pounds. R. The image of St George armed, sitting on horseback, attacking the
dragon with a broken spear surrounded by the inscription 'HONI SOIT QUI MAL
Y PENSE'.

2017 BU (Edition: 1,000)...£2400

—   Proof in gold *FDC** £3500

* Coins marked thus were originally issued in Royal Mint sets.

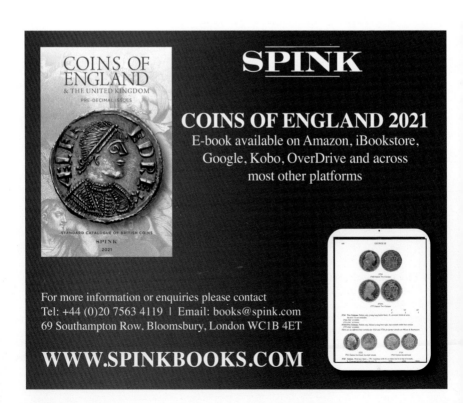

SPINK

COINS OF ENGLAND 2021

E-book available on Amazon, iBookstore,
Google, Kobo, OverDrive and across
most other platforms

For more information or enquiries please contact
Tel: +44 (0)20 7563 4119 | Email: books@spink.com
69 Southampton Row, Bloomsbury, London WC1B 4ET

WWW.SPINKBOOKS.COM

Many of the gold sovereign range of coins were issued as single pieces but most were also included in sets and others, especially a majority of the £5 pieces, only appear in cased sets.

Some sets contain a £2 commemorative of the year instead of the usual St. George & Dragon design and these are noted.

Proof Gold Sovereign Sets

			£
PGS01–**1980**	Gold £5 to half-sovereign (Issued: 10,000)	(4)	3500
PGS02–**1981**	U.K. Proof coin Commemorative collection. (Consists of £5, sovereign, 'Royal Wedding' Crown in silver, plus base metal proofs 50p to ½p), (Issued: 2080)	(9)	2500
PGS02A-**1981**	Gold sovereign and Royal Wedding silver proof crown (Issued: 2,107)	(2)	550
PGS03–**1982**	Gold £5 to half-sovereign (Issued: 2,500)	(4)	3600
PGS04–**1983**	Gold £2, sovereign and half-sovereign, (Not known)	(3)	1550
PGS05–**1984**	Gold £5, sovereign and half-sovereign, (Issued: 7,095)	(3)	2700
PGS06–**1985**	Gold £5 to half-sovereign (Issued: 5,849)	(4)	3500
PGS07–**1986**	Gold Commonwealth Games £2, sovereign and half-sovereign (Issued: 12,500)	(3)	1500
PGS08–**1987**	Gold £2, sovereign and half-sovereign (Issued: 12,500)	(3)	1500
PGS09–**1988**	Gold £2 to half-sovereign (Issued: 11,192)	(3)	1500
PGS10–**1989**	Sovereign Anniversary Gold £5 to half-sovereign (Issued: 5,000)	(4)	6000
PGS11–**1989**	Sovereign Anniversary Gold £2 to half-sovereign (Issued: 7,936)	(3)	3400
PGS12–**1990**	Gold £5 to half-sovereign (Issued: 1,721)	(4)	3500
PGS13–**1990**	Gold £2 to half-sovereign (Issued: 1,937)	(3)	1550
PGS14–**1991**	Gold £5 to half-sovereign (Issued: 1,336)	(4)	3500
PGS15–**1991**	Gold £2 to half-sovereign (Issued: 1,152)	(3)	1550
PGS16–**1992**	Gold £5 to half-sovereign (Issued: 1,165)	(4)	3500
PGS17–**1992**	Gold £2 to half-sovereign (Issued: 967)	(3)	1550
PGS18–**1993**	Gold £5 to half-sovereign with silver Pistrucci medal in case (Issued: 1,078)	(5)	3500
PGS19–**1993**	Gold £2 to half-sovereign (Issued: 663)	(3)	1550
PGS20–**1994**	Gold £5, Bank of England £2, sovereign and half-sovereign (Issued: 918)	(4)	3500
PGS21–**1994**	Gold Bank of England £2, sovereign and half-sovereign (Issued: 1,249)	(3)	1550
PGS22–**1995**	Gold £5, Dove of Peace £2, sovereign and half-sovereign (Issued: 718)	(4)	3500
PGS23–**1995**	Gold Dove of Peace £2, sovereign and half-sovereign (Issued: 1,112)	(3)	1550
PGS24–**1996**	Gold £5 to half-sovereign (Issued: 742)	(4)	3500
PGS25–**1996**	Gold £2 to half-sovereign (Issued: 868)	(3)	1550
PGS26–**1997**	Gold £5, Industry £2, sovereign and half-sovereign (Issued: 860)	(4)	3500
PGS27–**1997**	Gold Industry £2 to half-sovereign (Issued: 817)	(3)	1550
PGS28–**1998**	Gold £5 to half sovereign (Issued: 789)	(4)	3500
PGS29–**1998**	Gold £2 to half sovereign (Issued: 560)	(3)	1550
PGS30–**1999**	Gold £5, Rugby World Cup £2, sovereign and half sovereign (Issued: 991)	(4)	3500
PGS31–**1999**	Gold Rugby World Cup £2, sovereign and half sovereign (Issued: 912)	(3)	1550
PGS32–**2000**	Gold £5 to half-sovereign (Issued: 1,000)	(4)	3500
PGS33–**2000**	Gold £2 to half-sovereign (Issued: 1,250)	(3)	1550
PGS34–**2001**	Gold £5, Marconi £2, sovereign and half sovereign (Issued: 1,000)	(4)	3500
PGS35–**2001**	Gold Marconi £2, sovereign and half sovereign (Issued: 891)	(3)	1550
PGS36–**2002**	Gold £5 to half sovereign (Issued: 3,000)	(4)	4000
PGS37–**2002**	Gold £2 to half sovereign (Issued: 3,947)	(3)	1600
PGS38–**2003**	Gold £5 to half sovereign (Issued: 2,050)	(4)	3500
PGS39–**2003**	Gold DNA £2, sovereign and half sovereign (Issued: 1,737)	(3)	1550
PGS40–**2004**	Gold £5 to half sovereign (Issued: 1,749)	(4)	3500
PGS41–**2004**	Gold Locomotive £2, sovereign and half sovereign (Issued: 761)	(3)	1550
PGS42–**2005**	Gold £5 to half sovereign (Issued: 2,161)	(4)	3950
PGS43–**2005**	Gold £2 to half sovereign (Issued: 797)	(3)	1850
PGS44–**2006**	Gold £5 to half sovereign (Issued: 1,750)	(4)	3500

£

PGS45–**2006**	Gold £2 to half sovereign (Issued: 540)	(3)	1550
PGS46–**2007**	Gold £5 to half sovereign (Issued: 1,750)	(4)	3500
PGS47–**2007**	Gold £2 to half sovereign (Issued: 651)	(3)	1550
PGS48–**2007**	Gold sovereign and half sovereign (Issued: 818)..	(2)	800
PGS49–**2008**	Gold £5 to half sovereign (Issued: 1,750)	(4)	3500
PGS50–**2008**	Gold £2 to half sovereign (Issued: 583)	(3)	1550
PGS51–**2008**	Gold sovereign and half sovereign (Issued: 804)..	(2)	800
PGS52–**2009**	Gold £5, £2, sovereign, half sovereign, and quarter sovereign (Issued: 1,750)	(5)	3500
PGS53–**2009**	Gold £2, sovereign and half sovereign (Issued: 666)....................................	(3)	1550
PGS54–**2009**	Gold sovereign and half sovereign (Edition: 1,000)	(2)	800
PGS55–**2010**	Gold £5 to quarter sovereign (Issued: 1,461)	(5)	3600
PGS56–**2010**	Gold £2 to half sovereign (Issued: 558)	(3)	1550
PGS57–**2010**	Gold sovereign, half sovereign and quarter sovereign (Edition: 1,500)	(3)	900
PGS58–**2011**	Gold £5 to quarter sovereign (Issued: 1,028)...	(5)	3600
PGS59–**2011**	Gold £2 to quarter sovereign (Edition: 200)	(4)	1650
PGS60–**2011**	Gold £2 to half sovereign (Edition: 750)...	(3)	1550
PGS61–**2011**	Gold sovereign, half sovereign and quarter sovereign (Edition: 1,000)	(3)	900
PGS62–**2012**	Gold £5, £2, sovereign, half sovereign and quarter sovereign (Issued: 956)...	(5)	6250
PGS63–**2012**	Gold £2 to quarter sovereign (Issued: 605)	(4)	3000
PGS64–**2012**	Gold £2 to half sovereign (Issued: 335)...	(3)	2750
PGS65–**2012**	Gold sovereign, half sovereign and quarter sovereign (Issued: 701)..............	(3)	1600
PGS66–**2013**	Gold £5, £2, sovereign, half sovereign and quarter sovereign (Issued: 388)...	(5)	3600
PGS67–**2013**	Gold £2 to quarter sovereign (Issued: 495)	(4)	1650
PGS68–**2013**	Gold £2 to half sovereign (Issued: 380)...	(3)	1550
PGS69–**2013**	Gold sovereign, half sovereign and quarter sovereign (Issued: 652)	(3)	900
PGS70–**2014**	Gold £5, £2, sovereign, half sovereign and quarter sovereign (Issued: 375)...	(5)	3500
PGS71–**2014**	Gold £2 to half sovereign (Issued: 306)	(3)	1550
PGS72–**2014**	Gold sovereign, half sovereign and quarter sovereign (Issued: 669)..............	(3)	900
PGS73–**2015**	Gold £5, £2, sovereign, half sovereign and quarter sovereign (Issued: 507)....	(5)	3500
PGS74–**2015**	Gold £2 to half sovereign (Issued: 328)	(3)	1600
PGS75–**2015**	Gold sovereign, half sovereign and quarter sovereign (Issued: 664)...............	(3)	900
PGS76–**2015**	Gold £5, £2, sovereign, half sovereign and quarter sovereign (Issued: 598)....	(5)	5000
PGS77–**2015**	Gold £2 to half sovereign (Issued: 448)	(3)	1850
PGS78–**2016**	Gold £5 to quarter sovereign (Issued: 573)	(5)	6000
PGS79–**2016**	Gold £2 to half sovereign (Issued: 348)	(3)	2500
PGS80–**2016**	Gold sovereign, half sovereign and quarter sovereign (Issued: 745)	(3)	1300
PGS81–**2017**	Gold £5 to quarter sovereign (Issued: 749)	(5)	4000
PGS82–**2017**	Gold £2 to half sovereign (Issued: 449)	(3)	1750
PGS83–**2017**	Gold sovereign, half sovereign and quarter sovereign (Issued: 997)	(3)	950
PGS84–**2018**	Gold £5, £2, sovereign, half sovereign and quarter sovereign with '65th Anniversary Mint mark on the reverses (Edition: 750)...................................	(5)	4000
PGS85–**2018**	Gold £2, sovereign, half sovereign and quarter sovereign with '65th' Anniversary Mint Mark (Edition: 300)	(3)	1900
PGS86–**2018**	Gold £2, sovereign and half sovereign with '65th' Anniversary Mint Mark (Edition: 450)	(3)	1800
PGS87–**2018**	Gold sovereign, half sovereign and quarter sovereign with '65th' Anniversary Mint Mark (Edition: 1,000)	(3)	970
PGS88–**2019**	Gold £5, £2, sovereign, half sovereign and quarter sovereign (Edition: 750)..	(5)	4575
PGS89–**2019**	Gold £2, sovereign, half sovereign and quarter sovereign (Edition: 300)........	(4)	1960
PGS90–**2019**	Gold £2, sovereign and half sovereign (Edition: 450)	(3)	1800
PGS91–**2019**	Gold sovereign, half sovereign and quarter sovereign (Edition: 1,000)..........	(3)	970
PGS92–**2020**	Gold £5, £2, sovereign, half sovereign and quarter sovereign all with 'George III Royal Cypher' on the reverses (Edition: 500)..............................	(5)	4575

£

PGS93–**2020** Gold £2, sovereign, half sovereign and quarter sovereign all with 'George III Royal Cypher' on the reverses (Edition: 650) .... (4) 1960

PGS94–**2020** Gold sovereign, half sovereign and quarter sovereign all with 'George III Royal Cypher' on the reverses (Edition: 750) .... (3)   970

Uncirculated Gold Sovereign Sets

UGS01–**2012** (Formerly PGS66) £2 to half sovereign BU (Issued: 119) .... (3) 2000
This set was struck on the day of the commencement of the Diamond Jubilee Celebrations, 2nd June 2012.

UGS02–**2013** (Formerly PGS70) £2 to half sovereign BU (Issued: 124) .... (3) 1750
This set was struck on the day of the Diamond Jubilee of the Coronation, 2nd June 2013

Struck on the Day – A number of BU sovereigns were struck on significant dates and sold by the Royal Mint in a limited issue with appropriate certificate. The catalogue numbers, dates and associated event are as follows. Prices are for coins in original case with certificate. SSD1-7 also exist as regular coins so will generally be available uncased at lower prices.

SSD	Cat No.	Date	Event	Privy Mark	Edge	BU or Matt	Edition	Issued	£
1	SC8	2 /6/2012	Diamond Jubilee Celebration Day	None	Milled	BU	2012	1990	500
2	SC7	2 /6/2013	60th Anniversary of the Coronation	None	Milled	BU	2013	900	500
3	SC7	22/7/2013	Birth of Prince George	None	Milled	BU	2013	2013	600
4	SC7	22/7/2014	First birthday of Prince George	None	Milled	BU	400	398	700
5	SC7	2/5/2015	Birth of Princess Charlotte	None	Milled	BU	750	743	600
6	SC7	22/7/2015	Second birthday of Prince George	None	Milled	BU	400	301	700
7	SC9	11/6/2016	Queen's 90th Birthday	None	Milled	BU	500	499	550
8	SC9	6/2/2017	65th Anniversary of the Accession	None	Milled	BU	750	739	550
9	SC9C	1/7/2017	200th Anniversary of 1817 Sovereign	None	Plain	BU	1817	1793	850
10	SC9	20/11/2017	Platinum Wedding	None	Milled	BU	750	745	550
11	SC9E	2/6/2018	65th Anniversary of the Coronation	65	Plain	BU	650	323	750
12	SC9C	22/7/2018	Fifth birthday of Prince George	None	Plain	BU	750	457	750
13	SC9F	24/5/2019	200th Anniversary of Birth of Queen Victoria	VA	Plain	Matt	650	—	900
14	SC9F	26/8/2019	200th Anniversary of Birth of Prince Albert	VA	Plain	Matt	650	—	750
15	SC9H	31/1/2020	Brexit Day	Crowned Portcullis	Plain	Matt	1500	—	900
16	SC9J	8/5/2020	75th Anniversary of VE Day	VE75	Plain	Matt	750	—	800
17	SC9K	15/8/2020	75th Anniversary of End of World War II.	VJ75	Plain	Matt	750	—	800

SSD4 has a prooflike reverse.

Many of the gold sovereign coins were sold as both singles and in sets. The sales figures in the preceding text indicate the sales of coins sold singly in presentation cases. The numbers below show the total sales of each denomination year by year. There are some years where the Royal Mint has not published fully detailed sales figures and other years where the coins sold in sets came out of the authorised mintage for the single coin. In addition to the numbers sold we have listed the announced authorised mintage and as indicated in the introduction to this section there are just a few instances where the published numbers sold are in excess of the authorised. We will endeavour to keep this information updated.

Proof Gold Sets

1980	½ Sov.	Sov.	£2	£5	SET		Authorised
PS01	10000	10000	10000	10000	10000	(4)	10000
SC1		81200					100000
SB1	76700						100000
	86700	91200	10000	10000			

1981	½ Sov.	Sov.	£2	£5	SET		Authorised
PGS02		2080		2080			5000
PGS02A		2107			2107	(2)	
SE1				3320			10000
SC1		32960					50000
		37147		5400			

1982	½ Sov.	Sov.	£2	£5	SET		Authorised
PGS03	2500	2500	2500	2500	2500	(4)	2500
SC1		20000					20000
SB1	19090						20000
	21590	22500	2500	2500			

1983	½ Sov.	Sov.	£2	£5	SET		Authorised
PGS04		(figures below include coins in this set)				(3)	
SD1			12500				12500
SC1		21250					22500
SB1	19710						22500
	19710	21250	12500				

1984	½ Sov.	Sov.	£2	£5	SET		Authorised
PGS05	7095	7095		7095	7095	(3)	
SE1				905			8000
SC1		12880					22500
SB1	12410						22500
	19505	19975		8000			

1985	½ Sov.	Sov.	£2	£5	SET		Authorised
PGS06	5849	5849	5849	5849	5849	(4)	12500
SE3				281			
SC2		11393					12500
SB2	9951						12500
	15800	17242	5849	6130			

1986	½ Sov.	Sov.	£2 is K1	£5	SET		Authorised
PGS07	12500	12500	12500		12500	(3)	12500
K1			3277				5000
SC2		5079					12500
SB2	4575						12500
	17075	17579	15777				

1987	½ Sov.	Sov.	£2	£5	SET		Authorised
PGS08	12500	12500	12500		12500	(3)	12500
SD2			1801				2500
SC2		9979					10000
SB2	8187						10000
	20687	22479	14301				

1988	½ Sov.	Sov.	£2	£5	SET		Authorised
PGS09	11192	11192	11192		11192	(3)	12500
SD2			1551				2500
SC2		7670					12500
SB2	7074						10000
	18266	18862	12743				

1989	½ Sov.	Sov.	£2	£5	SET		Authorised
PGS10	5000	5000	5000	5000	5000	(4)	5000
PGS11	7936	7936	7936		7936	(3)	10000
SD3			2000				2000
SC3		10535					12500
SB3	8888						10000
	21824	23471	14936	5000			

1990	½ Sov.	Sov.	£2	£5	SET		Authorised
PGS12	1721	1721	1721	1721	1721	(4)	2500
PGS13	1937	1937	1937		1937	(3)	7500
SD2			716				2000
SC2		4767					10000
SB2	4231						10000
	7889	8425	4374	1721			

1984	½ Sov.	Sov.	£2	£5	SET		Authorised
PGS14	1336	1336	1336	1336	1336	(4)	1500
PGS15	1152	1152	1152		1152	(3)	2500
SD2			620				1000
SC2		4713					5000
SB2	3588						5000
	6076	7201	3108	1336			

1992	½ Sov.	Sov.	£2	£5	SET		Authorised
PGS16	1165	1165	1165	1165	1165	(4)	1250
PGS17	967	967	967		967	(3)	1250
SD2			476				500
SC2		4722					5000
SB2	3783						5000
	5915	6854	2608	1165			

1993	½ Sov.	Sov.	£2	£5	SET		Authorised
PGS18	1078	1078	1078	1078	1078	(4)	1250
PGS19	663	663	663		663	(3)	1250
SD2			414				500
SC2		4349					5000
SB2	2910						5000
	4651	6090	2155	1078			

1994	½ Sov.	Sov.	£2 is K4	£5	SET		Authorised
PGS20	918	918	918	918	918	(4)	1250
PGS21	1249	1249	1249		1249	(3)	1250
K4			1000				1000
SC2		4998					5000
SB2	5000						5000
	7167	7165	3167	918			

1995	½ Sov.	Sov.	£2 is K5	£5	SET		Authorised
PGS22	718	718	718	718	718	(4)	1250
PGS23	1112	1112	1112		1112	(3)	1250
K5			2500				2500
SC2		7500					7500
SB2	4900						5000
	6730	9330	4330	718			

1996	½ Sov.	Sov.	£2	£5	SET		Authorised
PGS24	742	742	742	742	742	(4)	1250
PGS25	868	868	868		868	(3)	1250
SC2		7500					7500
SB2	5730						7500
	7340	9110	1610	742			

1997	½ Sov.	Sov.	£2 is K8	£5	SET		Authorised
PGS26	860	860	860	860	860	(4)	1000
PGS27	817	817	817		817	(3)	1250
K8			2482				2500
SC2		7500					7500
SB2	7500						7500
	9177	9177	4159	860			

1998	½ Sov.	Sov.	£2	£5	SET		Authorised
PGS28	789	789	789	789	789	(4)	1500
PGS29	560	560	560		560	(3)	2000
SC4		10000					10000
SB4	6147						7500
	7496	11349	1349	789			

1999	½ Sov.	Sov.	£2 is K10	£5	SET		Authorised
PGS30	991	991	991	991	991	(4)	1000
PGS31	912	912	912		912	(3)	1250
K10			311				3250
SC4		10000					10000
SB4	7500						7500
	9403	11903	2214	991			

2000	½ Sov.	Sov.	£2	£5	SET		Authorised
PGS32	1000	1000	1000	1000	1000	(4)	1000
PGS33	1250	1250	1250		1250	(3)	1250
SC4		9909					10000
SB4	7458						7500
	9708	12159	2250	1000			

2001	½ Sov.	Sov.	£2 is K11	£5	SET		Authorised
PGS34	1000	1000	1000	1000	1000	(4)	1000
PGS35	891	891	891		891	(3)	1500
K11			1658				2500
SC4		8915					12500
SB4	4596						7500
	6487	10806	3549	1000			

2002	½ Sov.	Sov.	£2	£5	SET		Authorised
PGS36	3000	3000	3000	3000	3000	(4)	3000
PGS37	3947	3947	3947		3947	(3)	5000
SC5		12500					12500
SB5	10000						10000
	16947	19447	6947	3000			

2003	½ Sov.	Sov.	£2	£5	SET		Authorised
PGS38	2050	2050	2050	2050	2050	(4)	2250
PGS39	1737	1737	†		1737	(3)	2500
SC4		12433					15000
SB4	4868						10000
	8655	16220	2050	2050			†[£2 in 3 coin set is K16]

2004	½ Sov.	Sov.	£2	£5	SET		Authorised
PGS40	1749	1749	1749	1749	1749	(4)	2250
PGS41	761	761	†		761	(3)	2500
SC4		10175					15000
SB4	4446						10000
	6956	12685	1749	1749			†[£2 in 3 coin set is K17]

2005	½ Sov.	Sov.	£2	£5	SET		Authorised
PGS42	2161	2161	2161	2161	2161	(4)	2500
PGS43	797	797	797		797	(3)	2500
SC6		12500					12500
SB6	5011						7500
	7969	15458	2958	2161			

2006	½ Sov.	Sov.	£2	£5	SET		Authorised
PGS44	1750	1750	1750	1750	1750	(4)	1750
PGS45	540	540	540		540	(3)	1750
SC4		9195					12500
SB4	4173						5000
	6463	11485	2290	1750			

2007	½ Sov.	Sov.	£2	£5	SET		Authorised
PGS46	1750	1750	1750	1750	1750	(4)	1750
PGS47	651	651	651		651	(3)	750
PGS48	818	818			818	(2)	
SC4		8199					10000
SB4	2442						5000
	5661	11418	2401	1750			

2008	½ Sov.	Sov.	£2	£5	SET		Authorised
PGS49	1750	1750	1750	1750	1750	(4)	1750
PGS50	583	583	583			583	(3)	750
PGS51	804	804				804	(2)	
SC4		7735						12500
SB4	2465							5000
	5602	10872	2333	1750			

2009	¼ Sov.	½ Sov.	Sov.	£2	£5	SET		Authorised
PGS52	1750	1750	1750	1750	1750	1750	(5)	1750
PGS53		666	666	666		666	(3)	750
PGS54	*(figures below include coins in this set)*						(2)	1000
SC7			7354					12500
SB7		2996						2500
SA1	11745							21500
	13495	5412	9770	2416	1750			

2010	¼ Sov.	½ Sov.	Sov.	£2	£5	SET		Authorised
PGS55	1461	1461	1461	1461	1461	1461	(5)	1750
PGS56		558	558	558		558	(3)	750
PGS57	*(figures below include coins in this set)*						(3)	1500
SC7			6809					7500
SB7		3351						2500
SA1	4546							14000
	6007	5370	8828	2019	1461			

2011	¼ Sov.	½ Sov.	Sov.	£2	£5	SET		Authorised
PGS58	1028	1028	1028	1028	1028	1028	(5)	1500
PGS59	*(figures below include coins in this set)*						(4)	200
PGS60	*(figures below include coins in this set)*						(3)	750
PGS61	*(figures below include coins in this set)*						(3)	1000
SC7			7181					7500
SB7A		4259						2500
SA1	6736							5000
	7764	5287	8209	2149	1028			

2012	¼ Sov.	½ Sov.	Sov.	£2	£5	SET		Authorised
PGS62	956	956	956	956	956	956	(5)	999
PGS63	605	605	605	605		605	(4)	295
PGS64		335	335	335		335	(3)	750
PGS65	701	701	701			701	(3)	700
PGCS12				60				60
SC8			5501					5500
SB8		2303						2250
SA2	7579							6500
	9841	4900	8098	1956	956			

2013	¼ Sov.	½ Sov.	Sov.	£2	£5	SET		Authorised
PGS66	388	388	388	388	388	388	(5)	1000
PGS67	495	495	495	495		495	(4)	295
PGS68		380	380	380		380	(3)	400
PGS69	652	652	652			652	(3)	650
SC7			8243					7500
SB7A		1863						2250
SA1	1696							3500
	3231	3778	10158	1263	388			

2014	¼ Sov.	½ Sov.	Sov.	£2	£5	SET		Authorised
PGS70	375	375	375	375	375	375	(5)	750
PGS71		306	306	306		306	(3)	500
PGS72	669	669	669			669	(3)	750
SC7			3263					7500
SB7A		1367						2000
SA1	1886							3000
	2930	2717	4613	681	375			

2015	¼ Sov.	½ Sov.	Sov.	£2	£5	SET		Authorised
PGS73	407	407	407	407	407	407	(5)	500
	100	100	100	100	100	100	(5) Ω	100
PGS74		328	328	328		328	(3)	500
PGS75	664	664	664			664	(3)	1000
SC7			4346					7500
SC7			200				Ω	200
SB7A		1704						2500
SA1	1808							3000
	2979	3203	6045	835	507			

2015 New Portrait	¼ Sov.	½ Sov.	Sov.	£2	£5	SET		Authorised
PGS76	348	348	348	348	348	348	(5)	350
	250	250	250	250	250	250	(5) Ω	250
PGS77		448	448	448		448	(3)	500
SC9			6994					7000
SC9			500				Ω	500
SA3	550						Ω	550
	1148	1046	8540	1046	598			

2016	¼ Sov.	½ Sov.	Sov.	£2	£5	SET		Authorised
PGS78	348	348	348	348	348	348	(5)	350
	75	75	75	75	75	75	(5) Ω	75
PGS79		348	348	348		348	(3)	350
PGS80	745	745	745			745	(3)	750
SC10			7495					7500
SC10			500				Ω	500
SB10		1995						2000
SA4	1727							1750
	3045	3661	9661	921	573			

2017	¼ Sov.	½ Sov.	Sov.	£2	£5	SET		Authorised
PGS81	749	749	749	749	749	749	(5)	750
PGS82		449	449	449		449	(3)	450
PGS83	997	997	997			997	(3)	1000
SC11			10486					10500
SB11		2453						2500
SA5	2442							2500
	4188	4648	12681	1198	749			

2018	¼ Sov.	½ Sov.	Sov.	£2	£5	SET		Authorised
PGS84	#	#	#	#	#	#	(5)	750
PGS85	#	#	#	#		#	[4]	300
PGS86		#	#	#		#	(3)	450
PGS87	#	#	#			#	(3)	1000
SC9D			#					10500
SB9A		#						2500
SA3A	#							2500

Ω Coins sold to the US market and not in standard Royal Mint cases.
Mintages not yet known

2019	¼ Sov.	½ Sov.	Sov.	£2	£5	SET		Authorised
PGS88	#	#	#	#	#	#	(5)	750
PGS89	#	#	#	#		#	[4]	300
PGS90		#	#	#		#	(3)	450
PGS91	#	#	#			#	(3)	1000
SC9			#					10500
SB9		#						2500
SA3	#							2500

2020	¼ Sov.	½ Sov.	Sov.	£2	£5	SET		Authorised
PGS92	#	#	#	#	#	#	(5)	500
PGS93	#	#	#	#		#	(4)	600
PGS94	#	#	#			#	(3)	750
SC9G			#					7995
SB9B		#						2000

Uncirculated Gold Sets

2012	½ Sov.	Sov.	£2	SET		Authorised
UGS01	119	119	119	119	(3)	125
SC8		4559				
SB8	2137					
	2256	4678	119			

2013	½ Sov.	Sov.	£2	SET		Authorised
UGS02	124	124	124	124	(3)	125
SC7		2695				
SB7A	1051					
	1175	2819	124			

Ω Coins sold to the US market and not in standard Royal Mint cases.
Mintages not yet known

In 1987 the Mint decided to enter the market for bullion coins and launched a series of four gold coins with weights that corresponded to those already issued by a number of gold producing countries such as Australia, Canada, South Africa and China. The plan was to sell bullion quality coins in quantity to trade customers and investors at modest premiums over the ruling gold market price, and also to sell proof versions in limited editions to collectors.

Until 2013 the gold coins were struck in 22 carat gold (.9166), the standard for UK gold coins. From 1990 silver was included with copper which made the coins more yellow and more acceptable in the Far East market. From 2013 onwards the gold coins were struck in .999 gold, but in the absence of sales figures for much of the bullion issues, it appears that the major interest is now to be found among collectors of the proof versions.

To mark the 10th anniversary of the first design, silver coins struck in Britannia silver (0.958) were introduced in the same four weights in 1997 although only the £2 (one ounce) was issued in quantity as a bullion coin. The silver fineness was increased to .999 in 2013 and smaller denominations were introduced as proofs in 2013 & 2014.

There are some attractive and different interpretations of Britannia with the gold and silver issues sharing the same designs as they are changed, but by and large the bullion coins have retained the designs from the first series so as to make them more recognisable across the world as UK bullion coins.

Most of the fraction coins are only issued within sets but some along with the 1oz versions were issued individually. Prices given relate to cased coins with certificates; uncased coins from split sets can often be found at lower prices.

A table of specifications for the silver coins appears below and a similar table for the gold may be found immediately before the gold listings. Sets of silver and gold Britannia coins are now listed immediately after the listing of the individual coins.

Britannia Silver Coins Specifications

Denomination	Metal	Weight		Diameter
5p - from 2014	00.999 silver	$^1/_{40}$ ounce	0.80 g	8.00 mm
10p - from 2013	0.999 silver	$^1/_{20}$ ounce	1.58 g	12.00 mm
20p 1997-2002	0.958 silver	$^1/_{10}$ ounce	3.24 g	16.50 mm
- from 2013	0.999 silver	$^1/_{10}$ ounce	3.15 g	16.50 mm
50p 1997-2012	0.958 silver	$^1/_4$ ounce	8.11 g	22.00 mm
- from 2013	0.999 silver	$^1/_4$ ounce	7.86 g	22.00 mm
£1 1997-2012	0.958 silver	$^1/_2$ ounce	16.22 g	27.00 mm
- from 2013	0.999 silver	$^1/_2$ ounce	15.71 g	27.00 mm
£2 1997-2012	0.958 silver	1 ounce	32.45 g	40.00 mm
- from 2013	0.999 silver	1 ounce	31.21 g	38.61 mm
£10	0.999 silver	5 ounces	156.30 g	65.00 mm
£50	0.999 silver	1 kilo	1005 g	100.00 mm
£250	0.999 silver	20 ounces	643.65 g	100.00 mm
£500	0.999 silver	1 kilo	1005 g	100.00 mm

Obverse portrait by Ian Rank-Broadley
BA1 **Britannia Five Pence.** (1/40 oz of fine silver.) R̠. As BF13 with the inscription
'BRITANNIA 999 1/40 OZ FINE SILVER 2014'.
2014 Proof in silver *FDC** £15

Obverse portrait by Jody Clark
BA2 **Britannia Five Pence.** (1/40 oz of fine silver.) R̠. As BF14 with the inscription
'BRITANNIA 1/40 OZ FINE SILVER 999 2015'.
2015 Proof in silver *FDC** £15
BA3 **Britannia Five Pence.** (1/40 oz of fine silver.) R̠. As BF16 with the inscription
'BRITANNIA 1/40 OZ FINE SILVER 999 2016'.
2016 Proof in silver *FDC** £15
BA4 **Britannia Five Pence.** (1/40 oz of fine silver.) R̠. As BF17 with the inscription
'BRITANNIA 1/40 OZ FINE SILVER 999 2017' and with Trident mint mark to
mark the 20th Anniversary of the first Britannia silver issue.
2017 Proof in silver *FDC** £15
BA5 **Britannia Five Pence.** (1/40 oz of fine silver.) R̠. As BF18 with the inscription
'BRITANNIA 1/40 OZ FINE SILVER 999 2018'.
2018 Proof in silver *FDC** £15
BA6 **Britannia Five Pence.** (1/40 oz of fine silver.) R̠. As BF21 with the inscription
'BRITANNIA 1/40 OZ FINE SILVER 999 2019'.
2019 Proof in silver *FDC** £15
BA7 **Britannia Five Pence.** (1/40 oz of fine silver.) R̠. As BF22 with the inscription
'BRITANNIA 1/40 OZ FINE SILVER 999 2020'.
2020 Proof in silver *FDC** £15

Obverse portrait by Ian Rank-Broadley
BB1 **Britannia Ten Pence.** (1/20 oz of fine silver.) R̠. As BF11 with the inscription
'BRITANNIA 999 1/20 OUNCE FINE SILVER 2013'.
2013 Proof in silver *FDC** £20
BB2 **Britannia Ten Pence.** (1/20 oz of fine silver.) R̠. As BF13 with the inscription
'BRITANNIA 999 1/20 OZ FINE SILVER 2014'.
2014 Proof in silver *FDC** £20

Obverse portrait by Jody Clark
BB3 **Britannia Ten Pence.** (1/20 oz of fine silver.) R̠. As BF14 with the inscription
'BRITANNIA 1/20 OZ FINE SILVER 999 2015'.
2015 Proof in silver *FDC** £20
BB4 **Britannia Ten Pence.** (1/20 oz of fine silver.) R̠. As BF16 with the inscription
'BRITANNIA 1/20 OZ FINE SILVER 999 2016'.
2016 Proof in silver *FDC** £20
BB5 **Britannia Ten Pence.** (1/20 oz of fine silver.) R̠. As BF17 with the inscription
'BRITANNIA 1/20 OZ FINE SILVER 999 2017' and with Trident mint mark to
mark the 20th Anniversary of the first Britannia silver issue.
2017 Proof in silver *FDC** £20
BB6 **Britannia Ten Pence.** (1/20 oz of fine silver.) R̠. As BF18 with the inscription
'BRITANNIA 1/20 OZ FINE SILVER 999 2018'.
2018 Proof in silver *FDC** £20
BB7 **Britannia Ten Pence.** (1/20 oz of fine silver.) R̠. As BF21 with the inscription
'BRITANNIA 1/20 OZ FINE SILVER 999 2019'.
2019 Proof in silver *FDC** £20

For coin specifications please see table at the beginning of this section.

BB8 **Britannia Ten Pence.** (1/20 oz of fine silver.) R. As BF22 with the inscription
'BRITANNIA 1/20 OZ FINE SILVER 999 2020'.
2020 Proof in silver *FDC** £20

Obverse portrait by Raphael Maklouf
BC1 **Britannia Twenty Pence.** (1/10 oz of fine silver.) R. As BF1 with the inscription
'BRITANNIA TENTH OUNCE FINE SILVER 1997'.
1997 Proof in silver *FDC* (Issued: 8,686 plus coins in sets)...£25

Obverse portrait by Ian Rank-Broadley
BC2 **Britannia Twenty Pence.** (1/10 oz of fine silver.) R. As BF2 with the inscription
'BRITANNIA 1/10 OUNCE FINE SILVER' and the date of the year.
1998 Proof in silver *FDC* (Issued: 2,724 plus coins in sets)...£25
2006 BU £20
2012 Proof in silver *FDC** £25
BC3 **Britannia Twenty Pence.** (1/10 oz of fine silver.) R. As BF4 with the inscription
'BRITANNIA TENTH OUNCE FINE SILVER 2001'.
2001 Proof in silver *FDC* (Issued: 826 plus coins in sets)..£25
BC4 **Britannia Twenty Pence.** (1/10 oz of fine silver.) R. As BF5 with the inscription
'BRITANNIA TENTH OUNCE FINE SILVER 2003' .
2003 Proof in silver *FDC* (Issued: 1,179 plus coins in sets)...£25
BC5 **Britannia Twenty Pence.** (1/10 oz of fine silver.) R. As BF6 with the inscription
'BRITANNIA TENTH OUNCE FINE SILVER 2005'.
2005 Proof in silver *FDC* (Issued: 913 plus coins in sets)..£25
BC6 **Britannia Twenty Pence.** (1/10 oz of fine silver.) R. As BF7 with the inscription
'BRITANNIA TENTH OUNCE FINE SILVER 2007'.
2007 Proof in silver *FDC* (Issued: 901 plus coins in sets)..£25
BC7 **Britannia Twenty Pence.** (1/10 oz of fine silver.) R. As BF8 with the inscription
'BRITANNIA TENTH OUNCE FINE SILVER 2008'.
2008 Proof in silver *FDC* (Issued: 725 plus coins in sets)..£25
BC8 **Britannia Twenty Pence.** (1/10 oz of fine silver.) R. As BF 3 with the inscription
'BRITANNIA TENTH OUNCE FINE SILVER 2009'.
2009 Proof in silver *FDC* (Issued: 1,000 plus coins in sets)...£25
BC9 **Britannia Twenty Pence.** (1/10 oz of fine silver.) R. As BF9 with the inscription
'BRITANNIA TENTH OUNCE FINE SILVER 2010'.
2010 Proof in silver *FDC* (Issued: 989 plus coins in sets)..£25
BC10 **Britannia Twenty Pence.** (1/10 oz of fine silver.) R. As BF10 with the inscription
'BRITANNIA TENTH OUNCE FINE SILVER 2011'.
2011 Proof in silver *FDC** £25
BC11 **Britannia Twenty Pence.** (1/10 oz of fine silver.) R. As BF11 with the inscription
'BRITANNIA 1/10 OUNCE FINE SILVER 2013'.
2013 Proof in silver *FDC** £25
BC12 **Britannia Twenty Pence.** (1/10 oz of fine silver.) R. As BF13 with the inscription
'BRITANNIA 999 1/10 OZ FINE SILVER 2014'.
2014 Proof in silver *FDC** £25

Obverse portrait by Jody Clark
BC13 **Britannia Twenty Pence.** (1/10 oz of fine silver.) R. As BF14 with the inscription
'BRITANNIA 1/10 OZ FINE SILVER 999 2015'.
2015 Proof in silver *FDC** £25

For coin specifications please see table at the beginning of this section.

BC14 Britannia Twenty Pence. (1/10 oz of fine silver.) R. As BF16 with the inscription
'BRITANNIA 1/10 OZ FINE SILVER 999 2016'.
2016 Proof in silver *FDC**..£25

BC15 Britannia Twenty Pence. (1/10 oz of fine silver.) R. As BF17 with the inscription
'BRITANNIA 1/10 OZ FINE SILVER 999 2017' and with Trident mint mark to
mark the 20th Anniversary of the first Britannia silver issue.
2017 Proof in silver *FDC**..£25

BC16 Britannia Twenty Pence. (1/10 oz of fine silver.) R. As BF18 with the inscription
'BRITANNIA 1/10 OZ FINE SILVER 999 2018'.
2018 Proof in silver *FDC**..£25

BC17 Britannia Twenty Pence. (1/10 oz of fine silver.) R. As BF21 with the inscription
'BRITANNIA 1/10 OZ FINE SILVER 999 2019'.
2019 Proof in silver *FDC**..£25

BC18 Britannia Twenty Pence. (1/10 oz of fine silver.) R. As BF22 with the inscription
'BRITANNIA 1/10 OZ FINE SILVER 999 2020'.
2020 Proof in silver *FDC**..£25

Obverse portrait by Raphael Maklouf
BD1 **Britannia Fifty Pence.** (1/4 oz of fine silver.) R. As BF1 with the inscription
'BRITANNIA QUARTER OUNCE FINE SILVER 1997'.
1997 Proof in silver *FDC**..£30

Obverse portrait by Ian Rank-Broadley
BD2 **Britannia Fifty Pence.** (1/4 oz of fine silver.) R. As BF2 with the inscription
'BRITANNIA 1/4 OUNCE FINE SILVER' and the date of the year.
1998 Proof in silver *FDC**..£30
2012 Proof in silver *FDC**..£30

BD3 **Britannia Fifty Pence.** (1/4 oz of fine silver.) R. As BF4 with the inscription
'BRITANNIA QUARTER OUNCE FINE SILVER 2001'.
2001 Proof in silver *FDC**..£30

BD4 **Britannia Fifty Pence.** (1/4 oz of fine silver.) R. As BF5 with the inscription
'BRITANNIA QUARTER OUNCE FINE SILVER 2003'.
2003 Proof in silver *FDC**..£30

BD5 **Britannia Fifty Pence.** (1/4 oz of fine silver.) R. As BF6 with the inscription
'BRITANNIA 1/4 OUNCE FINE SILVER 2005'.
2005 Proof in silver *FDC**..£30

BD6 **Britannia Fifty Pence.** (1/4 oz of fine silver.) R. As BF7 with the inscription
'BRITANNIA QUARTER OUNCE FINE SILVER 2007'.
2007 Proof in silver *FDC**..£30

BD7 **Britannia Fifty Pence.** (1/4 oz of fine silver.) R. As BF8 with the inscription
'BRITANNIA 1/4 OUNCE FINE SILVER 2008'.
2008 Proof in silver *FDC**..£30

BD8 **Britannia Fifty Pence.** (1/4 oz of fine silver.) R. As BF3 with the inscription
'BRITANNIA 1/4 OUNCE FINE SILVER 2009'.
2009 Proof in silver *FDC**..£30

BD9 **Britannia Fifty Pence.** (1/4 oz of fine silver.) R. As BF9 with the inscription
'BRITANNIA 1/4 OUNCE FINE SILVER 2010'.
2010 Proof in silver *FDC**..£30

BD10 Britannia Fifty Pence. (1/4 oz of fine silver.) R. As BF10 with the inscription
'BRITANNIA 1/4 OUNCE FINE SILVER 2011'.
2011 Proof in silver *FDC**..£30

For coin specifications please see table at the beginning of this section.

BD11 Britannia Fifty Pence. (1/4 oz of fine silver.) Ŗ. As BF11 with the inscription
'BRITANNIA 1/4 OUNCE FINE SILVER 2013'.
2013 Proof in silver *FDC** £30
BD12 Britannia Fifty Pence. (1/4 oz of fine silver.) Ŗ. As BD2 with revised inscription
'1/4OZ 999 FINE SILVER', the date of the year and edge inscription 'SS Gairsoppa'.
2013 BU £10
2014 BU in pack (Issued: 19,214)...£25
The silver for these coins was salvaged from the wreck of the SS 'Gairsoppa' sunk in 1941.

BD13 Britannia Fifty Pence. (1/4 oz of fine silver.) Ŗ. As BF13 with the inscription
'BRITANNIA 999 1/4 OZ FINE SILVER 2014'.
2014 Proof in silver *FDC** £30
BD14 Britannia Fifty Pence. (1/4 oz of fine silver.) Ŗ. As BD2 with revised inscription
'1/4OZ 999 FINE SILVER' the date '2015' and textured background on the obverse
and reverse.
2015 Unc (Edition: 100 in a case with a 2015 bullion sovereign) £25
It is not known whether this coin exists in any other presentation.

Obverse portrait by Jody Clark
BD15 Britannia Fifty Pence. (1/4 oz of fine silver.) Ŗ. As BF14 with the inscription
'BRITANNIA 1/4 OZ FINE SILVER 999 2015'.
2015 Proof in silver *FDC** £30
BD16 Britannia Fifty Pence. (1/4 oz of fine silver.) Ŗ. As BF16 with the inscription
'BRITANNIA 1/4 OZ FINE SILVER 999 2016'.
2016 Proof in silver *FDC** ....   ,,,,,,,,,,,,,,,,,,,..£30
BD17 Britannia Fifty Pence. (1/4 oz of fine silver.) Ŗ. As BF17 with the inscription
'BRITANNIA 1/4 OZ FINE SILVER 999 2017' and with Trident mint mark to mark the
20th Anniversary of the first Britannia silver issue.
2017 Proof in silver *FDC** £30
BD18 Britannia Fifty Pence. (1/4 oz of fine silver.) Ŗ. As BF18 with the inscription
'BRITANNIA 1/4 OZ FINE SILVER 999 2018'.
2018 Proof in silver *FDC** £30
BD19 Britannia Fifty Pence. (1/4 oz of fine silver.) Ŗ. As BF21 with the inscription
'BRITANNIA 1/4 OZ FINE SILVER 999 2019'.
2019 Proof in silver *FDC** £30
BD20 Britannia Fifty Pence. (1/4 oz of fine silver.) Ŗ. As BF22 with the inscription
'BRITANNIA 1/4 OZ FINE SILVER 999 2020'.
2020 Proof in silver *FDC** £30

Obverse portrait by Raphael Maklouf
BE1   Britannia. One pound. (1/2 oz of fine silver.) Ŗ. As BF1 with the inscription
'BRITANNIA HALF OUNCE FINE SILVER 1997'.
1997 Proof in silver *FDC** £40

Obverse portrait by Ian Rank-Bradley
BE2   Britannia. One pound. (1/2 oz of fine silver.) Ŗ. As BF2 with the inscription
'BRITANNIA 1/2 OUNCE FINE SILVER' and the date of the year.
1998 Proof in silver *FDC** £40
2012 Proof in silver *FDC** £40
BE2A Britannia. One pound. (1/2 oz of fine silver.) Ŗ. As BE2 with satin finish on reverse.
2007 Proof in silver* £40

For coin specifications please see table at the beginning of this section.

BE3 **Britannia. One pound.** (1/2 oz of fine silver.) R. As BF4 with the inscription
'BRITANNIA HALF OUNCE FINE SILVER' and the date of the year.
2001 Proof in silver *FDC**...£35
2012 Proof in silver *FDC**...£40

BE3A **Britannia. One pound.** (1/2 oz of fine silver.) R. As BE3 with satin finish on reverse.
2007 Proof in silver*..£40

BE4 **Britannia. One pound.** (1/2 oz of fine silver.) R. As BF5 with the inscription
'BRITANNIA HALF OUNCE FINE SILVER' and the date of the year.
2003 Proof in silver *FDC**...£35
2012 Proof in silver *FDC**...£40

BE4A **Britannia. One pound.** (1/2 oz of fine silver.) R. As BE4 with satin finish on reverse.
2007 Proof in silver*..£40

BE5 **Britannia. One pound.** (1/2 oz of fine silver.) R. As BF6 with the inscription
'BRITANNIA 1/2 OUNCE FINE SILVER' and the date of the year.
2005 Proof in silver *FDC**...£35
2012 Proof in silver *FDC**...£40

BE5A **Britannia. One pound.** (1/2 oz of fine silver.) R. As BE5 with satin finish on reverse.
2007 Proof in silver*..£40

BE6 **Britannia. One pound.** (1/2 oz of fine silver.) R. As BF7 with the inscription
'BRITANNIA HALF OUNCE FINE SILVER' and the date of the year.
2007 Proof in silver *FDC**...£35
2012 Proof in silver *FDC**...£40

BE6A **Britannia. One pound.** (1/2 oz of fine silver.) R. As BE6 with satin finish on reverse.
2007 Proof in silver*..£40

BE7 **Britannia. One pound.** (1/2 oz of fine silver.) R. As BF8 with the inscription
'BRITANNIA HALF OUNCE FINE SILVER' and the date of the year.
2008 Proof in silver *FDC**...£35
2012 Proof in silver *FDC**...£40

BE8 **Britannia. One pound.** (1/2 oz of fine silver.) R. As BF 3 with the inscription
'BRITANNIA ½ OUNCE FINE SILVER' and the date of the year.
2009 Proof in silver *FDC**...£35
2012 Proof in silver *FDC**...£40

BE9 **Britannia. One pound.** (1/2 oz of fine silver.) R. As BF9 with the inscription
'BRITANNIA 1/2 OUNCE FINE SILVER' and the date of the year.
2010 Proof in silver *FDC**...£35
2012 Proof in silver *FDC**...£40

BE10 **Britannia. One pound.** (1/2 oz of fine silver.) R. As BF10 with the inscription
'BRITANNIA 1/2 OUNCE FINE SILVER' and the date of the year.
2011 Proof in silver *FDC**...£35
2012 Proof in silver *FDC**...£40

BE11 **Britannia. One pound.** (1/2 oz of fine silver.) R. As BF11 with the inscription
'BRITANNIA 1/2 OUNCE FINE SILVER 2013'.
2013 Proof in silver *FDC**...£35

BE12 **Britannia. One pound.** (1/2 oz of fine silver.) R. As BF13 with the inscription
'BRITANNIA 999 1/2 OZ FINE SILVER 2014'.
2014 Proof in silver *FDC**...£35

Obverse portrait by Jody Clark
BE13 **Britannia. One pound.** (1/2 oz of fine silver.) R. As BF14 with the inscription
'BRITANNIA 1/2 OZ FINE SILVER 999 2015'.
2015 Proof in silver *FDC**...£40

For coin specifications please see table at the beginning of this section.

BE14 Britannia. One pound. (1/2 oz of fine silver.) R. As BF16 with the inscription
'BRITANNIA 1/2 OZ FINE SILVER 999 2016'.
2016 Proof in silver *FDC** £40

BE15 Britannia. One pound. (1/2 oz of fine silver.) R. As BF17 with the inscription
'BRITANNIA 1/2 OZ FINE SILVER 999 2017' and with Trident mint mark to
mark the 20th Anniversary of the first Britannia silver issue.
2017 Proof in silver *FDC** £40

BE16 Britannia. One pound. (1/2 oz of fine silver.) R. As BF18 with the inscription
'BRITANNIA 1/2 OZ FINE SILVER 999 2018'.
2018 Proof in silver *FDC** £40

BE17 Britannia. One pound. (1/2 oz of fine silver.) R. As BF21 with the inscription
'BRITANNIA 1/2 OZ FINE SILVER 999 2019'.
2019 Proof in silver *FDC** £40

BE18 Britannia. One pound. (1/2 oz of fine silver.) R. As BF22 with the inscription
'BRITANNIA 1/2 OZ FINE SILVER 999 2020'.
2020 Proof in silver *FDC** £40

Obverse portrait by Raphael Maklouf

BF1

BF1 Britannia. Two pounds. (1 oz of fine silver.) 10th Anniversary of Britannia bullion
coins. R. The figure of Britannia standing in a chariot drawn along the seashore by
two horses, with the word 'BRITANNIA', the inscription 'ONE OUNCE FINE
SILVER' and the date of the year. (Reverse design: Philip Nathan.)
1997 Proof in silver *FDC* (Issued: 4,173 plus coins in sets)...£170

For coin specifications please see table at the beginning of this section.

Obverse portrait by Ian Rank-Broadley

BF2

BF2 Britannia. Two pounds. (1 oz of fine silver.) R. The figure of Britannia standing upon
a rock in the sea, her right hand grasping a trident and her left hand resting on a shield
and holding an olive branch, with the word 'BRITANNIA', the date of the year and the
inscription 'ONE OUNCE FINE SILVER'. (Reverse design: Philip Nathan.)

1998 Unc (Issued: 88,909) £40
— Proof in silver *FDC* (Issued: 2,168 plus coins in sets)...£80
2000 Unc (Issued: 81,301) £40
2002 Unc (Issued: 36,543) £40
2004 Unc (Edition: 100,000)..£40
— Proof in silver *FDC* (Issued: 2,174) £65
2006 Unc (Edition: 100,000)..£40
— Proof in silver *FDC* (Issued: 2,529) £65
2012 Unc (Edition: 100,0000 ....£40
— Proof in silver *FDC* (Issued: 2,937 plus coins in sets)...£80
2013 Unc (.999 silver)..£40
— BU (.999 silver) (Issued: 2,387)...£50

BF2A Britannia. Two pounds. (1 oz of fine silver.) R. As BF2 with selected gold plating of
obverse and reverse.
2006 Proof in silver *FDC** £70

BF2B Britannia. Two pounds. (1 oz of fine silver.) R. As BF2 but with plain edge and
decoration as indicated.
2013 Snake Unc. (.999 silver) £45

* Coins marked thus were originally issued in Royal Mint sets.
For coin specifications please see table at the beginning of this section.

BF3   BF4

BF3 **Britannia. Two pounds.** (1 oz of fine silver.) R. As BF1 with the word 'BRITANNIA', the inscription 'ONE OUNCE FINE SILVER' and the date of the year.

1999 Unc (Issued: 69,394)...£40

2009 Unc (Issued: 100,000)...£40

— Proof in silver *FDC* (Issued: 2,937 plus coins in sets) £65

BF3A Britannia. Two pounds. (1 oz of fine silver.) R. As BF3 with selected gold plating of obverse and reverse.

2006 Proof in silver *FDC** £70

BF4 **Britannia. Two pounds.** (1 oz of fine silver) R. The figure of Britannia, as guardian, with a shield in her left hand and a trident in her right hand, accompanied by a lion and, against the background of a wave motif, the words 'ONE OUNCE FINE SILVER' to the left and 'BRITANNIA' and the date of the year to the right. (Reverse design: Philip Nathan.)

2001 Unc (Issued: 44,816) £40

— Proof *FDC* (Issued: 3,047 plus coins in sets)......................................£60

BF4A Britannia. Two pounds. (1 oz of fine silver.) R. As BF4 with selected gold plating of obverse and reverse.

2006 Proof in silver *FDC** £70

BF5

BF5 **Britannia. Two pounds.** (1 oz fine silver.) R. Helmeted head of Britannia with, to the left, the word 'BRITANNIA' and, to the right, the inscription 'ONE OUNCE FINE SILVER' and the date of the year, the whole being overlaid with a wave pattern. (Reverse design: Philip Nathan.)

2003 Unc (Issued: 73,271) £40

— Proof *FDC* (Issued: 2,016 plus coins in sets)......................................£65

BF5A Britannia. Two pounds. (1 oz of fine silver.) R. As BF5 with selected gold plating of obverse and reverse.

2006 Proof in silver *FDC** £70

* Coins marked thus were originally issued in Royal Mint sets.

For coin specifications please see table at the beginning of this section.

BF6   BF7

BF6 **Britannia. Two pounds.** (1 oz of fine silver.) ℞. Seated figure of Britannia facing to
the left holding a trident with a shield at her side, with the word 'BRITANNIA', the
inscription 'ONE OUNCE FINE SILVER' and the date of the year. (Reverse design:
Philip Nathan.)
2005 Unc (Edition: 100,000)...£40
—   Proof *FDC* (Issued: 1,539 plus coins in sets)...£65
BF6A **Britannia. Two pounds.** (1 oz of fine silver.) ℞. As BF6 with selected gold plating of
obverse and reverse.
2006 Proof in silver *FDC** £70
BF7 **Britannia. Two pounds.** (1 oz of fine silver.) ℞. Seated figure of Britannia facing right
holding a trident in her right hand and a sprig of olive in the left hand with a lion at her
feet with the inscription 'ONE OUNCE FINE SILVER' and the word 'BRITANNIA' and
the date of the year. (Reverse design: Christopher Le Brun.)
2007 Unc (Edition: 100,000) £40
—   Proof *FDC* (Issued: 5,157 plus coins in sets)..£65

BF8

BF8 **Britannia. Two pounds.** (1 oz of fine silver) ℞. A Standing figure of Britannia holding a
trident with a shield at her side, the folds of her dress transforming into a wave, with the word
'BRITANNIA' and the date of the year and the inscription 'ONE OUNCE FINE SILVER'.
(Reverse design: John Bergdahl.)
2008 Unc (Edition: 100,000) £40
—   Proof *FDC* (Issued: 2,500 plus coins in sets)..£65

* Coins marked thus were originally issued in Royal Mint sets.
For coin specifications please see table at the beginning of this section.

BF9   BF10

BF9 **Britannia. Two pounds.** (1 oz fine silver.) R. A design depicting a profile bust of
Britannia wearing a helmet, accompanied by the name 'BRITANNIA', the inscription
'ONE OUNCE FINE SILVER' and the date '2010'. (Reverse design: Suzie Zamit.)

2010 Unc (Issued: 126,367) £40

— Proof *FDC* (Issued: 3,042 plus coins in sets).......................................£65

BF10 **Britannia. Two pounds.** (1 oz fine silver.) R. A design depicting a seated figure of
Britannia set against a background of a rippling Union Flag accompanied by the words
'ONE OUNCE FINE SILVER BRITANNIA' and the date '2011'. (Reverse design:
David Mach.)

2011 Unc (Edition: 500,000) £40

— Unc Matt...£45

— Proof *FDC* (Issued: 2,490 plus coins in sets) £90

BF11

BF11 **Britannia. Two pounds.** (1 oz of fine silver.) R. Seated figure of Britannia holding
a trident with a shield at her side and an owl upon her knee with the word
'BRITANNIA' and the date of the year above and the inscription 'ONE OUNCE
FINE SILVER' below the figure of Britannia. (Reverse design: Robert Hunt.)

2013 BU (Issued: 2,387)...£55

— Proof in silver *FDC* (Issued: 3,468 plus coins in sets) £93

For coin specifications please see table at the beginning of this section.

Obverse portrait by Ian Rank-Broadley

BF12

BF12 Britannia. Two pounds. (1 oz of fine silver.) R. As BF2 with revised inscription
'1oz 999 FINE SILVER' and the date of the year.

2013 Unc...£40
— BU(Issued: 2,387)...£50
2014 Unc...£40
— BU(Issued: 1,493)...£50
2015 Unc...£40
— BU (Issued: 2,870)..£50

BF12ABritannia. Two pounds. (1 oz of fine silver.) R. As BF12 but with plain edge and
decoration as indicated.

2014 Horse Unc £45

BF12 Error obverse – known as a mule. See 5100B in Chinese Lunar Year series.

BF12BBritannia. Two pounds. (1 oz of fine silver.) R. As BF12 but with textured background
on the obverse and reverse.

2015 Unc...£40

BF13

BF13 Britannia. Two pounds. (1 oz of fine silver.) R. A design of the standing figure of
Britannia bearing a trident and shield, with a lion at her feet, set against the backdrop
of a globe, and with the inscription 'BRITANNIA 999 1 OZ FINE SILVER 2014'.
(Reverse design: Jody Clark.)

2014 — Proof in silver *FDC* (Issued: 2,981 plus coins in sets) £85

For coin specifications please see table at the beginning of this section.

Obverse portrait by Jody Clark

BF14

BF14 Britannia. Two pounds. (1 oz of fine silver.) R. A figure of Britannia bearing a trident and shield, set against a backdrop of a sailing ship, cliffs and a lighthouse with the inscription 'BRITANNIA 1 OZ FINE SILVER 999 2015'. (Reverse design: Antony Dufort.)

2015 BU (Issued: 2,870)..£55
—   Proof in silver *FDC* (Issued: 4,240 plus coins in sets) £85

BF15

BF15 Britannia. Two pounds. (1 oz of fine silver.) R. As BF12.

2016 BU (Issued: 3,901)..£50
2017 BU (Edition: 10,000) £50
2018 BU (Edition: 12,000) £50

BF15ABritannia. Two pounds. (1 oz of fine silver.) R. As BF12B.

2016 Unc...£40
2018 Unc...£40

For coin specifications please see table at the beginning of this section.

BF15B

BF15BBritannia. Two pounds. (1 oz of fine silver.) ℞. As BF12 with textured background
of speckled radial sunburst on the reverse.

2017 Unc..£40
2018 Unc..£40
2019 Unc..£40
2020 Unc..£40

BF15C

BF15CBritannia. Two pounds. (1 oz of fine silver.) ℞. As BF15B but with Trident 20 mint
mark on reverse to mark the 20th anniversary of this Philip Nathan design and with
guilloche finish to the table area of the obverse.

2017 Unc (Edition:120,000) £50

BF15DBritannia Two pounds. (1 oz of fine silver.) ℞. As BF15B but with plain edge and
incuse decoration as indicated.

2017 Rooster Unc. £45
2018 Dog Unc..£45
2020 Rat Unc £45

For coin specifications please see table at the beginning of this section.

BF16

BF16 Britannia. Two pounds. (1 oz. of fine silver.) ℞. A standing figure of Britannia
holding in her left hand a trident and in her right hand a shield with a lion in the
background and the inscription 'BRITANNIA 1 OZ FINE SILVER 999 2016'.
(Reverse design: Suzie Zamit.)
2016 — Proof in silver *FDC* (Issued: 4,137 plus coins in sets) £83

BF17

BF17 Britannia. Two pounds. (1 oz of fine silver.) ℞. The figure of Britannia, holding
a shield and trident, with her body combined with the United Kingdom and the
inscription 'BRITANNIA 1 OZ FINE SILVER 999 2017' with a Trident mint mark
to mark the 20th Anniversary of the first Britannia silver issue. (Reverse design:
Louis Tamlyn.)
2017 — Proof in silver *FDC* (Edition: 7,500 plus coins in sets) £85

BF18 Britannia. Two pounds. (1 oz of fine silver.) ℞. As BF1 but with textured background
of speckled radial sunburst on the reverse, plain edge with inscription '1997-2017' to
mark the 20th anniversary of this Philip Nathan design.
2017 Unc £55

For coin specifications please see table at the beginning of this section.

BF19   BF20

BF19 Britannia. Two pounds. (1 oz of fine silver.) Ɍ. The figure of Britannia wearing a Corinthian helmet garlanded with the floral symbols of Britain and the inscription 'BRITANNIA 1 OZ FINE SILVER 999 2018'. (Reverse design: David Lawrence.)
2018 — Proof in silver *FDC* (Edition: 5,800 plus coins in sets) £85

BF20 Britannia. Two pounds. (1 oz of fine silver.) Ɍ. The centre design of Britannia as BF12 but with an Oriental Border and the inscription within the centre rather than around the design.
2018 Unc (Edition: 100,000)...£40
2019 Unc (Edition: 50,000)...£40
2020 Unc (Edition: 50,000)...£40

BF21   BF22

BF21 Britannia. Two pounds. (1 oz of fine silver.) Ɍ. Britannia raising trident towards a new dawn with a lion beside her as a steadfast companion with the word 'BRITANNIA', the date of the year and the inscription '1 OZ FINE SILVER 999'. (Reverse design: David Lawrence.)
2019 BU (Edition: 10,000)...£55
—   Proof in silver *FDC* (Edition: 3,390 plus coins in sets) £85

BF22 Britannia. Two pounds. (1 oz of fine silver.) Ɍ. Britannia standing amid a rocky ocean setting as waves crash around her with the word "BRITANNIA", the date of the year and the inscription "1 OZ 999 FINE SILVER". (Reverse design: James Tottle.)
2020 BU (Edition: 7,010)..£55
—   Proof in silver *FDC* (Edition: 3,000 plus coins in sets) £85

For coin specifications please see table at the beginning of this section.

Obverse portrait by Ian Rank-Broadley

BG1

BG1 Britannia. Ten pounds. (5 oz of fine silver.) R. Seated figure of Britannia holding
a trident with a shield at her side and an owl upon her knee with the word
'BRITANNIA' and the date of the year above and the inscription '5 OUNCES FINE
SILVER' below the figure of Britannia. (Reverse design: Robert Hunt.)
2013 — Proof in silver *FDC* (Issued: 4,054) £450

BG2

BG2 Britannia. Ten pounds. (5 oz of fine silver.) R. A design of the standing figure of
Britannia bearing a trident and shield, with a lion at her feet, set against the backdrop
of a globe, and with the inscription 'BRITANNIA 999 5 OZ FINE SILVER 2014'.
(Reverse design: Jody Clark.)
2014 — Proof in silver *FDC* (Issued: 1,348) £395

For coin specifications please see table at the beginning of this section.

Obverse portrait by Jody Clark

BG3

BG3 Britannia. Ten pounds. (5 oz of fine silver.) R. A figure of Britannia bearing a trident
and shield, set against a backdrop of a sailing ship, cliffs and a lighthouse with the
inscription 'BRITANNIA 5 OZ FINE SILVER 999 2015'. (Reverse design:
Antony Dufort.)
2015 — Proof in silver *FDC* (Issued: 995) £395

BG4

BG4   Britannia. Ten pounds. (5 oz of fine silver.) R. A standing figure of Britannia holding
in her left hand a trident and in her right hand a shield with a lion in the background
and the inscription 'BRITANNIA 5 OZ FINE SILVER 999 2016'. (Reverse design:
Suzie Zamit.)
2016 — Proof in silver *FDC* (Issued: 533) £395

For coin specifications please see table at the beginning of this section.

BG5

BG5 Britannia. Ten pounds. (5 oz of fine silver.) R. The figure of Britannia, holding a shield and trident, with her body combined with the United Kingdom and the inscription 'BRITANNIA 5 OZ FINE SILVER 999 2017' with a Trident mint mark to mark the 20th Anniversary of the first Britannia silver issue. (Reverse design: Louis Tamlyn.)

2017 — Proof in silver *FDC* (Edition: 1,600) £415

BG6 Britannia. Ten pounds. (5 oz of fine silver.) R. The figure of Britannia wearing a Corinthian helmet garlanded with the floral symbols of Britain and the inscription 'BRITANNIA 5 OZ FINE SILVER 999 2018'. (Reverse design: David Lawrence.)

2018 Proof in silver *FDC* (Edition: 650) £420

BG7 Britannia. Ten pounds. (5 oz of fine silver.) R. Britannia raising trident towards a new dawn with a lion beside her as a steadfast companion with the word 'BRITANNIA', the date of the year and the inscription '5 OZ FINE SILVER 999'. (Reverse design: David Lawrence.)

2019 Proof in silver *FDC* (Edition: 340) £420

BG8 Britannia. Ten pounds. (5 oz of fine silver.). R. Britannia standing amid a rocky ocean setting as waves crash around her with the word 'BRITANNIA', the date of the year and the inscription '5 OZ 999 FINE SILVER'. (Reverse design: James Tottle.)

2020 Proof in silver *FDC* (Edition: 250) £420

Obverse portrait by Ian Rank-Broadley

BI1 Britannia. Fifty pounds. (1 kilo of fine silver.) R. A design of the figure of Britannia on a textured background standing upon a rock in the sea, her right hand grasping a trident and her left hand on a shield and holding an olive branch, with the inscription 'BRITANNIA' (and the date of the year) '1 KILO OF 999 FINE SILVER'. (Original reverse design: Philip Nathan.)

2014 ....£1800

For coin specifications please see table at the beginning of this section.

Obverse portrait by Jody Clark

BJ1 Britannia. Two hundred and fifty pounds. (20 oz of fine silver.) ℞. As BG5 with revised inscription 'BRITANNIA 20 OZ FINE SILVER 999 2017' with a Trident mint mark to mark the 20th Anniversary of the first Britannia silver issue. (Reverse design: Louis Tamlyn.)

2017 — Proof in silver *FDC* (Edition: 350) £1650

BK2

BK1 Britannia. Five hundred pounds. (1 kilo of fine silver.) ℞. The figure of Britannia, holding a shield and trident, with her body combined with the United Kingdom and the inscription 'BRITANNIA 1 KILO FINE SILVER 999 2017' with a Trident mint mark to mark the 20th Anniversary of the first Britannia silver issue. Reverse as BG5. (Reverse design: Louis Tamlyn.)

2017 — Proof in silver *FDC* (Edition:) £2000

BK2 Britannia. Five hundred pounds. (1 kilo of fine silver.) ℞. The figure of Britannia wearing a Corinthian helmet garlanded with the floral symbols of Britain and the inscription 'BRITANNIA 1 KILO FINE SILVER 999 2018'. (Reverse design: David Lawrence)

2018 — Proof in silver *FDC* (Edition: 250) £2025

BK3 Britannia. Five hundred pounds. (1 kilo of fine silver.) ℞. Britannia raising trident towards a new dawn with a lion beside her as a steadfast companion with the word 'BRITANNIA', the date of the year and the inscription '1 KILO FINE SILVER 999'. (Reverse design: David Lawrence.)

2019 — Proof in silver *FDC* (Edition: 85) £2050

BK4 Britannia. Five hundred pounds. (1 kilo of fine silver.) As BF22.

2020 — Proof in silver *FDC* (Edition: 60) £2050

For coin specifications please see table at the beginning of this section.

Britannia Silver Proof Sets

			£
PBS01–**1997**	£2 – 20 pence (Issued: 11,832)	(4)	175
PBS02–**1998**	£2 – 20 pence (Issued: 3,045)	(4)	160
PBS03–**2001**	£2 – 20 pence (Issued: 4,596)	(4)	150
PBS04–**2003**	£2 – 20 pence (Issued: 3,669)	(4)	150
PBS06–**2005**	£2 – 20 pence (Issued: 2,360)	(4)	150
PBS07–**2006**	Britannia set of five different £2 designs with selected gold plating of obverse and reverse (Issued: 3,000)	(5)	350
PBS08–**2007**	£2 - 20 pence (Issued: 2,500)	(4)	150
PBS09–**2007**	Britannia set of six different proof £1 designs with satin finish on reverse (Issued: 2,000)	(6)	225
PBS10–**2008**	£2 – 20p (Issued: 2,500)	(4)	150
PBS11–**2009**	£2 – 20p (Issued: 2,500)	(4)	150
PBS12–**2010**	£2 – 20p (Issued: 3,497)	(4)	150
PBS13–**2011**	£2 – 20p (Issued: 2,483)	(4)	195
PBS14–**2012**	£2 – 20p (Issued: 2,595)	(4)	195
PBS15–**2012**	Britannia £1 proofs, set of nine different reverse designs (Issued: 1,656)	(9)	400
PBS16–**2013**	£2 – 10p (Issued: 3,087)	(5)	450
PBS17–**2013**	20p and 10p	(2)	39
PBS18–**2014**	£2 – 5 pence (Issued: 1,735)	(6)	200
PBS19–**2014**	20p – 5 pence (Issued: 998)	(3)	45
PBS20–**2015**	£2 – 5 pence (Issued: 1,009)	(6)	200
PBS21–**2015**	20p – 5 pence (Edition: 1,000)	(3)	45
PBS22–**2016**	£2 – 5 pence (Issued: 1,050)	(6)	200
PBS23–**2017**	£2 – 5 pence (Edition: 2,500)	(6)	215
PBS24–**2018**	£2 – 5 pence (Edition: 1,350)	(6)	215
PBS25–**2019**	£2 - 5 pence (Edition: 950)	(6)	215
PBS26–**2020**	£2 - 5 pence (Edition: 1,000)	(6)	225

Britannia Silver Uncirculated Set

UBS01–**MD**	£2 BF2, BF3. BF4, BF5 (Edition: 5,000)	(4)	160

SPINK

COINS OF ENGLAND 2021
E-book available on Amazon, iBookstore, Google, Kobo, OverDrive and across most other platforms

For more information or enquiries please contact
Tel: +44 (0)20 7563 4119 | Email: books@spink.com
69 Southampton Row, Bloomsbury, London WC1B 4ET

WWW.SPINKBOOKS.COM

1997	20p ($^1/_{10}$ oz)	50p (¼ oz)	£1 (½ oz)	£2 (1 oz)	SET		Authorised
PBS01	11832	11832	11832	11832	11832	(4)	15000
BF1				4173			20000
BC1	8686						50000
	20518	11832	11832	16005			

1998	20p ($^1/_{10}$ oz)	50p (¼ oz)	£1 (½ oz)	£2 (1 oz)	SET		Authorised
PBS02	3045	3045	3045	3045	3045	(4)	10000
BF2				2168			20000
BC2	2724						10000
	5769	3045	3045	5213			

2001	20p ($^1/_{10}$ oz)	50p (¼ oz)	£1 (½ oz)	£2 (1 oz)	SET		Authorised
PBS03	4596	4596	4596	4596	4596	(4)	5000
BF4				3047			10000
BC3	826						10000
	5422	4596	4596	7643			

2003	20p ($^1/_{10}$ oz)	50p (¼ oz)	£1 (½ oz)	£2 (1 oz)	SET		Authorised
PBS04	3669	3669	3669	3669	3669	(4)	5000
BF5				2016			5000
BC4	1179						5000
	4848	3669	3669	5685			

2005	20p ($^1/_{10}$ oz)	50p (¼ oz)	£1 (½ oz)	£2 (1 oz)	SET		Authorised
PBS06	2360	2360	2360	2360	2360	(4)	3500
BF6				1539			2500
BC5	913						2500
	3273	2360	2360	3899			

2007	20p ($^1/_{10}$ oz)	50p (¼ oz)	£1 (½ oz)	£2 (1 oz)	SET		Authorised
PBS08	2500	2500	2500	2500	2500	(4)	2500
BF7				5157			7500
BC6	901						2500
	3401	2500	2500	7657			

2008	20p ($^1/_{10}$ oz)	50p (¼ oz)	£1 (½ oz)	£2 (1 oz)	SET		Authorised
PBS10	2500	2500	2500	2500	2500	(4)	2500
BF8				2500			2500
BC7	725						2500
	3225	2500	2500	5000			

2009	20p (1/10 oz)	50p (1/4 oz)	£1 (1/2 oz)	£2 (1 oz)	SET		Authorised
PBS11	2500	2500	2500	2500	2500	(4)	2500
BF3				4284			3000
BC8	1000						1000
	3500	2500	2500	6784			

2010	20p (1/10 oz)	50p (1/4 oz)	£1 (1/2 oz)	£2 (1 oz)	SET		Authorised
PBS12	3497	3497	3497	3497	3497	(4)	3500
BF9				3042			4500
BC9	989						2500
	4486	3497	3497	6539			

2011	20p (1/10 oz)	50p (1/4 oz)	£1 (1/2 oz)	£2 (1 oz)	SET		Authorised
PBS13	2483	2483	2483	2483	2483	(4)	3500
BF11				2490			2500
	2483	2483	2483	4973			

2012	20p (1/10 oz)	50p (1/4 oz)	£1 (1/2 oz)	£2 (1 oz)	SET		Authorised
PBS14	2595	2595	2595	2595	2595	(4)	2600
PBS15			1656			(9)	2012
BF2				2937			2450
	2595	2595	4251	5532			

2013	10p (1/20 oz)	20p (1/10 oz)	50p (1/4 oz)	£1 (1/2 oz)	£2 (1 oz)	SET		Authorised
PBS16	3087	3087	3087	3087	3087	3087	(5)	3000
PBS17	#	#				#	(2)	7500
BF11					3468			2500
	3087	3087	3087	3087	6555			

2014	5p (1/40 oz)	10p (1/20 oz)	20p (1/10 oz)	50p (1/4 oz)	£1 (1/2 oz)	£2 (1 oz)	SET		Authorised
PBS18	1735	1735	1735	1735	1735	1735	1735	(6)	1750
		550	550	550	550	550	550	(5)Ω	550
PBS19	998	998	998				998	(3)	1000
BF13						2981			2500
	2733	3283	3283	2285	2285	5266			

Ω Coins sold to the US market and not in standard Royal Mint cases.
Mintages not yet known

2015	5p (1/40 oz)	10p (1/20 oz)	20p (1/10 oz)	50p (1/4 oz)	£1 (1/2 oz)	£2 (1 oz)	SET		Authorised
PBS20	1009	1009	1009	1009	1009	1009	1009	(6)	1750
		550	550	550	550	550	550	(5)Ω	550
PBS21	#	#	#					(3)	1000
BF14						2990			3000
BF14						1250		Ω	1250
	1009	1559	1559	1559	1559	5799			

2016	5p (1/40 oz)	10p (1/20 oz)	20p (1/10 oz)	50p (1/4 oz)	£1 (1/2 oz)	£2 (1 oz)	SET		Authorised
PBS22	1050	1050	1050	1050	1050	1050	1050	(6)	1100
BF16						4137			5900
	1050	1050	1050	1050	1050	5187			

2017	5p (1/40 oz)	10p (1/20 oz)	20p (1/10 oz)	50p (1/4 oz)	£1 (1/2 oz)	£2 (1 oz)	SET		Authorised
PBS23	#	#	#	#	#	#		(6)	2500
BF17						#			7500

2018	5p (1/40 oz)	10p (1/20 oz)	20p (1/10 oz)	50p (1/4 oz)	£1 (1/2 oz)	£2 (1 oz)	SET		Authorised
PBS24	#	#	#	#	#	#		(6)	1350
BF18						#			5800

2019	5p (1/40 oz)	10p (1/20 oz)	20p (1/10 oz)	50p (1/4 oz)	£1 (1/2 oz)	£2 (1 oz)	SET		Authorised
PBS25	#	#	#	#	#	#		(6)	950
BF21						#			3390

2020	5p (1/40 oz)	10p (1/20 oz)	20p (1/10 oz)	50p (1/4 oz)	£1 (1/2 oz)	£2 (1 oz)	SET		Authorised
PBS26	#	#	#	#	#	#		(6)	1000
BF22						#			3000

Ω Coins sold to the US market and not in standard Royal Mint cases.
Mintages not yet known

Until 2013 the gold coins were struck in 22 carat gold (.9166), the standard for UK gold coins, although from 1990 silver was included with copper which made the coins more yellow. From 2013 onwards the gold coins were struck in .999 gold.

Nearly all the ½ oz coins and many of the others are only issued within sets but some coins were issued individually. Prices given relate to cased coins with certificates where these were issued; uncased versions of these coins from split sets can often be found at lower prices.

A table of specifications for the gold coins appears below.

Britannia Gold Coins Specifications

Denomination	Metal	Weight		Diameter
50p from 2014	0.999 gold	$^1/_{40}$ ounce	0.80 g	8.00 mm
£1 from 2013	0.999 gold	$^1/_{20}$ ounce	1.58 g	12.00 mm
£10 1987-2012	0.916 gold	$^1/_{10}$ ounce	3.41 g	16.50 mm
- from 2013	0.999 gold	$^1/_{10}$ ounce	3.13 g	16.50 mm
£25 1987-2012	0.916 gold	$^1/_4$ ounce	8.51 g	22.00 mm
- from 2013	0.999 gold	$^1/_4$ ounce	7.80 g	22.00 mm
£50 1987-2012	0.916 gold	$^1/_2$ ounce	17.03 g	27.00 mm
- from 2013	0.999 gold	$^1/_2$ ounce	15.60 g	27.00 mm
£100 1987-2012	0.916 gold	1 ounce	34.05 g	32.69 mm
-2013	0.999 gold	1 ounce	31.11 g	38.61 mm
- from 2014	0.999 gold	1 ounce	31.11 g	32.69 mm
£200	0.999 gold	2 ounce	62.42 g	40.00 mm
£500	0.999 gold	5 ounce	156.30 g	50.00 mm
£800	0.999 gold	30 ounce	937.11 g	100.00 mm

Obverse portrait by Ian Rank-Broadley
BL1   **Britannia Fifty pence.** (1/40 oz of fine gold.) R. As BQ14 with the inscription 'BRITANNIA 999 1/40 OZ FINE GOLD 2014'.
2014 Proof in gold *FDC* (Issued: 5.521 plus coins in sets)...£50

Obverse portrait by Jody Clark
BL2   **Britannia Fifty pence.** (1/40 oz of fine gold.) R. As BQ16 with the inscription 'BRITANNIA 1/40 OZ FINE GOLD 999.9 2015'.
2015 Proof in gold *FDC* (Issued: 3,075 plus coins in sets)...£50
BL3   **Britannia Fifty pence.** (1/40 oz of fine gold.) R. As BQ18 with the inscription 'BRITANNIA 1/40 OZ FINE GOLD 999.9 2016'.
2016 Proof in gold *FDC* (Issued: 1,447 plus coins in sets)...£50
BL4   **Britannia Fifty pence.** (1/40 oz of fine gold.) R. As BQ19 with the inscription 'BRITANNIA 1/40 OZ FINE GOLD 999.9 2017' and with Trident mint mark to mark the 30th Anniversary of the first Britannia gold issue.
2017 Proof in gold *FDC* (Issued: 871 plus coins in sets)..£50

For coin specifications please see table at the beginning of this section.

BL5 Britannia Fifty pence. (1/40 oz of fine gold.) R. As BQ20 with the inscription
'BRITANNIA 1/40 OZ FINE GOLD 999.9 2018'.
2018 Proof in gold *FDC** £70
BL6 Britannia Fifty pence. (1/40 oz of fine gold.) R. As BQ22 with the inscription
'BRITANNIA 1/40 OZ FINE GOLD 999.9 2019'.
2019 Proof in gold *FDC** £70
BL7 Britannia Fifty pence. (1/40 oz of fine gold.) R. As BQ23 with the inscription
'BRITANNIA 1/40 OZ FINE GOLD 999.9 2020'.
2020 Proof in gold *FDC** £70

Obverse portrait by Ian Rank-Broadley
BM1 Britannia One pound. (1/20 oz of fine gold) R. As BQ13 with the inscription
'BRITANNIA 999 1/20 OUNCE FINE GOLD 2013'.
2013 Proof in gold *FDC* (Issued: 2,496 plus coins in sets) £100
BM2 Britannia One pound. (1/20 oz of fine gold) R. As BQ14 with the inscription
'BRITANNIA 999 1/20 OZ FINE GOLD 2014'.
2014 Proof in gold *FDC* (Issued: 993 plus coins in sets) £100

Obverse portrait by Jody Clark
BM3 Britannia One pound. (1/20 oz of fine gold.) R. As BQ16 with the inscription
'BRITANNIA 1/20 OZ FINE GOLD 999.9 2015'.
2015 Proof in gold *FDC** £100
BM4 Britannia One pound. (1/20 oz of fine gold) R. As BQ18 with the inscription
'BRITANNIA 1/20 OZ FINE GOLD 999.9 2016'.
2016 Proof in gold *FDC** £100
BM5 Britannia One pound. (1/20 oz of fine gold.) R. As BQ19 with the inscription
'BRITANNIA 1/20 OZ FINE GOLD 999.9 2017' and with Trident mint mark to mark the
30th Anniversary of the first Britannia gold issue.
2017 Proof in gold *FDC** £100
BM6 Britannia One pound. (1/20 oz of fine gold.) R. As BQ20 with the inscription
'BRITANNIA 1/20 OZ FINE GOLD 999.9 2018'.
2018 Proof in gold *FDC** £100
BM7 Britannia One pound. (1/20 oz of fine gold.) R. As BQ22 with the inscription
'BRITANNIA 1/20 OZ FINE GOLD 999.9 2019'.
2019 Proof in gold *FDC** £100
BM8 Britannia One pound. (1/20 oz of fine gold.) R. As BQ23 with the inscription
'BRITANNIA 1/20 OZ FINE GOLD 999.9 2020'.
2020 Proof in gold *FDC** £100

Obverse portrait by Raphael Maklouf
BN1 Britannia Ten pounds. (1/10 oz of fine gold.) R. As BQ1 with the inscription
'BRITANNIA 1/10 OUNCE FINE GOLD' and the date of the year.
1987 Unc £160
—   Proof in gold *FDC* (Issued: 3,500 plus coins in sets) £180
1988 Unc £160
—   Proof in gold *FDC* (Issued: 2,694 plus coins in sets) £180
1989 Unc £160
—   Proof in gold *FDC* (Issued: 1609 plus coins in sets) £180
1990 Unc £160
—   Proof in gold *FDC* (Issued: 1571 plus coins in sets) £180

* *Coins marked thus were originally issued in Royal Mint sets.*
For coin specifications please see table at the beginning of this section.

1991 Unc... £160
— Proof in gold *FDC* (Issued: 954 plus coins in sets).. £180
1992 Unc... £160
— Proof in gold *FDC* (Issued: 1,000 plus coins in sets)... £180
1993 Unc... £160
— Proof in gold *FDC* (Issued: 997 plus coins in sets).. £180
1994 Unc... £160
— Proof in gold *FDC* (Issued: 994 plus coins in sets).. £180
1995 Unc... £160
— Proof in gold *FDC* (Issued: 1,500 plus coins in sets)... £180
1996 Unc... £160
— Proof in gold *FDC* (Issued: 2,379 plus coins in sets)... £180

Obverse portrait by Ian Rank-Broadley
BN2 **Britannia Ten pounds.** (1/10 oz of fine gold.) Ŗ. As BQ2 with the inscription
'BRITANNIA TENTH OUNCE FINE GOLD' and the date of the year.
1997 Proof in gold *FDC* (Issued: 1,821 plus coins in sets)..................... £180
BN3 **Britannia Ten pounds.** (1/10 oz of fine gold.) Ŗ. As BQ1 with the inscription
'BRITANNIA 1/10 OUNCE FINE GOLD' and the date of the year.
1998 Proof in gold *FDC* (Issued: 392 plus coins in sets)......................... £180
1999 Unc... £160
— Proof in gold *FDC* (Issued: 1,058 plus coins in sets)... £180
2000 Unc... £160
— Proof in gold *FDC* (Issued: 659 plus coins in sets).. £180
2002 Unc... £160
— Proof in gold *FDC* (Issued: 1,500 plus coins in sets)... £180
2004 Unc... £160
— Proof in gold *FDC* (Issued: 929 plus coins in sets).. £180
2006 Proof in gold *FDC* (Issued: 700 plus coins in sets)......................... £180
2012 Unc... £160
— Proof in gold *FDC* (Issued: 1,249 plus coins in sets)... £180
BN4 **Britannia Ten pounds.** (1/10 oz of fine gold.) Ŗ. As BQ5 with the inscription
'BRITANNIA TENTH OUNCE FINE GOLD 2001'.
2001 unc £160
— Proof in gold *FDC* (Issued: 1,557 plus coins in sets.).. £180
BN5 **Britannia Ten pounds.** (1/10 oz of fine gold.) Ŗ. As BQ6 with the inscription
'BRITANNIA TENTH OUNCE FINE GOLD 2003'.
2003 Unc... £160
— Proof in gold *FDC* (Issued: 1,382 plus coins in sets)... £180
BN6 **Britannia Ten pounds.** (1/10 oz of fine gold.) Ŗ. As BQ7 with the inscription
'BRITANNIA TENTH OUNCE FINE GOLD 2005'.
2005 Proof in gold *FDC* (Issued: 1,225 plus coins in sets)..................... £180
BN7 **Britannia Ten pounds.** (1/10 oz of fine gold.) Ŗ. As BQ8 with the inscription
'BRITANNIA TENTH OUNCE FINE GOLD 2007'.
2007 Unc... £160
— Proof in gold *FDC* (Issued: 893 plus coins in sets).. £180
BN8 **Britannia Ten pounds.** (1/10 oz of fine gold.) Ŗ. As BQ9 with the inscription
'BRITANNIA TENTH OUNCE FINE GOLD 2008'.
2008 Proof in gold *FDC* (Issued: 748 plus coins in sets)......................... £180

For coin specifications please see table at the beginning of this section.

BN9 Britannia Ten pounds. (1/10 oz of fine gold.) R. As BQ 2 with the inscription
'BRITANNIA TENTH OUNCE FINE GOLD 2009'.
2009 Unc £160
  — Proof in gold *FDC* (Issued: 749 plus coins in sets) £180
BN10 Britannia Ten pounds. (1/10 oz of fine gold.) R. As BQ11 with the inscription
'BRITANNIA TENTH OUNCE FINE GOLD 2010'.
2010 Unc (Issued: 3,530) £160
  — Proof in gold *FDC* (Issued: 1,049 plus coins in sets) £180
BN11 Britannia Ten pounds. (1/10 oz of fine gold.) R. As BQ12 with the inscription
'BRITANNIA TENTH OUNCE FINE GOLD 2011'.
2011 Proof in gold *FDC* (Issued: 3,511 including coins in sets) £200
BN12 Britannia Ten pounds. (1/10 oz of fine gold.) R. As BQ13 with the inscription
'BRITANNIA 1/10 OUNCE FINE GOLD 2013'.
2013 Proof in gold *FDC* (Issued: 1,150 plus coins in sets) £200
BN13 Britannia Ten pounds. (1/10 oz of fine gold.) R. As BQ14 with the inscription
'BRITANNIA 999.9 1/10 OZ FINE GOLD 2014'.
2014 Proof in gold *FDC** £200
BN14 Britannia Ten pounds. (1/10 oz of fine gold.) R. As BN4 but with textured
background on the obverse and reverse, and with the inscription 'BRITANNIA
2015 1/10 OZ 999.9 FINE GOLD'.
2015 Unc £160

Obverse portrait by Jody Clark
BN15 Britannia Ten pounds. (1/10 oz of fine gold.) R. As BQ16 with the inscription
'BRITANNIA 1/10 OZ FINE GOLD 999.9 2015'.
2015 Proof in gold *FDC** £200
BN16 Britannia Ten pounds. (1/10 oz of fine gold.) As BN14.
2016 Unc £160
BN16A Britannia Ten pounds. (1/10 oz of fine gold.) As BN16 but with textured
background of a speckled radial sunburst on the reverse.
2017 Unc £160
2018 Unc £160
2019 Unc £160
2020 Unc £160
BN17 Britannia Ten pounds. (1/10 oz of fine gold.) R. As BQ18 with the inscription
'BRITANNIA 1/10 OZ FINE GOLD 999 2016'.
2016 Proof in gold *FDC** £200
BN18 Britannia Ten pounds. (1/10 oz of fine gold.) R. As BQ19 with the inscription
'BRITANNIA 1/10 OZ FINE GOLD 999 2017' and with Trident mint mark to mark the
30th Anniversary of the first Britannia gold issue.
2017 Proof in gold *FDC** £200
BN19 Britannia Ten pounds. (1/10 oz of fine gold.) R. As BQ20 with the inscription
'BRITANNIA 1/10 OZ FINE GOLD 999 2018'.
2018 Proof in gold *FDC** £200
BN20 Britannia Ten pounds. (1/10 oz of fine gold.) R. As BQ22 with the inscription
'BRITANNIA 1/10 OZ FINE GOLD 999 2019'.
2019 Proof in gold *FDC** £200
BN21 Britannia Ten pounds. (1/10 oz of fine gold.) R. As BQ23 with the inscription
'BRITANNIA 1/10 OZ FINE GOLD 999 2020'.
2020 Proof in gold *FDC** £200

* Coins marked thus were originally issued in Royal Mint sets.
For coin specifications please see table at the beginning of this section.

Obverse portrait by Raphael Maklouf
BO1 Britannia Twenty five pounds. (1/4 oz of fine gold.) R. As BQ1 with the inscription
'1/4 OUNCE FINE GOLD BRITANNIA' and the date of the year.

1987 Unc.. £400
— Proof in gold *FDC* (Issued: 3,500 plus coins in sets)... £450
1988 Unc.. £400
— Proof in gold *FDC**.. £450
1989 Unc.. £400
— Proof in gold *FDC**.. £450
1990 Unc.. £400
— Proof in gold *FDC**.. £450
1991 Unc.. £400
— Proof in gold *FDC**.. £450
1992 Unc.. £400
— Proof in gold *FDC**.. £450
1993 Unc.. £400
— Proof in gold *FDC**.. £450
1994 Unc.. £400
— Proof in gold *FDC**.. £450
1995 Unc.. £400
— Proof in gold *FDC**.. £450
1996 Unc.. £400
— Proof in gold *FDC**.. £450

BO2 Britannia Twenty five pounds. (1/4 oz of fine gold.) R. As BQ2 with the inscription
'BRITANNIA QUARTER OUNCE FINE GOLD' and the date of the year.
1997 Proof in gold *FDC* (Issued: 923 plus coins in sets)... £450

Obverse portrait by Ian Rank-Broadley
BO3 Britannia Twenty five pounds. (1/4 oz of fine gold.) R. As BQ1 with the inscription
'BRITANNIA 1/4 OUNCE FINE GOLD' and the date of the year.
1998 Proof in gold *FDC* (Issued: 560 plus coins in sets)... £450
1999 Unc.. £400
— Proof in gold *FDC* (Issued: 1,000 plus coins in sets).. £450
2000 Unc.. £400
— Proof in gold *FDC* (Issued: 500 plus coins in sets).. £450
2002 Proof in gold *FDC* (Issued: 750 plus coins in sets)... £450
2004 Proof in gold *FDC* (Issued: 750 plus coins in sets)... £450
2006 Proof in gold *FDC* (Issued: 728 plus coins in sets)... £450
2012 Proof in gold *FDC* (Issued: 316 plus coins in sets)... £450

BO4 Britannia Twenty five pounds. (1/4 oz of fine gold.) R. As BQ5 with the inscription
'BRITANNIA QUARTER OUNCE FINE GOLD' and the date of the year.
2001 Unc.. £400
— Proof in gold *FDC* (Issued: 500 plus coins in sets).. £450
2006 Proof in gold *FDC**.. £450

BO5 Britannia Twenty five pounds. (1/4 oz of fine gold.) R. As BQ6 with the inscription
'BRITANNIA QUARTER OUNCE FINE GOLD' and the date of the year.
2003 Proof in gold *FDC* (Issued 609 plus coins in sets)... £450
2006 Proof in gold *FDC**.. £450

* Coins marked thus were originally issued in Royal Mint sets.
For coin specifications please see table at the beginning of this section.

BO6 Britannia Twenty five pounds. (1/4 oz of fine gold.) R. As BQ7 with the inscription
'BRITANNIA 1/4 OUNCE FINE GOLD' and the date of the year.
2005 Proof in gold *FDC* (Issued: 750 plus coins in sets) £450
2006 Proof in gold *FDC** £450
BO7 Britannia Twenty five pounds. (1/4 oz of fine gold.) R. As BQ2 with the inscription
'BRITANNIA QUARTER OUNCE FINE GOLD' and the date of the year.
2006 Proof in gold *FDC** £450
2009 Proof in gold *FDC** £450
BO8 Britannia Twenty five pounds. (1/4 oz of fine gold.) R. As BQ8 with the inscription
'BRITANNIA QUARTER OUNCE FINE GOLD 2007'.
2007 Unc £400
— Proof in gold *FDC* (Issued: 1,000 plus coins in sets) £450
BO9 Britannia Twenty five pounds. (1/4 oz of fine gold.) R. As BQ9 with the inscription
'BRITANNIA 1/4 OUNCE FINE GOLD 2008'.
2008 Proof in gold *FDC* (Issued: 1,000 plus coins in sets) £450

BO10 Britannia Twenty five pounds. (1/4 oz of fine gold.) R. As BQ11 with the inscription
'BRITANNIA 1/4 OUNCE FINE GOLD 2010'.
2010 Unc (Issued: 1,501) £400
— Proof in gold *FDC* (Issued: 517 plus coins in sets) £450
BO11 Britannia Twenty five pounds. (1/4 oz of fine gold.) R. As BQ12 with the inscription
'BRITANNIA 1/4 OUNCE FINE GOLD 2011'.
2011 Proof in gold *FDC* (Issued: 698 plus coins in sets) £450
BO12 Britannia Twenty five pounds. (1/4 oz of fine gold.) R. As BQ13 with the inscription
'BRITANNIA 1/4 OUNCE FINE GOLD 2013'.
2013 Proof in gold *FDC** £500
BO13 Britannia Twenty five pounds. (1/4 oz of fine gold.) R. As BQ14 with the inscription
'BRITANNIA 999.9 1/4 OZ FINE GOLD 2014'.
2014 Proof in gold *FDC** £500
BO14 Britannia Twenty five pounds. (1/4 oz of fine gold.) R. As BO3 with revised
inscription '1/4OZ 999.9 FINE GOLD' the date '2015' and textured background
on the obverse and reverse.
2015 Unc £400

Obverse portrait by Jody Clark
BO15 Britannia Twenty five pounds. (1/4 oz of fine gold.) R. As BQ16 with the inscription
'BRITANNIA 1/4 OZ FINE GOLD 999.9 2015'.
2015 Proof in gold *FDC** £500
BO16 Britannia Twenty five pounds. (1/4 oz of fine gold.) As BO14.
2016 Unc £400
BO16A Britannia Twenty five pounds. (1/4 oz of fine gold.) As BO16 but with textured
background of a speckled radial sunburst on the reverse.
2017 Unc £400
2018 Unc £400
2019 Unc £400
2020 Unc £400

* Coins marked thus were originally issued in Royal Mint sets.
For coin specifications please see table at the beginning of this section.

BO17 **Britannia Twenty five pounds.** (1/4 oz of fine gold.) R. As BQ18 with the inscription
'BRITANNIA 1/4 OZ FINE GOLD 999.9 2016'.
2016 Proof in gold *FDC* (Issued: 829 plus coins in sets) £500
BO18 **Britannia Twenty five pounds.** (1/4 oz of fine gold.) R. As BQ19 with the inscription
'BRITANNIA 1/4 OZ FINE GOLD 999.9 2017' and with Trident mint mark to mark
the 30th Anniversary of the first Britannia GOLD issue.
2017 Proof in gold *FDC* (Edition: 2,500 plus coins in sets) £500
BO19 **Britannia Twenty five pounds.** (1/4 oz of fine gold.) R. As BQ20 with the inscription
'BRITANNIA 1/4 OZ FINE GOLD 999.9 2018'.
2018 Proof in gold *FDC* (Edition: 1,080 plus coins in sets) £500
BO20 **Britannia Twenty five pounds.** (1/4 oz of fine gold.) R. As BQ22 with the inscription
'BRITANNIA 1/4 OZ FINE GOLD 999.9 2019'.
2019 Proof in gold *FDC* (Edition: 645 plus coins in sets) £500
BO21 **Britannia Twenty five pounds.** (1/4 oz of fine gold.) R. As BQ23 with the inscription
'BRITANNIA 1/4 OZ FINE GOLD 999.9 2020'.
2020 Proof in gold *FDC* (Edition: 700 plus coins in sets) £585

Obverse portrait by Raphael Maklouf
BP1 **Britannia. Fifty pounds.** (1/2 oz of fine gold.) R. As BQ1 with the inscription
'BRITANNIA 1/2 OUNCE FINE GOLD' and the date of the year.
1987 Unc.. £800
— Proof in gold *FDC* (Issued: 2,485 plus coins in sets) £950
1988 Unc.. £800
— Proof in gold *FDC** £900
1989 Unc.. £800
— Proof in gold *FDC** £900
1990 Unc.. £800
— Proof in gold *FDC** £900
1991 Unc.. £800
— Proof in gold *FDC** £900
1992 Unc.. £800
— Proof in gold *FDC** £900
1993 Unc.. £800
— Proof in gold *FDC** £900
1994 Unc.. £800
— Proof in gold *FDC** £900
1995 Unc.. £800
— Proof in gold *FDC** £900
1996 Unc.. £800
— Proof in gold *FDC** £900
BP2 **Britannia. Fifty pounds.** (1/2 oz of fine gold.) R. As BQ2 with the inscription
'BRITANNIA HALF OUNCE FINE GOLD' and the date of the year.
1997 Proof in gold *FDC** £900

* Coins marked thus were originally issued in Royal Mint sets.
For coin specifications please see table at the beginning of this section.

Obverse portrait by Ian Rank-Broadley

BP3   Britannia. Fifty pounds. (1/2 oz of fine gold.) R. As BQ2 with the inscription
'BRITANNIA 1/2 OUNCE FINE GOLD' and the date of the year.
1998 Proof in gold *FDC** £900
1999 Unc.. £800
— Proof in gold *FDC** £900
2000 Unc.. £800
— Proof in gold *FDC** £900
2002 Proof in gold *FDC** £900
2004 Proof in gold *FDC** £900
2006 Proof in gold *FDC** £900
2012 Proof in gold *FDC** £900

BP4   Britannia. Fifty pounds. (1/2 oz of fine gold.) R. As BQ5 with the inscription
'BRITANNIA HALF OUNCE FINE GOLD' and the date of the year.
2001 Unc.. £800
— Proof in gold *FDC** £900
2012 Proof in gold *FDC** £900

BP5   Britannia. Fifty pounds. (1/2 oz of fine gold.) R. As BQ6 with the inscription
'BRITANNIA HALF OUNCE FINE GOLD' and the date of the year.
2003 Unc.. £800
— Proof in gold *FDC** £900
2012 Proof in gold *FDC** £900

BP6   Britannia. Fifty pounds. (1/2 oz of fine gold.) R. As BQ7 with the inscription
'BRITANNIA HALF OUNCE FINE GOLD' and the date of the year.
2005 Proof in gold *FDC** £900
2012 Proof in gold *FDC** £900

BP7   Britannia. Fifty pounds. (1/2oz of fine gold.) R. As BQ8 with the inscription
'BRITANNIA HALF OUNCE FINE GOLD' and the date of the year.
2007 Unc.. £800
— Proof in gold *FDC** £900
2012 Proof in gold *FDC** £900

BP8   Britannia. Fifty pounds. (1/2oz of fine gold.) R. As BQ9 with the inscription
'BRITANNIA 1/2 OUNCE FI NE GOLD' and the date of the year.
2008 Proof in gold *FDC** £900
2012 Proof in gold *FDC** £900

BP9   Britannia. Fifty pounds. (1/2 oz of fine gold.) R. As BQ 10 with the inscription
'BRITANNIA HALF OUNCE FINE GOLD' and the date of the year.
2009 Unc.. £800
— Proof in gold *FDC** £900
2012 Proof in gold *FDC** £900

BP10 Britannia. Fifty pounds. (1/2 oz of fine gold.) R. As BQ11 with the inscription
'BRITANNIA 1/2 OUNCE FINE GOLD' and the date of the year.
2010 Unc (Issued: 1,301).. £800
— Proof in gold *FDC** £900
2012 Proof in gold *FDC** £900

BP11 Britannia. Fifty pounds. (1/2 oz of fine gold.) R. As BQ12 with the inscription
'BRITANNIA 1/2 OUNCE FINE GOLD' and the date of the year.
2011 Proof in gold *FDC* (Issued: 847 including coins in sets).................................... £900
2012 Proof in gold *FDC** £900

* Coins marked thus were originally issued in Royal Mint sets.
For coin specifications please see table at the beginning of this section.

BP12 Britannia. **Fifty pounds.** (1/2 oz of fine gold.) R. As BQ13 with the inscription
'BRITANNIA 1/2 OUNCE FINE GOLD 2013'.
2013 Proof in gold *FDC** £900
BP13 Britannia. **Fifty pounds.** (1/2 oz of fine gold.) R. As BQ14 with the inscription
'BRITANNIA 999.9 1/2 OZ FINE GOLD 2014'.
2014 Proof in gold *FDC** £900
BP14 Britannia. **Fifty pounds.** (1/2 oz of fine gold.) R. As BP3 with revised inscription
'1/2 OZ 999.9 FINE GOLD' the date '2015' and textured background on the obverse
and reverse.
2015 Unc £800

Obverse portrait by Jody Clark
BP15 Britannia. **Fifty pounds.** (1/2 oz of fine gold.) R. As BQ16 with the inscription
'BRITANNIA 1/2 OZ FINE GOLD 999.9 2015'.
2015 Proof in gold *FDC** £900
BP16 Britannia. **Fifty pounds.** (1/2 oz of fine gold.) R. As BQ18 with the inscription
'BRITANNIA 1/2 OZ FINE GOLD 999.9 2016'.
2016 Proof in gold *FDC** £900
BP17 Britannia. **Fifty pounds.** (1/2 oz of fine gold.) R. As BQ19 with the inscription
'BRITANNIA 1/2 OZ FINE GOLD 999.9 2017' and with Trident mint mark to
mark the 30th Anniversary of the first Britannia gold issue.
2017 Proof in gold *FDC** £900
BP18 Britannia. **Fifty pounds.** (1/2 oz of fine gold.) R. As BP15 but with textured
background of a speckled radial sunburst on the reverse.
2017 Unc.. £800
2018 Unc.. £800
2020 Unc.. £800
BP19 Britannia. **Fifty pounds.** (1/2 oz of fine gold.) R. As BQ20 with the inscription
'BRITANNIA 1/2 OZ FINE GOLD 999.9 2018'.
2018 Proof in gold *FDC** £900
BP20 Britannia. **Fifty pounds.** (1/2 oz of fine gold.) R. As BQ22 with the inscription
'BRITANNIA 1/2 OZ FINE GOLD 999.9 2019'.
2019 Proof in gold *FDC** £900
BP21 Britannia. **Fifty pounds.** (1/2 oz of fine gold.) R. As BQ23 with the inscription
'BRITANNIA 1/2 OZ FINE GOLD 999.9 2020'.
2020 Proof in gold *FDC** £900

* Coins marked thus were originally issued in Royal Mint sets.
For coin specifications please see table at the beginning of this section.

Obverse portrait by Raphael Maklouf

BQ1

BQ1   Britannia. One hundred pounds. (1 oz of fine gold.) R. The figure of Britannia standing upon a rock in the sea, her right hand grasping a trident and her left hand resting on a shield and holding an olive branch, with the inscription 'ONE OUNCE FINE GOLD BRITANNIA' and the year of the date. (Reverse design: Philip Nathan.)

1987 Unc	£1600
— Proof in gold *FDC* (Issued: 2,486 plus coins in sets)	£1800
1988 Unc	£1600
— Proof in gold *FDC* (Issued: 626 plus coins in sets)	£1800
1989 Unc	£1600
— Proof in gold *FDC* (Issued: 338 plus coins in sets)	£1800
1990 Unc	£1600
— Proof in gold *FDC* (Issued: 262 plus coins in sets)	£1800
1991 Unc	£1600
— Proof in gold *FDC* (Issued: 143 plus coins in sets)	£1800
1992 Unc	£1600
— Proof in gold *FDC**	£1750
1993 Unc	£1600
— Proof in gold *FDC**	£1750
1994 Unc	£1600
— Proof in gold *FDC**	£1750
1995 Unc	£1600
— Proof in gold *FDC**	£1750
1996 Unc	£1600
— Proof in gold *FDC**	£1750

BQ2

BQ2   Britannia. One Hundred pounds. (1 oz of fine gold, alloyed with silver.) 10th Anniversary of Britannia issue. R. The figure of Britannia standing in a chariot drawn along the seashore by two horses, with the word 'BRITANNIA', the inscription. 'ONE OUNCE FINE GOLD' and the date of the year. (Reverse design: Philip Nathan.)

1997	£1650
— Proof in gold *FDC* (Issued: 164 plus coins in sets)	£1850

* Coins marked thus were originally issued in Royal Mint sets.
For coin specifications please see table at the beginning of this section.

Obverse portrait by Ian Rank-Broadley

BQ3

BQ3 **Britannia. One Hundred pounds.** (1 oz of fine gold.) R. The figure of Britannia
standing upon a rock in the sea, her right hand grasping a trident and her left hand
resting on a shield and holding an olive branch, with the word 'BRITANNIA', the date
of the year, and the inscription' ONE OUNCE FINE GOLD'. (Reverse design: Philip
Nathan).

1998 Proof in gold *FDC** £1800
1999 Unc £1600
1999 Proof in gold *FDC** £1800
2000 Unc £1600
2000 Proof in gold *FDC** £1800
2002 Proof in gold *FDC** £1800
2004 Unc £1600
2004 Proof in gold *FDC** £1800
2006 Proof in gold *FDC** £1800
2012 Unc £1600
2012 Proof in gold *FDC** £1800

BQ3A **Britannia. One Hundred pounds.** (1 oz of fine gold.) As BQ3 but .999 gold and
38.61mm diameter.

2013 Unc £1600

BQ4 **Britannia. One Hundred pounds.** (1 oz of fine gold) R. As BQ3 but with revised
inscription "BRITANNIA 2014 1OZ 999.9 FINE GOLD".

2014 Unc £1600

BQ5

BQ5 **Britannia. One Hundred pounds.** (1 oz of fine gold.) R. The figure of Britannia, as
guardian, with a shield in her left hand and a trident in her right hand, accompanied by
a lion and, against the background of a wave motif, the words 'ONE OUNCE FINE
GOLD' to the left and 'BRITANNIA' and the date of the year to the right.
(Reverse design: Philip Nathan.)

2001 ....£1600
2001 Proof in gold *FDC** £1800

* Coins marked thus were originally issued in Royal Mint sets.
For coin specifications please see table at the beginning of this section.

BQ6   BQ7   BQ8

BQ6 Britannia. One Hundred pounds. (1 oz of fine gold.) R. Helmeted head of Britannia
with, to the left, the word 'BRITANNIA' and, to the right, the inscription 'ONE OUNCE
FINE GOLD' and the date of the year, the whole being overlaid with a wave pattern.
(Reverse design: Philip Nathan.)
2003 ....£1600
2003 Proof in gold *FDC** £1800

BQ7 Britannia. One Hundred pounds. (1 oz of fine gold.) R. Seated figure of Britannia
facing to the left holding a trident with a shield at her side, with the word
'BRITANNIA', the inscription 'ONE OUNCE FINE GOLD' and the date of the year.
(Reverse design: Philip Nathan.)
2005 Proof in gold *FDC** £1800

BQ8 Britannia. One Hundred pounds. (1 oz of fine gold.) R. Seated figure of Britannia facing
right holding a trident in her right hand and a sprig of olive in the left hand with a lion at her
feet with the inscription 'ONE OUNCE FINE GOLD' and the word 'BRITANNIA' and the
date of the year. (Reverse design: Christopher Le Brun.)
2007 ....£1600
2007 Proof in gold *FDC** £1800

BQ9   BQ10

BQ9 Britannia. One Hundred pounds. (1 oz of fine gold,) R. A Standing figure of Britannia
holding a trident with a shield at her side, the folds of her dress transforming into a
wave, with the word 'BRITANNIA', the date of the year, and the inscription 'ONE
OUNCE FINE GOLD'. (Reverse design: John Bergdahl.)
2008 ....£1600
2008 Proof in gold *FDC** £1800

BQ10 Britannia. One Hundred pounds. (1 oz of fine gold.) R. Standing figure of Britannia
in horse drawn chariot. (Reverse design: Philip Nathan.)
2009 ....£1600
2009 Proof in gold *FDC** £1800

* Coins marked thus were originally issued in Royal Mint sets.
For coin specifications please see table at the beginning of this section.

BQ11   BQ12

BQ11 Britannia. One Hundred pounds. (1 oz of fine gold alloyed with silver.) R. A design
depicting **a** profile bust of Britannia wearing a helmet, accompanied by the name
'BRITANNIA', the inscription 'ONE OUNCE FINE GOLD' and the date '2010'.
(Reverse design: Suzie Zamit.)
2010 Unc (Issued: 13,860)..£1600
2010 Proof in gold *FDC**..£1800

BQ12 Britannia. One Hundred pounds. (1 oz of fine gold.) R. A design depicting a seated
figure of Britannia set against a background of a rippling Union Flag accompanied by
the words 'ONE OUNCE FINE GOLD BRITANNIA, and the date '2011'.
(Reverse design: David Mach.)
2011 Proof in gold *FDC** £1800

BQ13   BQ14

BQ13 Britannia. One Hundred pounds. (1 oz of fine gold.) R. Seated figure of Britannia
holding a trident with a shield at her side and an owl upon her knee with the word
'BRITANNIA' and 'ONE OUNCE FINE GOLD' and the date '2013' below the figure
of Britannia. (Reverse design: Robert Hunt).
2013 — Proof in gold *FDC** £1800

BQ14 Britannia. One Hundred pounds. (1 oz of fine gold.) R. A design of the standing
figure of Britannia bearing a trident and shield, with a lion at her feet, set against the
backdrop of a globe, and with the inscription 'BRITANNIA 999.9 1 OZ FINE GOLD
2014'. (Reverse design: Jody Clark.)
2014 Proof in gold *FDC** £2000

* Coins marked thus were originally issued in Royal Mint sets.
For coin specifications please see table at the beginning of this section.

BQ15

BQ15 Britannia. One Hundred pounds. (1 oz of fine gold.) R. As BQ4 but with textured
background on the obverse and reverse,
2015 Unc..£1600

Obverse portrait by Jody Clark

BQ16

BQ16 Britannia. One Hundred pounds. (1 oz of fine gold.) R. A figure of Britannia
bearing a trident and shield, set against a backdrop of a sailing ship, cliffs and a
lighthouse with the inscription 'BRITANNIA 1 OZ FINE GOLD 999.9 2015'.
(Reverse design: Antony Dufort.)
2015 – Proof in gold *FDC** £1800

BQ17

BQ17 Britannia. One Hundred pounds. (1 oz of fine gold.) R. As BQ15.
2016 Unc..£1600

* Coins marked thus were originally issued in Royal Mint sets.
For coin specifications please see table at the beginning of this section.

BQ17A   BQ17B

BQ17A Britannia. One Hundred pounds. (1 oz of fine gold.) R. As BQ15 but with textured background of a speckled radial sunburst on the reverse.

2017 Unc £1600
2018 Unc £1600
2019 Unc £1600
2020 Unc £1600

BQ17B Britannia. One hundred pounds. As BQ17A but with mint mark on reverse to mark thirtieth anniversary of first issue of the Nathan reverse design and guilloché finish to the table area of the obverse.

2017 Unc (Edition: 7,030) £1600

BQ18   BQ19

BQ18 Britannia. One Hundred pounds. (1 oz of fine gold.) R. A standing figure of Britannia holding in her left hand a trident and in her right hand a shield with a lion in the background and the inscription 'BRITANNIA 1 OZ FINE GOLD 999.9 2016'. (Reverse design: Suzie Zamit.)

2016 Proof in gold *FDC** £1800

BQ19 Britannia. One Hundred pounds. (1 oz of fine gold.) R. The figure of Britannia, holding a shield and trident, with her body combined with the United Kingdom and the inscription 'BRITANNIA 1 OZ FINE GOLD 999.9 2017' with a trident mintmark to mark the 30th Anniversary of the first Britannia issue. (Reverse design: Louis Tamlyn.)

2017 Proof in gold *FDC** £1800

* Coins marked thus were originally issued in Royal Mint sets.
For coin specifications please see table at the beginning of this section.

BQ20   BQ21

BQ20 Britannia. One hundred pounds. (1 oz of fine gold.) ℞. The figure of Britannia
wearing a Corinthian helmet garlanded with the floral symbols of Britain and the
inscription 'BRITANNIA 1 OZ FINE GOLD 999.9 2018'. (Reverse design:
David Lawrence.)
2018 Proof in gold *FDC**..£1800

BQ21 Britannia. One hundred pounds. (1 oz of fine gold.) ℞. The centre design of
Britannia as BQ17A but with an Oriental Border and the inscription within the centre
rather than around the design.
2018 Unc (Edition: 5,000)...£1600
2019 Unc (Edition: 5,000)...£1600
2020 Unc (Edition: 5,000)...£1600

BQ22

BQ22 Britannia. One hundred pounds. (1 oz of fine gold.) ℞. Britannia raising trident
towards a new dawn with a lion beside her as a steadfast companion with the word
'BRITANNIA', the date of the year and the inscription '1 OZ FINE GOLD 999.9'.
(Reverse design: David Lawrence.)
2019 Proof in gold *FDC** £1800

BQ23 Britannia. One hundred pounds. (1 oz of fine gold.) ℞. Britannia standing amid a
rocky ocean setting as waves crash around her with the word 'BRITANNIA', the
date of the year and the inscription '1 OZ 999.9 FINE GOLD'. (Reverse design:
James Tottle.)
2020 Proof in gold *FDC** £1800

* *Coins marked thus were originally issued in Royal Mint sets.*
For coin specifications please see table at the beginning of this section.

BR1   BR2

BR1 **Britannia. Two hundred pounds.** (2 oz of fine gold.) ℞. Britannia raising trident
towards a new dawn with a lion beside her as a steadfast companion with the word
'BRITANNIA', the date of the year and the inscription '2 OZ FINE GOLD 999.9'.
(Reverse design: David Lawrence.)
2019 Proof in gold *FDC* (Edition: 110) £4500

BR2 **Britannia. Two hundred pounds.** (2 oz of fine gold.) ℞. Britannia standing amid a
rocky ocean setting as waves crash around her with the word 'BRITANNIA', the
date of the year and the inscription '2 OZ 999.9 FINE GOLD'. (Reverse design:
James Tottle.)
2020 Proof in gold *FDC* (Edition: 160) £4500

Obverse portrait by Ian Rank-Broadley

BS1

BS1 **Britannia. Five Hundred pounds.** (5 oz of fine gold.) ℞. Seated figure of Britannia
holding a trident with a shield at her side and an owl upon her knee with the word
'BRITANNIA' and '5 OUNCES FINE GOLD' and the date '2013' below the figure of
Britannia. (Reverse design: Robert Hunt.)
2013 — Proof in gold *FDC* (Issued: 61) £11000

For coin specifications please see table at the beginning of this section.

BS2

BS2 Britannia. Five Hundred pounds. (5 oz of fine gold.) ℞ A design of the standing figure
of Britannia bearing a trident and shield, with a lion at her feet, set against the backdrop
of a globe, and with the inscription 'BRITANNIA 999.9 5 OZ FINE GOLD 2014'.
(Reverse design: Jody Clark.)
2014 — Proof in gold *FDC* (Issued: 75) £12000

BS3

BS3 Britannia. Five hundred pounds. (5 oz of fine gold.) R. A figure of Britannia bearing a
trident and shield, set against a backdrop of a sailing ship, cliffs and a lighthouse with the
inscription 'BRITANNIA 5 OZ FINE GOLD 999.9 2015'. (Reverse design: Anthony Dufort.)
2015 Proof in gold *FDC* (Issued: 50) £10000

BS4

BS4 Britannia. Five Hundred pounds. (5 oz of fine gold.) R. A standing figure of Britannia
holding in her left hand a trident and in her right hand a shield with a lion in the background and
the inscription 'BRITANNIA 5 OZ FINE GOLD 999.9 2016'. (Reverse design: Suzie Zamit.)
2016 Proof in gold *FDC* (Issued: 64)..£12000

For coin specifications please see table at the beginning of this section.

BS5

BS5 Britannia. Five Hundred pounds. (5 oz of fine gold.) R. The figure of Britannia,
holding a shield and trident, with her body combined with the United Kingdom
and the inscription 'BRITANNIA 5 OZ FINE GOLD 999.9 2017' with a trident
mintmark to mark the 30th Anniversary of the first Britannia issue. (Reverse design:
Louis Tamlyn.)
2017 Proof in gold *FDC* (Edition: 130)..£8250

BS6

BS6 Britannia. Five hundred pounds. (5 oz of fine gold.) R. The figure of Britannia
wearing a Corinthian helmet garlanded with the floral symbols of Britain and the
inscription 'BRITANNIA 5 OZ FINE GOLD 999.9 2018'. (Reverse design:
David Lawrence.)
2018 Proof in gold *FDC* (Edition: 95)..£8565

BS7 Britannia. Five hundred pounds. (5 oz of fine gold.) R. Britannia raising trident
towards a new dawn with a lion beside her as a steadfast companion with the word
'BRITANNIA', the date of the year and the inscription '5 OZ FINE GOLD 999.9'.
(Reverse design: David Lawrence.)
2019 Proof in gold *FDC* (Edition: 57)..£10000

BS8 Britannia. Five hundred pounds. (5 oz of fine gold.) R. Britannia standing amid a
rocky ocean setting as waves crash around her with the word 'BRITANNIA', the date of
the year and the inscription '5 OZ 999.9 FINE GOLD'. (Reverse design: James Tottle.)
2020 Proof in gold *FDC* (Edition: 58)..£10000

For coin specifications please see table at the beginning of this section.

BT1

BT1 Britannia. Eight hundred pounds. (30 oz of fine gold.) ℞. The figure of Britannia
holding a shield and trident, with her body combined with the United Kingdom and
the inscription 'BRITANNIA 30 OZ FINE GOLD 999.9 2017' with a trident
mintmark to mark the 30th Anniversary of the first Britannia issue. (Reverse design:
Louis Tamlyn.)
2017 Proof in gold *FDC* (Edition: 21)...£46995

For coin specifications please see table at the beginning of this section.

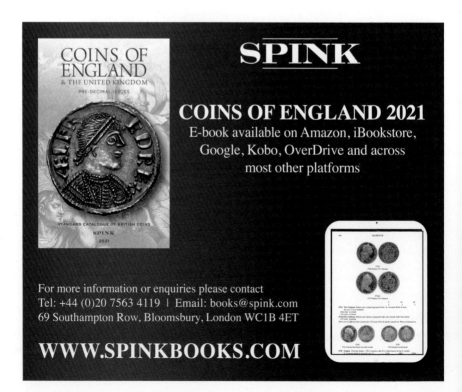

COINS OF ENGLAND
& THE UNITED KINGDOM
PRE-DECIMAL ISSUES

STANDARD CATALOGUE OF BRITISH COINS
SPINK
2021

SPINK

COINS OF ENGLAND 2021
E-book available on Amazon, iBookstore,
Google, Kobo, OverDrive and across
most other platforms

For more information or enquiries please contact
Tel: +44 (0)20 7563 4119 | Email: books@spink.com
69 Southampton Row, Bloomsbury, London WC1B 4ET

WWW.SPINKBOOKS.COM

Britannia Gold Proof Sets

			£
PBG01–**1987**	£100, £50, £25, £10 (Issued: 10,000) ....(4)	3250
PBG02–**1987**	£25, £10 (Issued: 11,100) ....(2)	600
PBG03–**1988**	£100, £50, £25, £10 (Issued: 3,505) ....(4)	3250
PBG04–**1988**	£25, £10 (Issued: 894) ....(2)	600
PBG05–**1989**	£100, £50, £25, £10 (Issued: 2,268) ....(4)	3250
PBG06–**1989**	£25, £10 (Issued: 451) ....(2)	600
PBG07–**1990**	£100, £50, £25, £10 (Issued: 527) ....(4)	3250
PBG08–**1991**	£100, £50, £25, £10 (Issued: 509) ....(4)	3250
PBG09–**1992**	£100, £50, £25, £10 (Issued: 500) ....(4)	3250
PBG10–**1993**	£100, £50, £25, £10 (Issued: 462) ....(4)	3250
PBG11–**1994**	£100, £50, £25, £10 (Issued: 435) ....(4)	3250
PBG12–**1995**	£100, £50, £25, £10 (Issued: 500) ....(4)	3250
PBG13–**1996**	£100, £50, £25, £10 (Issued: 483) ....(4)	3250
PBG14–**1997**	£100, £50, £25, £10 (Issued: 892) ....(4)	3300
PBG15–**1998**	£100, £50, £25, £10 (Issued: 750) ....(4)	3250
PBG16–**1999**	£100, £50, £25, £10 (Issued: 740) ....(4)	3250
PBG17–**2000**	£100, £50, £25, £10 (Issued: 750) ....(4)	3250
PBG18–**2001**	£100, £50, £25, £10 (Issued: 1,000) ....(4)	3250
PBG19–**2002**	£100, £50, £25, £10 (Issued: 945) ....(4)	3250
PBG20–**2003**	£100, £50, £25, £10 (Issued: 1,250) ....(4)	3250
PBG21–**2003**	£50, £25, £10 (Issued: 825) ....(3)	1550
PBG22–**2004**	£100, £50, £25, £10 (Issued: 973) ....(4)	3250
PBG23–**2004**	£50, £25, £10 (Issued: 223) ....(3)	1550
PBG24–**2005**	£100, £50, £25, £10 (Issued: 1,439) ....(4)	3250
PBG25–**2005**	£50, £25, £10 (Issued: 417) ....(3)	1550
PBG26–**2006**	£100, £50, £25, £10 (Issued: 1,163) ....(4)	3250
PBG27–**2006**	£25 BO3,4,5,6,7 (Issued: 250) ....(5)	2250
PBG28–**2007**	£100, £50, £25, £10 (Issued: 1,250) ....(4)	3250
PBG29–**2008**	£100, £50, £25, £10 (Issued: 1,250) ....(4)	3250
PBG30–**2009**	£100, £50, £25, £10 (Issued: 797) ....(4)	3250
PBG31–**2010**	£100, £50, £25, £10 (Issued: 867) ....(4)	3250
PBG32–**2010**	£50, £25, £10 (Issued: 186) ....(3)	1550
PBG33–**2011**	£100, £50, £25, £10 (Issued: 1,000) ....(4)	3250
PBG34–**2011**	£50, £25, £10 (Issued: 250) ....(3)	1550
PBG35–**2012**	£100, £50, £25, £10 (Issued: 352) ....(4)	3250
PBG36–**2012**	£50, £25, £10 (Issued: 99) ....(3)	1550
PBG37–**2012**	£50 BP3,4,5,6,7,8,9,10,11 (Issued: 25) ....(9)	8000

£

PBG38–**2013**	£100, £50, £25, £10, £1 (Issued: 261) ....(5)	3400
PBG39–**2013**	£50, £25, £10 (Issued: 90) ....(3)	1650
PBG40–**2013**	£25, £10, £1 (Issued: 136) ....(3)	700
PBG41–**2014**	£100, £50, £25, £10, £1,50p (Issued: 225) ....(6)	3850
PBG42–**2014**	£50, £25, £10 (Issued: 98) ....(3)	1750
PBG43–**2014**	£25, £10, £1 (Issued: 140) ....(3)	700
PBG44–**2015**	£100, £50, £25, £10, £1, 50p (Issued: 138) ....(6)	3500
PBG45–**2015**	£50, £25, £10 (Issued: 99) ....(3)	1650
PBG46–**2015**	£10, £1, 50p (Issued: 176) ....(3)	360
PBG47–**2016**	£100, £50, £25, £10, £1, 50p (Issued: 174) ....(6)	3850
PBG48–**2016**	£50, £25, £10 (Issued: 69) ....(3)	1750
PBG49–**2017**	£100, £50, £25, £10, £1, 50p (Edition 250) ....(6)	3800
PBG50–**2017**	£50, £25, £10 Edition 200) ....(3)	1700
PBG51–**2018**	£100, £50, £25, £10, £1, 50p (Edition 220) ....(6)	4000
PBG52–**2018**	£50, £25, £10 Edition 200) ....(3)	1700
PBG53–**2019**	£100, £50, £25, £10, £1, 50p (Edition 150) ....(6)	4200
PBG54–**2019**	£50, £25, £10 Edition 130) ....(3)	1800
PBG55–**2020**	£100, £50, £25, £10, £1, 50p (Edition 150) ....(6)	4400
PBG56–**2020**	£50, £25, £10 Edition 130) ....(3)	1945

Britannia gold uncirculated sets

UBG1–**MD**	£100 BQ1, 2, 5, 6 (Edition 2,500) ....(4)	6400

1987	£10 ($^1/_{10}$ oz)	£25 (¼ oz)	£50 (½ oz)	£100 (1 oz)	SET		Authorised
PBG01	10000	10000	10000	10000	10000	(4)	10000
PBG02	11100	11100			11100	(2)	12500
BQ1				2486			2500
BP1			2485				2500
BO1		3500					3500
BN1	3500						3500
	24600	24600	12485	12486			

1988	£10 ($^1/_{10}$ oz)	£25 (¼ oz)	£50 (½ oz)	£100 (1 oz)	SET		Authorised
PBG03	3505	3505	3505	3505	3505	(4)	6500
PBG04	894	894			894	(2)	7500
BQ1				626			2000
BN1	2694						5000
	7093	4399	3505	4131			

1989	£10 ($^1/_{10}$ oz)	£25 (¼ oz)	£50 (½ oz)	£100 (1 oz)	SET		Authorised
PBG05	2268	2268	2268	2268	2268	(4)	2500
PBG06	451	451			451	(2)	1500
BQ1				338			1000
BN1	1609						2500
	4328	2719	2268	2606			

1990	£10 ($^1/_{10}$ oz)	£25 (¼ oz)	£50 (½ oz)	£100 (1 oz)	SET		Authorised
PBG07	527	527	527	527	527	(4)	2500
BQ1				262			1000
BN1	1571						2500
	2098	527	527	789			

1991	£10 ($^1/_{10}$ oz)	£25 (¼ oz)	£50 (½ oz)	£100 (1 oz)	SET		Authorised
PBG08	509	509	509	509	509	(4)	750
BQ1				143			500
BN1	954						2000
	1463	509	509	652			

1992	£10 ($^1/_{10}$ oz)	£25 (¼ oz)	£50 (½ oz)	£100 (1 oz)	SET		Authorised
PBG09	500	500	500	500	500	(4)	500
BN1	1000						1000
	1500	500	500	500			

1993	£10 (^{1}/$_{10}$ oz)	£25 (¼ oz)	£50 (½ oz)	£100 (1 oz)	SET		Authorised
PBG10	462	462	462	462	462	(4)	500
BN1	997						1000
	1459	462	462	462			

1994	£10 (^{1}/$_{10}$ oz)	£25 (¼ oz)	£50 (½ oz)	£100 (1 oz)	SET		Authorised
PBG11	435	435	435	435	435	(4)	500
BN1	994						1000
	1429	435	435	435			

1995	£10 (^{1}/$_{10}$ oz)	£25 (¼ oz)	£50 (½ oz)	£100 (1 oz)	SET		Authorised
PBG12	500	500	500	500	500	(4)	500
BN1	1500						1500
	2000	500	500	500			

1996	£10 (^{1}/$_{10}$ oz)	£25 (¼ oz)	£50 (½ oz)	£100 (1 oz)	SET		Authorised
PBG13	483	483	483	483	483	(4)	500
BN1	2379						2500
	2862	483	483	483			

1997	£10 (^{1}/$_{10}$ oz)	£25 (¼ oz)	£50 (½ oz)	£100 (1 oz)	SET		Authorised
PBG14	892	892	892	892	892	(4)	1500
BQ2				164			1000
BO2		923					2500
BN2	1821						5000
	2713	1815	892	1056			

1998	£10 (^{1}/$_{10}$ oz)	£25 (¼ oz)	£50 (½ oz)	£100 (1 oz)	SET		Authorised
PBG15	750	750	750	750	750	(4)	750
BO3		560					1000
BN3	392						5000
	1142	1310	750	750			

1999	£10 (^{1}/$_{10}$ oz)	£25 (¼ oz)	£50 (½ oz)	£100 (1 oz)	SET		Authorised
PBG16	740	740	740	740	740	(4)	750
BO3		1000					1000
BN3	1058						5000
	1798	1740	740	740			

2000	£10 ($^1/_{10}$ oz)	£25 (¼ oz)	£50 (½ oz)	£100 (1 oz)	SET		Authorised
PBG17	750	750	750	750	750	(4)	750
BO3		500					500
BN3	659						5000
	1409	1250	750	750			

2001	£10 ($^1/_{10}$ oz)	£25 (¼ oz)	£50 (½ oz)	£100 (1 oz)	SET		Authorised
PBG18	1000	1000	1000	1000	1000	(4)	1000
BO4		500					500
BN4	1557						2500
	2557	1500	1000	1000			

2002	£10 ($^1/_{10}$ oz)	£25 (¼ oz)	£50 (½ oz)	£100 (1 oz)	SET		Authorised
PBG19	945	945	945	945	945	(4)	1000
BO3		750					1750
BN3	1500						2500
	2445	1695	945	945			

2003	£10 ($^1/_{10}$ oz)	£25 (¼ oz)	£50 (½ oz)	£100 (1 oz)	SET		Authorised
PBG20	1250	1250	1250	1250	1250	(4)	1250
PBG21	825	825	825		825	(3)	1500
BO5		609					750
BN5	1382						1500
	3457	2684	2075	1250			

2004	£10 ($^1/_{10}$ oz)	£25 (¼ oz)	£50 (½ oz)	£100 (1 oz)	SET		Authorised
PBG22	973	973	973	973	973	(4)	1250
PBG23	223	223	223		223	(3)	1500
BO3		750					750
BN3	929						1500
	2125	1946	1196	973			

2005	£10 ($^1/_{10}$ oz)	£25 (¼ oz)	£50 (½ oz)	£100 (1 oz)	SET		Authorised
PBG24	1439	1439	1439	1439	1439	(4)	1500
PBG25	417	417	417		417	(3)	500
BO6		750					750
BN6	1225						1500
	3081	2606	1856	1439			

2006	£10 (¹/₁₀ oz)	£25 (¼ oz)	£50 (½ oz)	£100 (1 oz)	SET		Authorised
PBG26	1163	1163	1163	1163	1163	(4)	1250
PBG27		250				(5)	
BO3		728					1000
BN3	700						1500
	1863	2141	1163	1163			

2007	£10 (¹/₁₀ oz)	£25 (¼ oz)	£50 (½ oz)	£100 (1 oz)	SET		Authorised
PBG28	1250	1250	1250	1250	1250	(4)	1250
BO7		1000					1000
BN7	893						1500
	2143	2250	1250	1250			

2008	£10 (¹/₁₀ oz)	£25 (¼ oz)	£50 (½ oz)	£100 (1 oz)	SET		Authorised
PBG29	1250	1250	1250	1250	1250	(4)	1250
BO8		1000					1000
BN8	748						1000
	1998	2250	1250	1250			

2009	£10 (¹/₁₀ oz)	£25 (¼ oz)	£50 (½ oz)	£100 (1 oz)	SET		Authorised
PBG30	797	797	797	797	797	(4)	1250
BO9		770					2250
BN9	749						2000
	1546	1567	797	797			

2010	£10 (¹/₁₀ oz)	£25 (¼ oz)	£50 (½ oz)	£100 (1 oz)	SET		Authorised
PBG31	867	867	867	867	867	(4)	1250
PBG32	186	186	186		186	(3)	500
BO10		517					1250
BN10	1049						1250
	2102	1670	1053	867			

2011	£10 (¹/₁₀ oz)	£25 (¼ oz)	£50 (½ oz)	£100 (1 oz)	SET		Authorised
PBG33	#	#	#	#		(4)	1000
PBG34	#	#	#			(3)	250
BN11	#						1000
	3511	698	847	5735			

2012	£10 ($^1/_{10}$ oz)	£25 (¼ oz)	£50 (½ oz)	£100 (1 oz)	SET		Authorised
PBG35	365	365	365	365	365	(4)	550
PBG36	99	99	99		99	(3)	100
PBG37			25			(9)	
BO3		316					620
BN3	1249						750
	1713	780	489	365			

2013	£1 ($^1/_{20}$ oz)	£10 ($^1/_{10}$ oz)	£25 (¼ oz)	£50 (½ oz)	£100 (1 oz)	SET		Authorised
PBG38	261	261	261	261	261	261	(5)	250
PBG39		90	90	90		90	(3)	125
PBG40	136	136	136			136	(3)	350
BN12		1150						1125
BM1	2496							1000
	2893	1637	487	351	261			

2014	50p ($^1/_{20}$ oz)	£1 ($^1/_{20}$ oz)	£10 ($^1/_{10}$ oz)	£25 (¼ oz)	£50 (½ oz)	£100 (1 oz)	SET		Authorised
PBG41	225	225	225	225	225	225	225	(6)	250
PBG42			98	98	98		98	(3)	100
PBG43		140	140	140			140	(3)	150
BM2		993							1000
BL1	5521								9650
	5746	1358	463	463	323	225			

2015	50p ($^1/_{20}$ oz)	£1 ($^1/_{20}$ oz)	£10 ($^1/_{10}$ oz)	£25 (¼ oz)	£50 (½ oz)	£100 (1 oz)	SET		Authorised
PBG44	138	138	138	138	138	138	138	(6)	250
PBG45			99	99	99		99	(3)	100
PBG46		176	176	176			176	(3)	250
BL2	3075								7500
	3213	314	413	413	237	138			

2016	50p ($^1/_{20}$ oz)	£1 ($^1/_{20}$ oz)	£10 ($^1/_{10}$ oz)	£25 (¼ oz)	£50 (½ oz)	£100 (1 oz)	SET		Authorised
PBG47	174	174	174	174	174	174	174	(6)	175
		50	50	50	50	50	50	(5) Ω	50
PBG48			69	69	69		69	(3)	70
BO17				729					730
BO17				100				Ω	100
BL3	1447								2250
	1621	224	293	1122	293	224			

2017	50p (1/20 oz)	£1 (1/20 oz)	£10 (1/10 oz)	£25 (¼ oz)	£50 (½ oz)	£100 (1 oz)	SET		Authorised
PBG49	#	#	#	#	#	#		(6)	250
		#	#	#	#	#		(5) Ω	
PBG50			#	#	#			(3)	200
BO18				#					2500
BL4	871								1500
	871	0	0	0	0	0			

2018	50p (1/20 oz)	£1 (1/20 oz)	£10 (1/10 oz)	£25 (¼ oz)	£50 (½ oz)	£100 (1 oz)	SET		Authorised
PBG51	#	#	#	#	#	#		(6)	220
PBG52			#	#	#			(3)	170
BO19				#					1080
	0	0	0	0	0	0			

2019	50p (1/20 oz)	£1 (1/20 oz)	£10 (1/10 oz)	£25 (¼ oz)	£50 (½ oz)	£100 (1 oz)	SET		Authorised
PBG53	#	#	#	#	#	#		(6)	150
PBG54			#	#	#			(3)	130
BO20				#					645
	0	0	0	0	0	0			

2020	50p (1/20 oz)	£1 (1/20 oz)	£10 (1/10 oz)	£25 (¼ oz)	£50 (½ oz)	£100 (1 oz)	SET		Authorised
PBG55	#	#	#	#	#	#		(6)	150
PBG56			#	#	#			(3)	130
BO21				#					700
	0	0	0	0	0	0			

Ω Coins sold to the US market and not in standard Royal Mint cases.
Mintages not yet known

The range of Britannia platinum coins is so far quite small, and they were previously included within the listing of the gold pieces.

Britannia Platinum Coins Specifications

Denomination	Metal	Weight		Diameter
£10	0.995 platinum	$^1/_{10}$ ounce	3.14 g	15.00 mm
£25	0.995 platinum	$^1/_4$ ounce	7.85 g	20.00 mm
£50	0.995 platinum	$^1/_2$ ounce	15.69 g	25.00 mm
£100	0.995 platinum	1 ounce	31.39 g	32.69 mm

Obverse portrait by Ian Rank-Broadley
BU1 Britannia. Ten pounds. (1/10 oz platinum.) R. As BQ8 with the inscription 'TENTH OUNCE PLATINUM BRITANNIA 2007'.
2007 Proof *FDC* (Issued: 691 plus coins in sets.) £200
BU2 Britannia. Ten pounds. (1/10 oz platinum.) R. As BQ9 with the inscription 'BRITANNIA 2008 1/10 OUNCE 999.5 PLATINUM'.
2008 Proof *FDC* (Issued: 268 plus coins in sets.) £220

Obverse portrait by Jody Clark
BU3 Britannia. Ten pounds. (1/10 oz platinum.) R. As BQ1 with the inscription 'BRITANNIA 1/10 OUNCE 999.5 PLATINUM' and the date of the year.
2018 Unc...£100
2019 Unc...£100
2020 Unc...£100

Obverse portrait by Ian Rank-Broadley
BV1 Britannia. Twenty five pounds. (1/4 oz platinum.) R. As BQ8 with the inscription 'QUARTER OUNCE PLATINUM BRITANNIA 2007'.
2007 Proof *FDC* (Issued: 210 plus coins in sets) £400
BV2 Britannia. Twenty five pounds. (1/4 oz platinum.) R. As BQ9 with the inscription 'BRITANNIA 2008 1/4 OUNCE 999 .5 PLATINUM'.
2008 Proof *FDC* (Issued: 100 plus coins in sets) £400

Obverse portrait by Jody Clark
BV3 Britannia. Twenty five pounds. (1/4 oz platinum.) R. As BQ19 with the inscription 'BRITANNIA 1/4 OUNCE PLATINUM 999.5 2017'.
2017 Proof *FDC* (Issued: 750) £450
BV4 Britannia. Twenty five pounds. (1/4 oz platinum.) R. As BQ22 with the inscription 'BRITANNIA 1/4 OUNCE PLATINU M 999.5 2018'.
2018 Proof *FDC* (Edition: 650)..£450
BV5 Britannia. Twenty five pounds. (1/4 oz platinum.) R. As BQ24 with the inscription 'BRITANNIA 1/4 OUNCE PLATINUM 999.5 2019'.
2019 Proof *FDC* (Edition: 240)..£500
BV6 Britannia. Twenty five pounds. (1/4 oz platinum.) R. As BQ25 with the inscription 'BRITANNIA 1/4 OUNCE PLATINUM 999.5 2020'.
2020 Proof *FDC* (Edition: 150)..£525

Obverse portrait by Ian Rank-Broadley
BW1 Britannia. Fifty pounds. (1/2 oz platinum.) R. As BQ8 with the inscription 'HALF OUNCE PLATINUM BRITANNIA 2007'.
2007 Proof *FDC** £800

* Coins marked thus were originally issued in Royal Mint sets.

BW2 Britannia. Fifty pounds. (1/2 oz platinum.) Ŗ. As BQ9 with the inscription
'BRITANNIA 2008 1/2 OUNCE 999.5 PLATINUM'.
2008 Proof *FDC** £800

Obverse portrait by Ian Rank-Broadley
BX1 Britannia. One hundred pounds. (1 oz platinum.) Ŗ. As BQ8 with the inscription
'ONE OUNCE PLATINUM BRITANNIA 2007'.
2007 Proof *FDC** £1600

BX2 Britannia. One hundred pounds. (1 oz platinum.) Ŗ. As BQ9 with the inscription
'BRITANNIA 2008 ONE OUNCE 999.5 PLATINUM'.
2008 Proof *FDC** £1600

Obverse portrait by Jody Clark
BX3 Britannia. One hundred pounds. (1 oz platinum.) Ŗ. As BQ1 with the inscription
'BRITANNIA 1 OZ 999.5 PLATINUM' and the date of the year.
2018 Unc...£1100
2019 Unc £1100
2020 Unc £1100

* Coins marked thus were originally issued in Royal Mint sets.

Britannia Platinum Proof Sets

                                                                                        £
PBP1-2007   £100, £50, £25, £10 (Issued: 250) 3000
PBP2-2008   £100, £50, £25, £10 (Issued: 150) 3000

Britannia Platinum Proof Coin Sales

2007	£10 ($^1/_{10}$ oz)	£25 (¼ oz)	£50 (½ oz)	£100 (1 oz)	SET		Authorised
PBP1	250	250	250	250	250	(4)	250
BV1		210					1000
BU1	691						1000
	941	460	250	250			

2008	£10 ($^1/_{10}$ oz)	£25 (¼ oz)	£50 (½ oz)	£100 (1 oz)	SET		Authorised
PBP2	150	150	150	150	150	(4)	250
BV2		100					500
BU2	268						750
	418	250	150	150			

As the Royal Mint issued a considerable number of coins to mark the London 2012 Olympic and Paralympic Games, it was decided that it would be easier for collectors if these coins were grouped together rather than be included with other coins of the same denomination. As a consequence the £2 coins issued in 2008 (previously listed as 4585 and 4586) have been renumbered and are now listed within this section.

The Olympic series commenced in 2008 with the issue of two £2 coins – one for the centenary of the first London Olympic Games and the other for the handover of the Olympic flag from Beijing to London following the end of the Beijing Olympics that year. 2009 saw the first of an annual issue of £5 crown coins marking the Countdown to 2012 followed by the first of 29 50p coins depicting the range of sports to be seen at the games. Also in 2009 the first six silver crowns from a set of 18 celebrating the Best of Britain were issued depicting the Mind of Britain. The final coin in this series depicted Olaudah Equiano, the first person from a slave background to feature on a British coin. Gold coins were issued from 2010 depicting the legendary gods associated with the ancient Greek games, and finally in 2012 the UK's first 5oz and kilo coins were issued. A third £2 coin was issued late in 2012 to mark the passing of the Olympic flag from London to Rio de Janeiro the host for the 2016 games.

Specifications of the coins from 50p to £5 are the same as those in the specification table in the introduction and for the £10 and higher gold and silver coins, readers may refer to the tables at the head of the relevant Britannia coins.

Numbers issued are quoted where these are available but there are still some gaps where we are waiting for figures from the Royal Mint.

4960

4960 Fifty pence. Athletics. To commemorate the London 2012 Olympic and Paralympic Games. R. A design which depicts an athlete clearing a high jump bar, with the London 2012 logo above and the denomination '50 pence' below. (Reverse design: Florence Jackson.)

2009
- — BU in presentation folder (Issued: 19,722) £95
- — Gold *FDC* – presented to the artist
2011 ....£1
- — BU in card (3/29) (Issued: 195,608)...£3
- — BU in presentation folder signed by Daley Thompson (Issued: 490) £50
- — BU in presentation folder signed by Dame Kelly Holmes (Issued: 485).................£50
- — BU in presentation folder signed by Lord Sebastian Coe (Issued: 376) £50
- — Silver BU (Issued: 7,640)* £25
- — Proof piedfort in gold *FDC* (Issued: 26 including coins in sets) £4000

* Coins marked thus were originally issued in Royal Mint sets.

4961   4962

4961 Fifty pence. Aquatics. To commemorate the London 2012 Olympic and Paralympic
Games. R. A design which depicts a swimmer submerged in water, with the London
Olympic logo above and the denomination '50 PENCE' below. (Reverse design:
Jonathan Olliffe.)

2011 ....£1
— BU in card (1/29) (Issued: 183,749)..£3
— Silver BU (Issued: 6,600)* £25
— Gold *FDC* – presented to the artist

4961A Fifty pence. As 4961 but with lines over face.

2011 ....£900

4962 Fifty pence. Archery. To commemorate the London 2012 Olympic and Paralympic
Games. R. A design which depicts a bow being drawn, with the London Olympic logo
above and the denomination '50 PENCE' below. (Reverse design: Piotr Powaga.)

2011 ....£1
— BU in card (2/29) (Issued: 165,954)..£3
— Silver BU (Issued: 5,205)* £25
— Gold *FDC* – presented to the artist

4963   4964

4963 Fifty pence. Badminton. To commemorate the London 2012 Olympic and Paralympic
Games. R. A design which depicts a shuttlecock and a diagram of badminton actions, with
the London Olympic logo above and the denomination '50 PENCE' below.
(Reverse design: Emma Kelly.)

2011 ....£1
— BU in card (4/29) (Issued: 149,996)..£3
— Silver BU (Issued: 5,257)* £25
— Gold *FDC* – presented to the artist

4964 Fifty pence. Basketball. To commemorate the London 2012 Olympic and Paralympic
Games. R. A design which depicts basketball players against a textured background
of a large basketball, with the London Olympic logo above and the denomination '50
PENCE' below. (Reverse design: Sarah Payne.)

2011 ....£1
— BU in card (5/29) (Issued:162,916)..£3
— Silver BU (Issued: 11,445)* £25
— Gold *FDC* – presented to the artist

* Coins marked thus were originally issued in Royal Mint sets.

4965   4966

4965 Fifty pence. Boccia. To commemorate the London 2012 Olympic and Paralympic
Games. R. A design which depicts a boccia player in a wheelchair throwing a ball, with
the London Olympic logo above and the denomination '50 PENCE' below.
(Reverse design: Justin Chung.)
2011 ....£1
— BU in card (6/29) (Issued: 152,421)...£3
— Silver BU (Issued: 5,229)*..£25
— Gold *FDC* – presented to the artist

4966 Fifty pence. Boxing. To commemorate the London 2012 Olympic and Paralympic
Games. R. A design which depicts a pair of boxing gloves against the background of a
boxing ring, with the London Olympic logo above and the denomination '50 PENCE'
below. (Reverse design: Shane Abery.)
2011. ....£1
— BU in card (7/29) (Issued: 167,910)...£3
— Silver BU (Issued: 5,872)*..£25
— Proof piedfort in gold *FDC* (Issued: 18)* £4000
Gold *FDC* – presented to the artist

4967   4968

4967 Fifty pence. Canoeing. To commemorate the London 2012 Olympic and Paralympic Games.
R. A design which depicts a figure in a canoe on a slalom course, with the London Olympic
logo above and the denomination '50 PENCE' below. (Reverse design: Timothy Lees.)
2011 ....£1
— BU in card (8/29) (Issued: 141,873 ....£3
— Silver BU (Issued: 8,498)*..£25
— Proof piedfort in gold *FDC* (Issued: 17)* £4000
— Gold *FDC* – presented to the artist

4968 Fifty pence. Cycling. To commemorate the London 2012 Olympic and Paralympic
Games. R. A design which depicts a cyclist in a velodrome, with the London Olympic logo
above and the denomination '50 PENCE' below. (Reverse design: Theo Crutchley- Mack.)
2010
— Gold *FDC* – presented to the artist
2011 ....£1
— BU in card (9/29) (Issued: 182,631) £3
— Silver BU (Issued: 16,379)*..£25
— Proof piedfort in gold *FDC* (Issued: 26 including coins in sets) £4000

* Coins marked thus were originally issued in Royal Mint sets.

4969   4970

4969 Fifty pence. Equestrian. To commemorate the London 2012 Olympic and Paralympic
Games. ℞. A design which depicts a horse and rider jumping over a fence, with the
London Olympic logo above and the denomination '50 PENCE' below.
(Reverse design: Thomas Babbage.)

2011 ....£1
—   BU in card (10/29) (Issued: 170,881)...£3
—   Silver BU (Issued: 5,382)* £25
—   Proof piedfort in gold *FDC* (Issued: 22)* £4000
—   Gold *FDC* – presented to the artist

4970 Fifty pence. Fencing. To commemorate the London 2012 Olympic and Paralympic
Games. ℞. A design which depicts two figures fencing, with the London Olympic logo
above and the denomination "50 PENCE" below. (Reverse design: Ruth Summerfield.)

2011 ....£1
—   BU in card (11/29) (Issued: 156,574)...£3
—   Silver BU (Issued: 7,183)* £25
—   Gold *FDC* – presented to the artist

4971   4972

4971 Fifty pence. Football. To commemorate the London 2012 Olympic and Paralympic
Games. ℞. A diagrammatic explanation of the offside rule in football, with the London
Olympic logo above and the denomination '50 PENCE' below. (Reverse design:
Neil Wolfson.)

2011 ....£10
—   BU in card (12/29) (Issued: 214,021)...£12
—   Silver BU (Issued: 6,688)* £25
—   Gold *FDC* – presented to the artist

4972 Fifty pence. Goalball. To commemorate the London 2012 Olympic and Paralympic
Games. ℞. A design which depicts a goalball player throwing a ball, with the London
Olympic logo above and the denomination '50 PENCE' below. (Reverse design:
Jonathan Wren.)

2011 ....£1
—   BU in card (13/29) (Issued: 140,093)...£3
—   Silver BU (Issued: 5,131)* £25
—   Gold *FDC* – presented to the artist

* Coins marked thus were originally issued in Royal Mint sets.

4973   4974

4973 Fifty pence. Gymnastics. To commemorate the London 2012 Olympic and Paralympic
Games. ℞. A design which depicts a gymnast with a ribbon, with the London Olympic
logo above and the denomination '50 PENCE' below. (Reverse design: Jonathan Olliffe.)
2011 ....£1
—   BU in card (14/29) (Issued: 171,654)...£3
—   Silver BU (Issued: 7,083)* £25
—   Gold *FDC* – presented to the artist

4974 Fifty pence. Handball. To commemorate the London 2012 Olympic and Paralympic
Games. ℞. A design which depicts a handball player throwing a ball against a
background of a handball court, with the London Olympic logo above and the
denomination '50 PENCE' below. (Reverse design: Natasha Ratcliffe.)
2011 ....£1
—   BU in card (15/29) (Issued: 143,325)...£3
—   Silver BU (Issued: 5,593)* £25
—   Gold *FDC* – presented to the artist

4975   4976

4975 Fifty pence. Hockey. To commemorate the London 2012 Olympic and Paralympic
Games. ℞. A design which depicts two hockey players challenging for the ball, with the
London Olympic logo above and the denomination '50 PENCE' below. (Reverse design:
Robert Evans.)
2011 ....£1
—   BU in card (16/29) (Issued:156,572) £3
—   Silver BU (Issued: 5,642)* £25
—   Gold *FDC* – presented to the artist

4976 Fifty pence. Judo. To commemorave the London 2012 Olympic and Paralympic
Games. ℞. A depiction of a judo throw, with the London Olympic logo above and the
denomination '50 PENCE' below. (Reverse design: David Cornell.)
2011 ....£1
—   BU in card (17/29) (Issued: 154,201)...£3
—   Silver BU (Issued: 5,624)* £25
—   Gold *FDC* – presented to the artist

* Coins marked thus were originally issued in Royal Mint sets.

4977   4978

4977 Fifty pence. Modern Pentathlon. To commemorate the London 2012 Olympic and
Paralympic Games. ℞. A montage of the five sports which form the modern pentathlon,
with the London Olympic logo above and the denomination '50 PENCE' below.
(Reverse design: Daniel Brittain.)

2011 ....£1
— BU in card (18/29) (Issued: 149,116 ....£3
— Silver BU (Issued: 5,889)* £25
— Gold *FDC* – presented to the artist

4978 Fifty pence. Rowing. To commemorate the London 2012 Olympic and Paralympic
Games. ℞. A design which depicts a rowing boat accompanied by a number of words
associated with the Olympic movement, with the London Olympic logo above and the
denomination '50 PENCE' below. (Reverse design: David Podmore.)

2011 ....£1
— BU in card   (19/29) (Issued 167,222) £3
— BU in presentation folder signed by Sir Steve Redgrave (Issued: 486) £50
— Silver BU (Issued: 9,043)* £25
— Proof piedfort in gold FDC (Issued: 26)* £4000
— Gold *FDC* – presented to the artist

4979   4980

4979 Fifty pence. Sailing. To commemorate the London 2012 Olympic and Paralympic
Games. ℞. A design which depicts three sailing boats accompanied by a map of the coast
of Weymouth, with the London Olympic logo above and the denomination '50 PENCE'
below. (Reverse design: Bruce Rushin.)

2011 ....£1
— BU in card (20/29) (Issued: 164,294) £3
— Silver BU (Issued: 7,267)* £25
— Proof piedfort in gold *FDC* (Issued: 17)* £4000
— Gold *FDC* – presented to the artist

4980 Fifty pence. Shooting. To commemorate the London 2012 Olympic and Paralympic
Games. ℞. A design which depicts a figure shooting, with the London Olympic logo
above and the denomination '50 PENCE' below. (Reverse design: Pravin Dewdhory.)

2011 ....£1
— BU in card (21/29) (Issued: 151,157) £3
— Silver BU (Issued: 5,358)* £25
— Proof piedfort in gold *FDC* (Issued: 17)* £4000
— Gold *FDC* – presented to the artist

* Coins marked thus were originally issued in Royal Mint sets.

4981   4982

4981 Fifty pence. Table Tennis. To commemorate the London 2012 Olympic and
Paralympic Games. R. A design which depicts two table tennis bats against the
background of a table and net, with the London Olympic logo above and the
denomination '50 PENCE' below. (Reverse design: Alan Linsdell.)
2011 ....£1
—   BU in card (22/29) (Issued: 148,954) £3
—   Silver BU (Issued: 5,797)* £25
—   Gold *FDC* – presented to the artist

4982 Fifty pence. Taekwondo. To commemorate the London 2012 Olympic and Paralympic
Games. R. A design which depicts two athletes engaged in Taekwondo, with the London
Olympic logo above and the denomination '50 PENCE' below. (Reverse design:
David Gibbons.)
2011 ....£1
—   BU in card (23/29) (Issued: 145,969) £3
—   Silver BU (Issued: 5,305)* £25
—   Proof piedfort in gold *FDC* (Issued: 15)* £5000
—   Gold *FDC* – presented to the artist

4983   4984

4983 Fifty pence. Tennis. To commemorate the London 2012 Olympic and Paralympic Games.
R. A design which depicts a tennis net and tennis ball, with the London Olympic logo
above and the denomination '50 PENCE' below. (Reverse design: Tracy Baines.)
2011 ....£1
—   BU in card (24/29) (Issued: 170,294) £3
—   Silver BU (Issued: 6,137)* £25
—   Proof piedfort in gold *FDC* (Issued: 25)* £4000
—   Gold *FDC* – presented to the artist

4984 Fifty pence. Triathlon. To commemorate the London 2012 Olympic and Paralympic
Games. R. A montage of the three sports which form the triathlon, with the London
Olympic logo above and the denomination '50 ' below. (Reverse design: Sarah Harvey.)
2011 ....£1
—   BU in card (25/29) (Issued: 172,113) £3
—   Silver BU (Issued: 7,247)* £25
—   Proof piedfort in gold *FDC* (Issued: 22)* £4000
—   Gold *FDC* – presented to the artist

* Coins marked thus were originally issued in Royal Mint sets.

4985   4986

4985 Fifty pence. Volleyball. To commemorate the London 2012 Olympic and Paralympic
Games. ℞. A design which depicts three figures playing beach volleyball, with the
London Olympic logo above and the denomination '50 PENCE' below. (Reverse design:
Daniela Boothman.)

2011 ....£1
—   BU in card (26/29) (Issued: 149,874)...£3
—   Silver BU (Issued: 5,870)* £25
—   Gold *FDC* – presented to the artist

4986 Fifty pence. Weight Lifting. To commemorate the London 2012 Olympic and
Paralympic Games. ℞. A design which depicts the outline of a weightlifter starting a
lift, with the London Olympic logo above and the denomination '50 PENCE' below.
(Reverse design:Rob Shakespeare.)

2011 ....£1
—   BU in card (27/29) (Issued: 147,537)...£3
—   Silver BU (Issued: 5,500)* £25
—   Gold *FDC* – presented to the artist

4987   4988

4987 Fifty pence. Wheelchair Rugby. To commemorate the London 2012 Olympic and
Paralympic Games. ℞. A design which depicts a wheelchair rugby player in action,
with the London Olympic logo above and the denomination '50 PENCE' below.
(Reverse design: Natasha Ratcliffe.)

2011 ....£1
—   BU in card (28/29) (Issued: 146,934 ....£3
—   Silver BU (Issued: 5,956)* £25
—   Gold *FDC* – presented to the artist

4988 Fifty pence. Wrestling. To commemorate the London 2012 Olympic and Paralympic
Games. ℞. A design which depicts two figures wrestling in a stadium, with the London
Olympic logo above and the denomination '50 PENCE' below. (Reverse design:
Roderick Enriquez.)

2011 ....£1
—   BU in card (29/29) (Issued: 153,038)..£3
—   Silver BU (Issued: 5,727)* £25
—   Gold *FDC* – presented to the artist

* Coins marked thus were originally issued in Royal Mint sets.

4951 4952 4953

4951 Two pounds. Centenary of the Olympic Games of 1908 held in London. R. A running track on which is superimposed the date '1908' accompanied by the denomination 'TWO POUNDS' and the date '2008', the whole design being encircled by the inscription 'LONDON OLYMPIC CENTENARY' with the edge inscription 'THE 4TH OLYMPIAD LONDON'. (Reverse design: Thomas T Docherty.)

2008 (Issued: 910,000) ....Unc £6; BU £8
— BU in presentation folder (Issued: 29,594) £12
— Proof *FDC* (in 2008 set, see PS93)* £18
— Proof in Silver *FDC* (Issued: 6,481) £35
— Proof piedfort in silver *FDC* (Issued: 1,619) £55
— Proof in gold *FDC* (Issued: 1,908 including coins in sets) £900

4952 Two pounds. London Olympic Handover Ceremony. R. The Olympic flag being passed from one hand to another, encircled by the inscription 'BEIJING 2008 LONDON 2012' and with the London 2012 logo below with the edge inscription 'I CALL UPON THE YOUTH OF THE WORLD'. (Reverse design: Royal Mint Engraving Department.)

2008 (Issued: 918,000) ....Unc £5, BU £8
— BU in presentation folder (Issued: 47,765) £10
— Proof in Silver *FDC* (Issued: 30,000) £38
— Proof piedfort in silver *FDC* (Issued: 3,000) £60
— Proof in gold *FDC* (Issued: 3,250 including coins in sets) £900

4953 Two pounds. London to Rio Olympic Handover coin. R. A design which depicts a baton being passed from one hand to another, accompanied by the conjoined Union and Brazilian Flags. The reverse design is set against the background of a running track motif, with the London 2012 logo above and the surrounding inscription 'LONDON 2012 RIO 2016'. With the edge inscription 'I CALL UPON THE YOUTH OF THE WORLD'. (Reverse design: Jonathan Olliffe.)

2012 (Issued: 845,000) ....Unc £8; BU £8
— BU in presentation card (Issued: 28,356)..£12
— Proof in silver *FDC* (Issued: 3,781) £60
— Proof piedfort in silver *FDC* (Issued: 2,000) £105
— Proof in gold *FDC* (Issued: 771)...£1250

* Coins marked thus were originally issued in Royal Mint sets.

4920   4921

4920 Five pounds. (Crown.) UK countdown to 2012 Olympic Games. ℞. In the centre a
depiction of two swimmers as faceted figures accompanied by the number '3' with
a section of a clock face to the right and the London 2012 logo to the left printed in
coloured ink on the precious metal versions and surrounded by a plan view of the main
Olympic Stadium incorporating the date '2009' with the words 'COUNTDOWN' above
and the inscription 'XXX OLYMPIAD' below. (Reverse design: Claire Aldridge.)
2009
-   BU in presentation folder (Issued: combined with below) £8
-   BU in presentation folder (Issued: 184,921) £15
-   Proof in silver *FDC* (Issued: 26,645) £50
-   Proof piedfort in silver *FDC* (Issued: 4,874) £80
-   Proof in gold *FDC* (Issued: 1,860) £2000

4921 Five pounds. (Crown.) UK countdown to 2012 Olympic Games. ℞. In the centre a
depiction of two runners as faceted figures accompanied by the number '2' with a section
of a clock face to the right and the London 2012 logo to the left printed in coloured
ink on the precious meta versions and surrounded by a plan view of the main Olympic
Stadium incorporating the date '2010' with the words 'COUNTDOWN' above and the
inscription 'XXX OLYMPIAD' below. (Reverse design: Claire Aldridge.)
2010
-   BU in presentation folder (Issued: combined with below) £8
-   BU in presentation folder (Issued: 153,080) £15
-   Proof in silver *FDC* (Issued: 20,159) £50
-   Proof piedfort in silver *FDC* (Issued: 2,179) £100
-   Proof in gold *FDC* (Issued: 1,562) £2000

4922   4923

4922 Five pounds. (Crown.) UK countdown to 2012 Olympic Games. R. In the centre a
depiction of a cyclist as a faceted figure, accompanied by the number '1' with a
section of a clock face to the right, below and to the left, and the London 2012 logo to
the right printed in coloured ink on the precious metal versions and surrounded by a
plan view of the main Olympic Stadium incorporating the date '2011' with the words
'COUNTDOWN' above and the inscription 'XXX OLYMPIAD' below.
(Reverse design: Claire Aldridge.)
2011
— BU in presentation folder (Issued: combined with below) £8
— BU in presentation folder (Issued: 163,235) £15
— Proof in silver *FDC* (Issued: 25,877) £50
— Proof piedfort in silver *FDC* (Issued: 4,000)...£80
— Proof in gold *FDC* (Issued: 1,300) £2000

4923 Five pounds. (Crown.) UK countdown to 2012 Olympic Games. R. A depiction of
three athletes as faceted figures standing on a victory podium, with a section of a
clock-face to the right, to the left and above, and the London 2012 logo to the right.
The reverse design is surrounded by a plan view of the main Olympic Stadium,
incorporating the date '2012' at the top, and the word 'COUNTDOWN' above and the
inscription 'XXX OLYMPIAD' below. (Reverse design: Claire Aldridge.)
2012
— BU in presentation card   (Edition: combined with below).....................................£8
— BU in presentation folder (Edition: 250,000)...£15
— Proof in silver *FDC* (Issued: 12,670) £60
— Proof piedfort in silver *FDC* (Issued: 2,324) £90
— Proof in gold *FDC* (Issued: 1,007)..£2000

4924

4924 Five pounds. (Crown.) The London 2012 Olympic Games. ℞. An image of the skyline of some of the most well-known landmarks and buildings in London reflected in the River Thames, with the inscription 'LONDON 2012' above. Surrounding the skyline image is a selection of sports from the London 2012 Games with the London 2012 logo at the top. (Reverse design: Saiman Miah.)
2012
— BU in presentation folder (Issued: 283,523) £15
— BU in folder with L24 (2012 Diamond Jubilee) (Issued: 1,815) £35
— Proof in silver *FDC* (Edition: 100,000) £70
— Proof in silver with gold plating *FDC* (Issued: 8,180)...£80
— Proof piedfort in silver *FDC* (Edition: 7,000)..£100
— Proof in gold *FDC* (Edition: 5,000) £2000

4925

4925 Five pounds. (Crown.) The London 2012 Paralympic Games. ℞. A design showing segments of a target, a spoked wheel, a stopwatch and the clock face of the Palace of Westminster. The inscription 'LONDON 2012' appears on the target and the London 2012 Paralympic logo appears on the stopwatch. On the gold and silver coins the London Paralympic logo is printed in coloured ink, while on the cupro-nickel coin the logo is struck into the surface. (Reverse design: Pippa Anderson.)
2012
— BU in presentation folder (Edition: 250,000; Issued: 50,387) £15
— Proof in silver *FDC* (Edition: 10,000) £75
— Proof in silver with gold plating *FDC* (Edition: 3,000) £85
— Proof piedfort in silver *FDC* (Edition: 2,012)...£120
— Proof in gold *FDC* (Edition: 2,012) £2100

4930

4930 Five pounds. (Crown.) The Mind of Britain. R. A depiction of the clock-face of the
Palace of Westminster accompanied by the London 2012 logo, printed in coloured ink
and a quotation From Walter Bagehot, 'NATIONS TOUCH AT THEIR SUMMITS'.
(Reverse design: Shane Greeves and the Royal Mint Engraving Department.)
2009
— Proof *FDC* (Edition: 100,000; Issued: 9,681) £20
— Proof in silver *FDC* (Issued: 26,630) £60

*The authorised mintage of the 18 coins 4930-4947 is 95,000 each. The numbers sold indicated
against each coin include the numbers sold in various sets as listed at the end of this Olympic
section but the numbers may not yet be complete. Even at this late stage we hope for more
information from the Royal Mint.*

4931   4932

4931 Five pounds. (Crown.) The Mind of Britain. R. A depiction of Stonehenge accompanied
by the London 2012 logo, printed in coloured ink on the silver version and a quotation
from William Blake 'GREAT THINGS ARE DONE WHEN MEN AND MOUNTAINS
MEET'. (Reverse design: Shane Greeves and the Royal Mint Engraving Department.)
2009
— Proof in silver *FDC* (Issued: 26,824)* £60

4932 Five pounds. (Crown.) The Mind of Britain. R. A depiction of the Angel of the North
accompanied   by the London 2012 logo printed in coloured ink on the silver version
and a quotation from William Shakespeare 'I HAVE TOUCHED THE HIGHEST
POINT OF MY GREATNESS'. (Reverse design: Shane Greeves and the Royal Mint
Engraving Department.)
2009
— Proof in silver *FDC* (Issued: 24,700)* £100

* Coins marked thus were originally issued in Royal Mint sets.

4933   4934

4933 Five pounds. (Crown.) The Mind of Britain. ℞. A depiction of the Flying Scotsman
accompanied   by the London 2012 logo printed in coloured ink on the silver version and
a quotation from William Shakespeare 'TRUE HOPE IS SWIFT'. (Reverse design:
Shane Greeves and the Royal Mint Engraving Department.)
2009
— Proof in silver *FDC* (Issued: 24,700)* £60

4934 Five pounds. (Crown.) The Mind of Britain. ℞. A depiction of Eduardo Paolozzi's
sculpture of Isaac Newton North accompanied by the London 2012 logo printed in
coloured ink on the silver version and a quotation from William Shakespeare 'MAKE
NOT YOUR THOUGHTS YOUR PRISONS'. (Reverse design: Shane Greeves and the
Royal Mint Engraving Department).
2009
— Proof in silver *FDC* (Issued: 24,734)* £60

4935   4936

4935 Five pounds. (Crown.) The Mind of Britain. ℞. A depiction of the Globe Theatre
accompanied by the London 2012 logo printed in coloured ink on the silver version and
a quotation from William Shakespeare 'WE ARE SUCH STUFF AS DREAMS ARE
MADE ON'. (Reverse design: Shane Greeves and the Royal Mint Engraving Department.)
2009
— Proof in silver *FDC* (Issued: 24,708)* £60

4936 Five pounds. (Crown.) The Body of Britain. ℞. A depiction of Rhossili Bay accompanied
by the London 2012 logo printed in coloured ink, and a quotation from William Blake
'TO SEE A WORLD IN A GRAIN OF SAND'. (Reverse design: Shane Greeves and the
Royal Mint Engraving Department.)
2010
— Proof in silver *FDC* (Issued: 4,311)* £70

* Coins marked thus were originally issued in Royal Mint sets.

4937   4938

4937 Five pounds. (Crown.) The Body of Britain R. A depiction of Giant's Causeway
accompanied by the London 2012 logo printed in coloured ink, and a quotation
from Alice Oswald 'WHEN THE STONE BEGAN TO DREAM'. (Reverse design:
Shane Greeves and the Royal Mint Engraving Department.)
2010

—   Proof in silver *FDC* (Issued: 4,310) £70

4938 Five pounds. (Crown.) The Body of Britain R. A depiction of the River Thames
accompanied by the London 2012 logo printed in coloured ink, and a quotation from
Percy Bysshe Shelley, 'TAMELESS, AND SWIFT AND PROUD'. (Reverse design:
Shane Greeves and the Royal Mint Engraving Department.)
2010

—   Proof in silver *FDC* (Issued: 6,209) £70

4939   4940

4939 Five pounds. (Crown.) The Body of Britain. R. A depiction of a barn owl accompanied
by the London 2012 logo printed in coloured ink, and a quotation from Samuel Johnson
'THE NATURAL FLIGHTS OF THE HUMAN MIND'. (Reverse design: Shane
Greeves and the Royal Mint Engraving Department.)
2010

—   Proof in silver *FDC* (Issued: 4,341) £70

4940 Five pounds. (Crown.) The Body of Britain. R. A depiction of oak leaves and an
acorn accompanied by the London 2012 logo printed in coloured ink, and a quotation
from Alfred, Lord Tennyson, 'TO STRIVE, TO SEEK . . . AND NOT TO YIELD'.
(Reverse design: Shane Greeves and the Royal Mint Engraving Department.)
2010

—   Proof in silver *FDC* (Issued: 4,313) £70

* Coins marked thus were originally issued in Royal Mint sets.

4941   4942

4941 Five pounds. (Crown.) The Body of Britain. ℞. A depiction of a weather-vane accompanied
by the London 2012 logo printed in coloured ink, and a quotation from Charlotte Bronte,
NEVER MAY A CLOUD COME O'ER THE SUNSHINE OF YOUR MIND'.
(Reverse design: Shane Greeves and the Royal Mint Engraving Department.)
2010
— Proof in silver *FDC* (Issued: 4,341)* £70

4942 Five pounds. (Crown.) The Spirit of Britain. ℞. A depiction of the intertwined national
emblems of England, Scotland, Wales and Northern Ireland accompanied by the
London 2012 logo, printed in coloured ink, and a quotation from John Lennon, 'AND
THE WORLD WILL BE ONE'. (Reverse design: Shane Greeves and the Royal Mint
Engraving Department.)
2010
— Proof in silver *FDC* (Issued: 5,019)* £75

4943   4944

4943 Five pounds. (Crown.) The Spirit of Britain. ℞. A depiction of the White Rabbit from
Lewis Carroll's *Alice in Wonderland* accompanied by the London 2012 logo, printed
in coloured ink, and a quotation from T S Eliot, 'ALL TOUCHED BY A COMMON
GENIUS'. (Reverse design: Shane Greeves and the Royal Mint Engraving Department.)
2010
— Proof in silver *FDC* (Issued: 5,048)* £75

4944 Five pounds. (Crown.) The Spirit of Britain. ℞. A view down the Mall of cheering
crowds accompanied by the London 2012 logo, printed in coloured ink, and a quotation
from Alfred, Lord Tennyson, 'KIND HEARTS ARE MORE THAN CORONETS'.
(Reverse design: Shane Greeves and the Royal Mint Engraving Department.)
2010
— Proof *FDC* (Edition; 100,000; Issued: 8,986) £20
— Proof in silver *FDC* (Issued: 6,949)* £75

* *Coins marked thus were originally issued in Royal Mint sets.*

4945   4946

4945 Five pounds. (Crown.) The Spirit of Britain. ℞. A depiction of the statue of Winston
   Churchill in Parliament Square accompanied by the London 2012 logo, printed in
   coloured ink, and a quotation from Anita Roddick, 'BE DARING, BE FIRST, BE
   DIFFERENT, BE JUST'. (Reverse design: Shane Greeves and the Royal Mint
   Engraving Department.)
   2010
   —   Proof *FDC* (Edition; 100,000; Issued: 14,930) £20
   —   Proof in silver *FDC* (Issued: 7,103)* £75

4946 Five pounds. (Crown.) The Spirit of Britain. ℞. An arrangement of musical
   instruments based on a well known sculpture accompanied by the London 2012 logo,
   printed in coloured ink, and a quotation from John Lennon and Paul McCartney,
   'ALL YOU NEED IS LOVE'. (Reverse design: Shane Greeves and the Royal Mint
   Engraving Department.)
   2010
   —   Proof in silver *FDC* (issued: 7,047)* £75

4947

4947 Five pounds. (Crown.) The Spirit of Britain. ℞. An image of the nineteenth-century anti-
   slavery campaigner Equiano accompanied by the London 2012 logo, printed in coloured
   ink, and a quotation from William Shakespeare, 'TO THINE OWN SELF
   BE TRUE'. (Reverse design: Shane Greeves and the Royal Mint Engraving
   Department.)
   2010
   —   Proof in silver *FDC* (Issued: 5,005)* £100

* Coins marked thus were originally issued in Royal Mint sets.

4950

4950 Ten pounds. (5 oz of fine silver.) R. A design of the winged horse Pegasus rearing on its hind legs surrounded by the inscription 'LONDON OLYMPIC GAMES', and the London 2012 logo and the date '2012'. (Reverse design: Christopher Le Brun.)
2012
— Proof in 0.999 fine silver *FDC* (Issued: 5,056)...£525
— Proof in 0.999 fine gold *FDC* (Issued: 193)..£11500
Illustration shown at reduced size – actual coin diameter 65 mm.

     4905   4906   4907

4905 Twenty five pounds. Faster. R. An image of Diana accompanied by a depiction of the sport of cycling, specifically pursuit racing ,with Olympic Rings above, the name 'DIANA' to the left, the Latin word for faster 'CITIUS', to the right, and the inscription 'LONDON 2012' below. (Reverse design: John Bergdah.)
2010
— Proof in gold *FDC* (Issued: 7,275)*...£500
4906 Twenty five pounds. Faster. R. An image of Mercury accompanied by a depiction of the sport of running, with Olympic Rings above, the name 'MERCURY' to the left, the Latin word for faster 'CITIUS', to the right, and the inscription 'LONDON 2012' below. (Reverse design: John Bergdahl.)
2010
— Proof in gold *FDC* (Issued: 7,230)*...£500
4907 Twenty five pounds. Higher. R. An image of Apollo accompanied by a depiction of the sport of rhythmic gymnastics, with Olympic Rings above, the name 'APOLLO' to the left, the Latin word for higher 'ALTIUS', to the right, and the inscription 'LONDON 2012' below. (Reverse design: John Bergdahl.)
2011
— Proof in gold *FDC* (Issued: 3,152)*...£500

* Coins marked thus were originally issued in Royal Mint sets.

4908   4909   4910

4908 Twenty five pounds. Higher. R. An image of Juno accompanied by a depiction of the sport of pole vaulting, with Olympic Rings above, the name 'JUNO' to the left, the Latin word for higher 'ALTIUS', to the right, and the inscription 'LONDON 2012' below. (Reverse design: John Bergdahl.)
2011
—   Proof in gold *FDC* (Issued: 3,257)* £500

4909 Twenty five pounds. Stronger. R. An image of Vulcan accompanied by a depiction of the sport of hammer throwing, with the Olympic Rings above, the name 'VULCAN' to the left, and the Latin word for stronger 'FORTIUS', to the right, and the inscription 'LONDON 2012' below. (Reverse design: John Bergdahl.)
2012
—   Proof in gold *FDC* (Issued 2,500)* £500

4910 Twenty five pounds. Stronger. R. An image of Minerva accompanied by a depiction Of the sport of javelin throwing, with the Olympic Rings above, the name 'MINERVA' to the left , the Latin word for stronger, 'FORTIUS', to the right, and the inscription 'LONDON 2012' below. (Reverse design: John Bergdahl.)
2012
—   Proof in gold *FDC* (Issued: 2,268)* £500

4915   4916

4915 One hundred pounds. Faster. R. An image of Neptune, accompanied by a depiction of the sport of sailing, with the Olympic Rings above, the name 'NEPTUNE' to the left, the Latin word for faster 'CITIUS' to the right, and the inscription 'LONDON 2012' below. (Reverse design: John Bergdahl.)
2010
—   Proof in gold *FDC* (Issued: 3,178)* £1800

4916 One hundred pounds. Higher. R. An image of Jupiter, accompanied by a depiction of the sport of diving, with the Olympic Rings above, the name 'JUPITER' to the left, the Latin word for higher 'ALTIUS' to the right, and the inscription 'LONDON 2012' below. (Reverse design: John Bergdahl.)
2011
—   Proof in gold *FDC* (Issued: 1,858)* £1800

* Coins marked thus were originally issued in Royal Mint sets.

4917

4917 One hundred pounds. Stronger. R. An image of Mars accompanied by a depiction of
the sport of boxing, with the Olympic Rings above, the name 'MARS' to the left, the
Latin word for stronger, 'FORTIUS', to the right, and the inscription 'LONDON 2012'
below. (Reverse design: John Bergdahl.)
2012
—   Proof in gold *FDC* (Issued 1,514)* £1800

4920

4918 Five hundred pounds. (1 kilo of fine silver.) R. A design consisting of celebratory
pennants and the inscription 'XXX OLYMPIAD' surrounded by the epigram 'UNITE
OUR DREAMS TO MAKE THE WORLD A TEAM OF TEAMS'. (Reverse design:
Tom Phillips.)
2012
—   Proof in silver (Issued: 910) £3000
Illustration shown at reduced size – actual coin diameter 100 mm

4921

4919 One thousand pounds. (1 kilo of fine silver.) R. A design depicting individual pieces of
sporting equipment encircled by a laurel of victory. (Reverse design: Sir Anthony Caro)
2012
—   Proof in gold (Issued: 20) £100000
Illustration shown at reduced size – actual coin diameter 100 mm

* *Coins marked thus were originally issued in Royal Mint sets.*

LONDON 2012 OLYMPIC AND PARALYMPIC GAMES PROOF SETS

Uncirculated coin sets

			£
OCNS1–**2011**	Set of 29 50 pence coins in individual card packs	(29)	90
OCNS2–**2011**	Set of 29 50 pence coins in folder with Completer medallion (Issued: 25,759)	(30)	125
OCNS3	Gold Medal Winners set of 50 pence Cuni and £5 Olympic 2012 £5, (Athletics, Boxing, Canoeing, Cycling, Equestrian, Rowing, Sailing, Shooting, Taekwondo, Tennis, Triathlon, and £5) (Edition: 2,012)	(12)	45
OCNS4	Five pounds.(crowns). Set of the four Countdown issues and the Official Olympic and Paralympic £5 cuni coins (Edition: 2,012; Issued 244)	(6)	70
OCNS5	Five pounds. (crowns). Set of four Countdown folders in box	(4)	50

Silver coin sets

OSS1–**2009.**	The Mind of Britain. Set of six £5 silver proofs (Issued: 1,480)	(6)	350
OSS2–**2010**	The Body of Britain. Set of six £5 silver proofs (Issued: 854)	(6)	400
OSS3–**2010**	The Spirit of Britain. Set of six £5 silver proofs (Issued: 1,564)	(6)	425
OSS4–**MD**	Great British Icons. Set of six £5 silver proofs (4930, 4931, 4938, 4944, 4945, 4946) (Edition: 10,000 taken from individual coin limits of 95,000)	(6)	425
OSS5–**MD**	'Countdown to London'. Set of four £5 silver proof coins	(4)	200
OSS6–**2011**	'Countdown to London'. Set of four £5 silver proof piedfort coins	(4)	325
OSS7–**MD**	The Mind, Body and Sprit of Britain. Set of 18 £5 silver proofs (Issued: 3,407)	(18)	1200
OSS8–**2011**	Set of 29 50 pence silver brilliant uncirculated coins (Issued: 384)	(29)	700
OSS9–**2011**	Gold Medal Winners set ot 50 pence silver brilliant uncirculated coins and £5 Olympic 2012 silver proof, (Athletics, Boxing, Canoeing, Cycling, Equestrian, Rowing, Sailing, Shooting, Taekwondo, Triathlon, and £5) (Edition: 999 but coins taken from individual issue limits)	(12)	350
OSS10–**2011**	Accuracy. Set of six 50 pence silver brilliant uncirculated coins depicting various sports (Badminton, Basketball, Fencing, ..Football, Hockey, and Tennis) (Edition: 2,012 but taken from individual issue limits; Issued: 40)	(6)	150
OSS11–**2011**	Agility. Set of six 50 pence silver brilliant uncirculated coins depicting various sports (Boxing, Equestrian, Gymnastics, Judo, Sailing, and Taekwondo) (Edition: 2,012 but taken from individual issue limits; Issued: 19)	(6)	150
OSS12–**2011**	Speed. Set of six 50 pence silver brilliant uncirculated coins depicting various sports (Athletics, Aquatics, Canoeing, Cycling, Rowing, Triathlon) (Edition: 2,012 but taken from individual issue limits; Issued: 41)	(6)	150
OSS13–**MD**	Five pounds.(crowns). Set of the four Countdown issues and the Official Olympic and Paralympic £5 proof silver coins (Edition: 800 taken from individual issue limits; Issued: 224)	(6)	400

Gold coin sets

OGS1–**2008**	'Bimetallic' 'Centenary of Olympic Games of 1908' £2 and 'Bimetallic' 'United Kingdom Olympic Handover Ceremony' £2 gold proofs (Edition: 250)	(2)	1800
OGS2–**2010**	'Faster' 2-coin proof set, two £25 (Issued: 246)	(2)	900
OGS3–**2010**	'Faster' 3-coin proof set, £100, and two £25 (Issued: 1079)	(3)	2750
OGS4–**2011**	'Higher' 2-coin proof set, two £25 (Issued: 229)	(2)	900
OGS5–**2011**	'Higher' 3-coin proof set, £100, and two £25 (Issued: 381)	(3)	2750

£

OGS6–**2012**	'Stronger' 2-coin proof set, two £25 (Issued: 156)..................................... (2)		900
OGS7–**2012**	'Stronger' 3-coin proof set, £100, and two £25 (Issued: 243)..................... (3)		2750
OGS8–**MD**	'Faster', 'Higher' and 'Stronger' set of three £100 and six £25 (Issued: 477) (9)		11000
OGS9–**MD**	'Countdown to London'. Set of four £5 gold proof coins .... (4)		8000
OGS10–**2012**	Set of £5 proof London Olympic Games and Paralympic Games (Edition: taken from individual coin limits) .... (2)		4000
OGS11–**2012**	Set of eleven different 50 pence gold piedfort proofs depicting designs of sports where there were United Kingdom gold medals winners. (Issued: 15)... (11)		40000

Olympic and Paralympic Gold Coin Sales

2010	**£25.00**	**£25.00**	**£100.00**	**SET**		*Authorised*
OGS2	1079	1079	1079	1079	(3)	
OGS3	246	246		246	(2)	
OGS8	477	477	477	477	(9)	
4915			1622			7500
4905	5473					20000
4906		5428				20000
	7275	7230	3178			

2011	**£25.00**	**£25.00**	**£100.00**	**SET**		*Authorised*
OGS4	555	555	555	555	(3)	
OGS5	125	125		125	(2)	
OGS8	477	477	477	477	(9)	
4916			826			7500
4907	1995					20000
4908		2100				20000
	3152	3257	1858			

2012	**£25.00**	**£25.00**	**£100.00**	**SET**		*Authorised*
OGS6	243	243	243	243	(3)	
OGS7	156	156		90	(2)	
OGS8	477	477	477	477	(9)	
4917			794			7500
4909	1624					20000
4910		1392				20000
	2500	2268	1514			

Following the decision to group the 2012 London Olympic and Paralympic coins separately, it seemed natural to follow the same policy for the WWI Centenary issues once the total number of issues became clear.

Most of the silver proof crowns were only sold in cased sets of 6 so prices are only shown for individual coins where these were available.

For specifications of £10 and higher coins, see the table on page 135.

4850

4850 Five pound. (Crown.) R. A design depicting British troops waving to crowds as they embark on a ship with the inscription '1914 THE FIRST WORLD WAR 1918. BEF' with the edge inscription 'SALUTE THE OLD CONTEMPTIBLES'. (Reverse design: John Bergdahl)

4851   4852

4851 Five pound. (Crown.) R. A design depicting three Howitzers with the inscription '1914 THE FIRST WORLD WAR 1918' and the edge inscription 'NEW AND FURIOUS BOMBARDMENT' (Reverse design: Edwina Ellis.)

4852 Five pound. (Crown.) R. A design depicting an effigy of Walter Tull in uniform with soldiers walking out over no man's land and the inscription '1914 THE FIRST WORLD WAR 1918' and 'WALTER TULL' around the coin, separated by poppy flowers with barbed wire with the edge inscription 'A HERO ON AND OFF THE FIELD'. (Reverse design: David Cornell.)

4853   4854

4853 Five pound. (Crown.) R. A design depicting a naval gun being loaded on board the deck of a battleship with the inscription '1914 THE FIRST WORLD WAR 1918. NAVY' and the edge inscription 'THE KING'S SHIPS WERE AT SEA'. (Reverse design: David Rowlands)

4854 Five pound. (Crown.) R. A design depicting a man putting up propaganda posters onto a brick wall with the inscription '1914 THE FIRST WORLD WAR 1918' and the edge inscription 'FOLLOW ME! YOUR COUNTRY NEEDS YOU'. (Reverse design: David Lawrence.)

4855   4856

4855 Five pound. (Crown.) R. A design depicting a woman working fields with a plough with the inscription '1914 THE FIRST WORLD WAR 1918. HOMEFRONT' and the edge inscription 'SPEED THE PLOUGH AND THE WOMAN WHO DRIVES IT'. (Reverse design: David Rowlands.)

PSS61-2014 £5 (4850-4855) silver proofs (6) (Issued: 839)...£465
PGC16-2014 £5 (4850-4855) gold proofs (6) (Issued: 20)..£15000

4856   Five pounds. (Crown.) R. A design of troops landing on the beaches below a map showing the Gallipoli landings with the inscription '1914 THE FIRST WORLD WAR 1918 – GALLIPOLI' with the edge inscription 'HEROES THAT SHED THEIR BLOOD'. (Reverse design : John Bergdahl.)
2015 — Proof in silver *FDC* (Edition: 2,500 plus coins in sets)* £80

4857   4858

4857 Five pounds. (Crown.) R. An effigy of Edith Cavell together with a nurse tending a patient and the inscription '1914 THE FIRST WORLD WAR 1918' and 'EDITH CAVELL' around the coin, separated by poppy flowers attached with barbed wire and the edge inscription 'SHE FACED THEM GENTLE AND BOLD'. (Reverse design: David Cornell.)

4858 Five pounds. (Crown.) R. An effigy of Albert Ball with First World War fighter planes and the inscription '1914 THE FIRST WORLD WAR 1918' and 'ALBERT BALL VC' around the coin , separated by poppy flowers attached with barbed wire and with the edge inscription 'BY FAR THE BEST ENGLISH FLYING MAN'. (Reverse design: David Cornell.)

4859   4860

4859 Five pounds. (Crown.) R. A First World War submarine and the inscription '1914 THE FIRST WORLD WAR 1918'and the edge inscription 'IN LITTLE BOXES MADE OF TIN'. (Reverse design: Edwina Ellis.)

2015 — Proof in silver *FDC* (Edition:2,500 including coins in sets, see PSS66)

4860 Five pounds. (Crown.) R. A horse carrying munitions and a howitzer in the background with the inscription '1914 THE FIRST WORLD WAR 1918' with the edge inscription ' PATIENT EYES COURAGEOUS HEARTS'. (Reverse design: David Lawrence.)

4861

4861 Five pounds. (Crown.) R. A sailor standing on deck below a red ensign with a ship in the background and the inscription '1914 THE FIRST WORLD WAR 1918 MERCHANT NAVY' and the edge inscription 'SEPULCHRED IN THE HARBOUR OF THE DEEP'. (Reverse design: David Rowlands.)

PSS67-2015 £5 (4856-4861) silver proofs (6) (Edition: 2,500) £465
PGC17-2015 £5 (4856-4861) gold proofs (6) (Edition: 25) £15,000

Obverse portrait by Jody Clark

4862   4863

4862 **Five pounds.** (Crown.) R. Troops accompanying a tank across the battle field with the inscription '1914 THE FIRST WORLD WAR 1918 SOMME' around the coin with the edge inscription 'DEAD MEN CAN ADVANCE NO FURTHER'. (Reverse design: John Bergdahl.)
2016 — Proof in silver *FDC* (Issued: 2,177 plus coins in sets).................................... £80

4863 **Five pounds.** (Crown.) R. An image of Jack Cornwell accompanied by an image of a naval gun and a battleship with the inscription '1914 THE FIRST WORLD WAR 1918' and 'JACK CORNWELL VC' around the coin, separated by poppy flowers attached with barbed wire and the edge inscription 'MOTHER, DON'T WATCH FOR POSTIE'. (Reverse design: David Cornell.)

4864   4865

4864 Five pounds. (Crown.) R. A depiction of battleships under fire and the inscription
'1914 THE FIRST WORLD WAR 1918 JUTLAND' around the coin and the edge
inscription 'OUR CHILDREN SHALL MEASURE THEIR WORTH'
(Reverse design: John Bergdahl.)

4865 Five pounds. (Crown.) R. A line of troops walking across the battlefield accompanied
by the inscription 'THERE SHALL BE IN THAT RICH EARTH A RICHER DUST
CONCEALED' and the inscription '1914 THE FIRST WORLD WAR 1918' and the
edge inscription 'THE TRUTH UNTOLD, THE PITY OF WAR'. (Reverse design:
David Lawrence.)
2016 — Proof in silver *FDC* (Edition: 4.000 plus coins in sets) £80

4866   4867

4866 Five pounds. (Crown.) R. A group of soldiers sat in a trench and the inscription
'1914 THE FIRST WORLD WAR 1918' 'ARMY' and the edge inscription 'MEN
WHO MARCH AWAY'. (Reverse design: David Rowlands.)
2016 — Proof in silver *FDC* (Edition: 500 plus coins in sets)

4867 Five pounds. (Crown.) R. A depiction of a naval gun on a Dreadnought and the
inscription '1914 THE FIRST WORLD WAR 1918' and the edge inscription
'WATCH-DOGS OF THE NATION'. (Reverse design: Edwina Ellis.)

PSS72-2016 £5 (4862-4867) silver proofs (6) (Issued: 499)..£465
PGC19-2016 £5 (4862-4867) gold proofs (6) (Issued: 25)..£15,000

4868   4869

4868 Five pounds. (Crown.) R. A portrait of Noel Chavasse VC accompanied by an image
of him tendingto a wounded soldier with the inscription '1914 THE FIRST WORLD
WAR 1918'and 'NOEL CHAVASSE VC' around the coin, separated by poppy flowers
attached with barbed wire with the edge inscription 'DUTY CALLED AND CALLED
ME TO OBEY'. (Reverse design: David Cornell.)

4869 Five pounds. (Crown.) R. A depiction of the Battle of Arras, showing howitzers with
planes flying overhead and the inscription '1914 THE FIRST WORLD WAR 1918 -
ARRAS' with the edge inscription 'THE MONSTROUS ANGER OF THE GUNS'.
(Reverse design: John Bergdahl.)

4870   4871

4870 Five pounds. (Crown.) R A view of a Sopwith Camel shown from directly in front of
the propellerand the inscription '1914 THE FIRST WORLD WAR 1918' with the edge
inscription 'IRRITATUS LACESSIT CRABRO'. (Reverse design: Edwina Ellis.)

4871 Five pounds. (Crown.) R. An image of a First World War gas mask and the inscription
'1914 THE FIRST WORLD WAR 1918' with the edge inscription 'GUTTERING,
CHOKING, DROWNING'. (Reverse design: Edwina Ellis.)

4872   4873

4872 Five pounds. (Crown.) R.A depiction of a First World War medical station with troops
carrying a stretcher and the inscription '1914 THE FIRST WORLD WAR 1918 -
MEDICAL SERVICES' with the edge inscription 'IN ARDUIS FIDELIS'.
(Reverse design: David Rowlands.)

4873 Five pounds. (Crown.) R. A design showing a war artist sketching a line of soldiers
who have been gassed and the inscription '1914 THE FIRST WORLD WAR 1918'
with the edge inscription 'WAR AS IT IS'. (Reverse design: David Lawrence).

PSS76-2017 £5 (4868-4873) silver proofs (6) (Edition: 1,197) £465
PGC21-2017 £5 (4868-4873) gold proofs (6) (Edition: 20) £15,000

4874   4875

4874 Five pounds. (Crown.) R. A portrait of T.E.Lawrence accompanied by an image of
soldiers on camels with the inscription '1914 THE FIRST WORLD WAR 1918' and
'T.E.LAWRENCE' around the coin, separated by poppy flowers attached with
barbed wire and with the edge inscription 'I WROTE MY WILL ACROSS THE
SKY IN STARS'. (Reverse design: David Cornell.)

4875 Five pounds. (Crown.) R. A depiction of the aftermath of the Battle of Ypres, showing
soldiers by a grave and the inscription '1914 THE FIRST WORLD WAR – YPRES'
and with the edge inscription ' HERE WAS THE WORLD'S WORST WOUND'.
(Reverse design: John Bergdahl.)

4876   4877

4876 **Five pounds.** (Crown.) R. A view of a First World War tank and the inscription '1914 THE FIRST WORLD WAR 1918' and with the edge inscription 'THE DEVIL IS COMING'. (Reverse design: Edwina Ellis.)

4877 **Five pounds.** (Crown.) R. A view of a woman working in a factory and the inscription '1914 THE FIRST WORLD WAR 1918' and with the edge inscription 'ON HER THEIR LIVES DEPEND'. (Reverse design: David Lawrence.)

4878   4879

4878 **Five pounds.** (Crown.) R. A depiction of a bi-plane from the First World War and the inscription '1914 THE FIRST WORLD WAR 1918 – ROYAL AIR FORCE' and with the edge inscription 'TUMULT IN THE CLOUDS'. (Reverse designs: David Rowlands.)

4879 **Five pounds.** (Crown.) R. A design showing a Victory Medal on a letter in front of a family portrait and the inscription '1914 THE FIRST WORLD WAR 1918' and with the edge inscription ' THE WATCHES BY LONELY HEARTHS'. (Reverse design: David Lawrence.)

PSS81-2018 £5 (4874-4879) silver proofs (6) (Edition: 2,000) £465
PGC24-2018 £5 (4874-4879) gold proofs (6) (Edition: 25) £15,000

4880   4881

4880 Five Pounds. (Crown.) Remembrance Day design. ℞. Poppy wreath with centred
inscription '11:00 11 NOVEMBER 1918 LEST WE FORGET 2018'. (Reverse design:
David Lawrence.)

2018
—   Proof in silver *FDC* – (Edition: 300 in individual leather cases plus the sets) £750
—   Proof in gold *FDC* (Edition: 50 in individual leather cases plus the sets) £4000

4881 Five pounds. (Crown.) War Memorial design. ℞. A design showing the Cenotaph
centred with the inscription 'THE GLORIOUS DEAD 1914-1918 2018'.
(Reverse design: John Bergdahl.)

4882   4883

4882 Five pounds. (Crown.) ℞. A design with poppies and barbed wire and the inscription
'REMEMBER'. (Reverse design: Edwina Ellis.)

*In addition to the six coin sets, 1111 silver proofs were made available for sale in a three coin
set with Australia and New Zealand $1 silver coins.*

4883 Five pounds. (Crown.) ℞. A design representing Imperial War Museums with the
inscription 'IMPERIAL WAR MUSEUMS 1918-2018'. (Reverse design:
David Rowlands.)

                    4884   4885

4884 Five pounds. (Crown.) R̩. A design representing War Graves with the inscription
'COMMONWEALTH WAR GRAVES COMMISSION 2018'. (Reverse design:
David Cornell.)

4885 Five pounds. (Crown.) R̩. A design showing the Dove of Peace with the incscription
'PEACE 1918'. (Reverse design: David Lawrence.)

PSS83-2018 £5 (4880-4885) silver proofs (6) (Edition: 800) £450
PGC25-2018 £5 (4880-4885) gold proofs (6) (Edition: 27) £15,000

Obverse portrait by Ian Rank Broadley

                                   4890

4890 Ten pounds. (Five ounce.) 100th Anniversary of the Outbreak of the First World
War. R̩. A depiction of a lion behind the figure of Britannia holding a shield and a
trident, watching over departing ships from a cliff top, with the inscription 'THE
FIRST WORLD WAR 1914 1918' and the date at the base of the coin.
(Reverse design: John Bergdahl.)
2014
— Proof in silver *FDC* (Issued: 606) £395
— Proof in gold *FDC* (Issued: 36)...£9000

Obverse portrait by Jody Clark

4891

4891 Ten pounds. (Five ounce.) World War One. R.A depiction of the landscape of the Western Front with the inscription '1914–1918'. (Reverse design: James Butler.) 2015
— Proof on silver *FDC* (Issued: 355) £395
— Proof in gold *FDC* (Issued: 17)...£9500

4892

4892 Ten pounds. (Five ounce.) R. A line of troops walking across the battlefield accompanied by the inscription 'THERE SHALL BE IN THAT RICH EARTH A RICHER DUST CONCEALED' and the inscription '1914 THE FIRST WORLD WAR 1918' and the edge inscription 'THE TRUTH UNTOLD, THE PITY OF WAR'. (Reverse design: David Lawrence.)
2016 — Proof in silver *FDC* (Edition: 500) £395
— Proof in gold *FDC* (Edition: 30)..£9000

4893   4894

4893 Ten pounds. (Five ounce.) ℞. A soldier from the First World War encircled by a
wreath. (Reverse design: Philip Jackson.)

    2017 – Proof in silver *FDC* (Edition: 450) £415

    —   Proof in gold *FDC* (Edition: 50) £9000

4894 Ten pounds. (Five ounce.) Centenary of Armistice. ℞. A design depicting a kneeling
soldier accompanied by the inscription 'ARMISTICE THE GUNS FALL SILENT'.
(Reverse design: Paul Day.)

    2018

    —   Proof in silver *FDC* (Edition: 525) £420

    —   Proof in gold *FDC* (Edition: 50) £9000

Obverse portrait by Ian Rank Broadley

4905

4905 One hundred pounds. (1 oz of fine platinum.) World War I. ℞. A depiction of
Lord Kitchener pointing above the inscription 'YOUR COUNTRY NEEDS YOU'
and the inscription 'THE FIRST WORLD WAR 1914-1918' and the date '2014'
surrounding the design. (Reverse design: John Bergdahl.)

    2014

    —   Proof in Platinum *FDC* (Issued: 325) £2000

WW50

WW50Five hundred pounds. (1 kilo of fine silver.) World War 1. ℞. A design depicting
British soldiers marching through no man's land with the figure of a British soldier
with rifle and helmet in the foreground and the dates '1914-1918' at the base of the coin.
(Reverse design: Michael Sandle.)
2014
— Proof in silver *FDC* (Issued: 165) £2000

Obverse portrait by Jody Clark

WW51

WW51Five hundred pounds. (1 kilo of fine silver.) Centenary of Armistice. ℞. A design
depicting a kneeling soldier accompanied by the inscription 'ARMISTICE THE
GUNS FALL SILENT'. (Reverse design: Paul Day.)
2018
— Proof in silver *FDC* (Edition: 100) £2025

WW100

WW100 One thousand pounds. (1 kilo of fine gold.) World War 1. ℞. A design depicting
British soldiers marching through no man's land with the figure of a British soldier
with rifle and helmet in the foreground and the dates '1914-1918' at the base of the
coin. (Reverse design: Michael Sandle, Obverse Ian Rank Broadley.)
2014
— Proof in gold *FDC* (Issued: 10)..£65000

WW101 One thousand pounds. (1 kilo of fine gold.) Centenary of Armistice. ℞. A design
depicting a kneeling soldier accompanied by the inscription 'ARMISTICE THE
GUNS FALL SILENT'. (Reverse design: Paul Day, obverse: Jody Clark.)
2018
— Proof in gold *FDC* (Edition: 10) £65000

For other World War I related Coins, please see: K34, K35, K41, K44, K49 and N2

In 2014 the Royal Mint launched the first of a series of Chinese Lunar Calendar coins starting with the animal for that year – the horse. Centuries old, the Shengxiao relates each year to one of 12 animals. The specifications for the coins match those in the Britannia series so see the tables on p187, p211 and p239 for further details. Proof coins are issued in a range of sizes in gold and silver. Some of these plus one platinum have also been issued as bullion uncirculated coins and these carry an additional inscription stating the coin weight. In 2021 a cupro-nickel £5 crown is added to the range.

CUPRO-NICKEL

Obverse portrait by Jody Clark

5000 Five pounds. (Crown.) Year of the Ox. Ŗ. As 5107.
2021 — BU in presentation folder £13

SILVER

5050 One pound. (1/2 oz of fine silver.) Ŗ. As 5104A but with the inscription 'YEAR OF THE DOG -2018 ½ OZ FINE SILVER'. (Reverse design: Wuon-Gean Ho.)
2018 — Unc £20

Obverse portrait by Ian Rank-Broadley

5100

5100 Two pounds. (1 oz of fine silver.) Year of the Horse. Ŗ. Design depicting a horse prancing past the Uffington chalk white horse, with the inscription 'YEAR OF THE HORSE. 2014' and the Chinese symbol for horse. (Reverse design: Wuon-Gean Ho.)
2014 — Proof in silver *FDC* (Issued: 8,347)............£83

5100A

5100A Two pounds. (1 oz of fine silver). R. Design as above but with the additional inscription '1 OZ FINE SILVER 999'.
2014—Unc £30

5100B Two pounds. Error obverse – known as a Mule. The obverse design of The Queen used for the £2 Silver Britannia uncirculated coin was paired with the reverse design of the Year of the Horse £2 silver coin.
2014 ....£50

5101   5101A

5101 Two pounds. (1 oz of fine silver.) Year of the Sheep. R. Design depicting two Swaledale sheep, with the inscription 'YEAR OF THE SHEEP 2015' and the Chinese symbol for sheep. (Reverse design: Wuon-Gean Ho.)
2015
— Proof in silver *FDC* (Issued: 4,463) £83
— Proof in silver with gold plating *FDC* (Issued: 1,358) £110

5101A Two pounds. (1 oz of fine silver.) Year of the Sheep. R. As above but with the additional inscription '1 OZ FINE SILVER 999'.
2015—Unc £30

Obverse portrait by Jody Clark

5102   5102A

5102 Two pounds. (1 oz of fine silver.) Year of the Monkey. ℞. Design depicting a monkey
leaping through the trees with the inscription 'YEAR OF THE MONKEY 2016' and the
Chinese symbol for monkeys. (Reverse design: Wuon-Gean Ho.)
2016 — Proof in silver *FDC* (Edition: 8,054) £83
5102A Two pounds. Year of the Monkey. ℞ As above but with the additional inscription
'1 OZ FINE SILVER 999'.
2016 — Unc (Edition: 138,888) £30

5103   5104

5103 Two pounds. (1 oz of fine silver.) Year of the Rooster. ℞. Design depicting a
crowing rooster accompanied by a number of gladiola flowers with the inscription
'YEAR OF THE ROOSTER 2017' and the Chinese symbol for a rooster.
(Reverse design: Wuon-Gean Ho.)
2017 — Proof in silver *FDC* (Issued: 3,846)...£85
5103A Two pounds. (1 oz of fine silver.) Year of the Rooster. ℞. As above but with the
additional inscription '1 OZ FINE SILVER 999'. (Reverse design: Wuon-Gean Ho.)
2017 — Unc £30
5104 Two pounds. (1 oz of fine silver.) Year of the Dog. ℞. Design depicting a running dog
with the inscription 'YEAR OF THE DOG 2018' and the Chinese lunar symbol for
a dog. (Reverse design: Wuon-Gean Ho.)
2018 — Proof in silver *FDC* (Edition:5,008) £85
5104A Two pounds. (1 oz of fine silver.) Year of the Dog. ℞. As above but with the
additional inscription '1 OZ FINE SILVER 999).
2018 — Unc £30

5105   5106

5105 Two pounds. (1 oz of fine silver.) Year of the Pig. ℞. Design depicting a cottage on a hill at night and in the foreground piglets suckling from a sow with the inscription 'YEAR OF THE PIG 2019' and the Chinese symbol for a pig. (Reverse design: Harry Brockway.)

2019 — Proof in silver *FDC* (Edition: 3,888) £85

5105A Two pounds. (1 oz of fine silver.) Year of the Pig. R. As above but with the additional inscription '1 OZ FINE SILVER 999'.

2019 Unc £30

5106 Two pounds. (1 oz of fine silver.) Year of the Rat. ℞. Design depicting an agile and inquisitive rat crouching against a backdrop of peonies with the inscription 'YEAR OF THE RAT 2020' and Chinese symbol for a rat. (Reverse design: P J Lynch.)

2020 Proof in silver *FDC* (Edition: 3,898) £85

5106A Two pounds. (1 oz of fine silver.) Year of the Rat. ℞. As above but with the additional inscription '1 OZ FINE SILVER 999'.

2020 Unc £30

5107

5107 Two pounds. (1 oz of fine silver.) Year of the Ox. ℞. Design depicting a powerful ox grazing in a meadow with bluebells in the foreground and blossom trees beyond with inscription 'YEAR OF THE OX 2021' and Chinese symbol for Ox. (Reverse design: Harry Brockway.)

2021 Proof in silver *FDC* (Edition: 3,998) £85

5107A Two pounds. (1 oz of fine silver.) Year of the Ox. ℞. As above but with the additional inscription '1 OZ FINE SILVER 999'.

2021 Unc £30

Obverse portrait by Ian Rank-Broadley

5120

5120 Ten pounds. (5 oz of fine silver.) Year of the Horse. R. As 5100.
2014 — Proof in silver *FDC* (Issued: 799) £450

5121

5121 Ten pounds. (5 oz of fine silver.) Year of the Sheep. R. As 5101.
2015 — Proof in silver *FDC* (Issued: 331) £395

Obverse portrait by Jody Clark

5122

5122 Ten pounds. (5 oz of fine silver.) Year of the Monkey. R. As 5102.
2016 — Proof in silver *FDC* (Edition: 588) £395

5123   5124

5123 Ten pounds. (5 oz of fine silver.) Year of the Rooster. ℞. As 5103.
2017 — Proof in silver *FDC* (Issued: 369) £415

5124 Ten pounds. (5 oz of fine silver.) Year of the Dog. ℞. As 5104.
2018 — Proof in silver *FDC* (Edition: 388) £420

5125 Ten pounds. (5 oz of fine silver.) Year of the Pig. ℞. As 5105.
2019 — Proof in silver *FDC* (Edition: 288) £420

5126 Ten pounds. (5 oz of fine silver.) Year of the Rat. ℞. As 5106.
2020 — Proof in silver *FDC* (Edition: 198) £420

5127 Ten pounds. (5 oz of fine silver.) Year of the Ox. ℞. As 5107.
2021 Proof in silver *FDC* (Edition: 198) £420

Obverse portrait by Ian Rank-Broadley

5140 Five hundred pounds. (1 kilo of fine silver.) Year of the Sheep. ℞. As 5101.
2015 — Proof in silver *FDC* £2000

Obverse portrait by Jody Clark

5141

5141 Five hundred pounds. (1 kilo of fine silver.) Year of the Monkey. ℞. As 5102.
2016 — Proof in silver *FDC* (1 Kilo) (Edition: 88) £2000

5142 Five hundred pounds. (1 kilo of fine silver.) Year of the Rooster. ℞. As 5103.
2017 — Proof in silver *FDC* (Edition: 68) £2050

5143 Five hundred pounds. (1 kilo of fine silver.) Year of the Dog. ℞. As 5104.
2018 — Proof in silver *FDC* (Edition: 108) £2025

5144 Five hundred pounds. (1 kilo of fine silver.) Year of the Pig. ℞. As 5105.
2019 — Proof in silver *FDC* (Edition: 38) £2025
5145 Five hundred pounds. (1 kilo of fine silver.) Year of the Rat. ℞. As 5106.
2020 — Proof in silver *FDC* (Edition: 38) £2025
5146 Five hundred pounds. (1 kilo fine silver.) Year of the Ox. ℞. As 5107.
2021 Proof in silver *FDC* (Edition: 38) £2050

GOLD

Obverse portrait by Ian Rank-Broadley

5160 Ten pounds. (1/10 oz of fine gold.) Year of the Horse. ℞. As 5180.
2014 BU (Issued; 1,779) £225
5161 Ten pounds. (1/10 oz of fine gold.) Year of the Sheep. ℞. As 5181.
2015 BU (Issued: 922) £225

Obverse portrait by Jody Clark

5162 Ten pounds. (1/10 oz of fine gold.) Year of the Monkey. ℞. As 5182.
2016 BU £200
5162A Ten pounds. (1/10 oz of fine gold.) Year of the Monkey. ℞. As 5162 but with the
additional inscription '1 /10 OZ FINE GOLD 999.9'. (Reverse design:
Wuon-Gean Ho.)
2016 Unc £180
5163 Ten pounds. (1/10 oz of fine gold.) Year of the Rooster. ℞. As 5183.
2017 BU (Issued: 980) £200
5163A Ten pounds. (1/4 oz of fine gold.) Year of the Rooster. ℞. As 5163 but with the
additional inscription 1/4 OZ FINE GOLD 999.9'.
2017 Unc £180
5164 Ten pounds. (1/10 oz of fine gold.) Year of the Dog. ℞. As 5184
2018 BU (Edition: 1,008) £200
5165 Ten pounds. (1/10 oz of fine gold.) Year of the Pig. ℞. As 5185.
2019 BU (Edition: 1,088) £200
5166 Ten pounds. (1/10 oz of fine gold.) Year of the Rat. ℞. As 5186.
2020 BU (Edition: 1,088) £200

5175 Twenty five pounds. (1/4 oz fine gold.) Year of the Dog. ℞. As 5184 but with the
additional inscription '1/4 OZ FINE GOLD 999.9'.
2018 Unc £450
5176 Twenty five pounds. (1/4 oz of fine gold.) Year of the Rat. ℞. As 5176.
2020 — Proof in gold *FDC* (Edition: 398) £550
5176A Twenty five pounds. (1/4 oz of fine gold.) Year of the Rat. ℞. As 5176 but with
the additional inscription '1/4 OZ FINE GOLD 999.9'.
2020 Unc £450
5177 Twenty five pounds. (1/4 oz of fine gold.) Year of the Ox. ℞. As 5187.
2021 Proof in gold *FDC* (Edition: 388) £585

Obverse portrait by Ian Rank-Broadley

5180   5180A

5180 One hundred pounds. (1 oz of fine gold.) Year of the Horse. R. Design depicting
a horse prancing past the Uffington chalk white horse, with the inscription 'YEAR
OF THE HORSE . 2014' and the Chinese symbol for horse. (Reverse design:
Wuon-Gean Ho.)

2014 — Proof in gold *FDC* (Issued: 811).. £2000

5180AOne hundred pounds. (1 oz of fine gold.) Year of the Horse. R. As 5180 but with
the additional inscription '1 OZ FINE GOLD 999.9'.

2014 Unc (Edition: 30,000)... £1700

5181   5181A

5181 One hundred pounds. (1 oz of fine gold.) Year of the Sheep. R. Design depicting
two Swaledale sheep, with the inscription 'YEAR OF THE SHEEP 2015' and the
Chinese symbol for sheep. (Reverse design: Wuon-Gean Ho.)

2015 — Proof in gold *FDC* (Issued: 548).. £2200

5181AOne hundred pounds. (1 oz of fine gold.) Year of the Sheep. R. As 5181 but with the
additional inscription '1OZ FINE GOLD 999.9'.

2015 Unc £1700

SPINK

COINS OF ENGLAND 2021
E-book available on Amazon, iBookstore,
Google, Kobo, OverDrive
and across most other platforms

For more information or enquiries please contact
Tel: +44 (0)20 7563 4119 | Email: books@spink.com
69 Southampton Row, Bloomsbury, London WC1B 4ET

WWW.SPINKBOOKS.COM

Obverse portrait by Jody Clark

5182   5183

5182 One hundred pounds. (1 oz of fine gold.) Year of the Monkey. R. Design depicting
a monkey leaping through the trees with the inscription 'YEAR OF THE
MONKEY 2016' and the Chinese symbol for monkeys. (Reverse design:
Wuon-Gean Ho.)

2016 — Proof in gold *FDC* (Edition; 888) £2000

5182A One hundred pounds. (1 oz of fine gold.) Year of the Monkey. R. As 5182 but
with the additional inscription '1OZ FINE GOLD 999.9'.

2016 Unc £1700

5183 One hundred pounds. (1 oz of fine gold.) Year of the Rooster. R. Design depicting
a crowing rooster accompanied by a number of gladiola flowers with the inscription
'YEAR OF THE ROOSTER 2017' and the Chinese symbol for a rooster.
(Reverse design: Wuon-Gean Ho.)

2017 — Proof in gold *FDC* (Edition. 688) £2000

5183A One hundred pounds. (1 oz of fine gold.) Year of the Rooster. R. As 5183 but
with the additional inscription '1 OZ FINE GOLD 999.9'.

2017 Unc £1700

5184

5184 One hundred pounds. (1 oz of fine gold.) Year of the Dog. R. Design depicting
a running dog with the inscription 'YEAR OF THE DOG 2018' and the Chinese
lunar symbol for a dog. (Reverse design: Wuon-Gean Ho.)

2018 — Proof in gold (Edition: 888) £2000

5184A One hundred pounds. (1 oz of fine gold.) Year of the Dog. R. As 5184 but with the
additional inscription '1 OZ FINE GOLD'

2018 Unc £1700

5185   5186

5185 One hundred pounds. (1 oz of fine gold.) Year of the Pig. R. Design depicting a
cottage on a hill at night and in the foreground piglets suckling from a sow with
the inscription 'YEAR OF THE PIG 2019' and Chinese symbol for a pig.
(Reverse design: Harry Brockway.)
2019 Proof in gold *FDC* (Edition: 888) £2100

5185A One hundred pounds. (1 oz of fine gold.) Year of the Pig. R. As 5185 but with the
additional inscription '1OZ FINE GOLD 999.9'.
2019 Unc £1700

5186 One hundred pounds. (1 oz of fine gold.) Year of the Rat. R. Design depicting
an agile and inquisitive rat crouching against a backdrop of peonies with the
inscription 'YEAR OF THE RAT 2020' and Chinese symbol for a rat.
(Reverse design: P J Lynch.)
2019 Proof in gold *FDC* (Edition: 898) £2100

5186A One hundred pounds. (1 oz of fine gold.) Year of the Rat. R. As 5186 but with the
additional inscription '1OZ FINE GOLD 999.9'.
2020 Unc £1700

5187 One hundred pounds. (1 oz of fine gold.) Year of the Ox. R. Design depicting a
powerful ox grazing in a meadow with bluebells in the foreground and blossom
trees beyond with inscription 'YEAR OF THE OX 2021' and Chinese symbol for
Ox. (Reverse design: Harry Brockway.)
2021 Proof in gold *FDC* (Edition: 898) £2320

5187A One hundred pounds. (1 oz of fine gold.) Year of the Ox. R. As 5187 but with the
additional inscription '1OZ FINE GOLD 999.9',
2021 Unc £1700

COINS OF
ENGLAND
& THE UNITED KINGDOM
PRE-DECIMAL ISSUES

SPINK

COINS OF ENGLAND 2021
E-book available on Amazon, iBookstore,
Google, Kobo, OverDrive and across
most other platforms

For more information or enquiries please contact
Tel: +44 (0)20 7563 4119 | Email: books@spink.com
69 Southampton Row, Bloomsbury, London WC1B 4ET

WWW.SPINKBOOKS.COM

Obverse portrait by Ian Rank-Broadley

5200 **Five hundred pounds.** (5 oz of fine gold.) Year of the Horse. R. As 5180.
2014 — Proof in gold *FDC* (Edition:) £9000

5201

5201 **Five hundred pounds.** (5 oz of fine gold.) Year of the Sheep. R. As 5181.
2015 — Proof in gold *FDC* (Issued: 26) £9500

Obverse portrait by Jody Clark

5202

5202 Five hundred pounds. (5 oz of fine gold.) Year of the Monkey. R. As 5182.
2016 — Proof in gold *FDC* (Edition: 38) £9500

5203

5203 **Five hundred pounds.** (5 oz of fine gold.) Year of the Rooster. R. As 5183.
2017 — Proof in gold *FDC* (Issued: 35) £9500

5204

5204 Five hundred pounds. (5 oz of fine gold.) Year of the Dog. ℞. As 5184.
2018 — Proof in gold *FDC* (Edition: 58) £9000
5205 Five hundred pounds. (5 oz of fine gold.) Year of the Pig. ℞. As 5185.
2019 — Proof in gold *FDC* (Edition: 38) £9500
5206 Five hundred pounds. (5 oz of fine gold.) Year of the Rat. ℞. As 5186.
2020 — Proof in gold *FDC* (Edition: 30) £10000
5207 Five hundred pounds. (5 oz fine gold.) Year of the Ox. ℞. As 5187.
2021 — Proof in gold *FDC* (Edition: 38) £10600

Obverse portrait by Ian Rank-Broadley

5220

5220 One thousand pounds. (1 kilo of fine gold.) Year of the Sheep. ℞. As 5181.
2015 — Proof in gold *FDC* (Edition:) £65000

Obverse portrait by Jody Clark

5221 One thousand pounds. (1 kilo of fine gold.) Year of the Monkey. ℞. As 5182.
2016 — Proof in gold *FDC* (Edition: 8) £65000

5222

5222 One thousand pounds. (1 kilo of fine gold.) Year of the Rooster. R. As 5183.
2017 — Proof in gold *FDC* (Issued: 8) £65000

5223   5225

5223 One thousand pounds. (1 kilo of fine gold.) Year of the Dog. R. As 5184.
2018 — Proof in gold *FDC* (Edition: 10) £65000
5224 One thousand pounds. (1 kilo of fine gold.) Year of the Pig. R. As 5185.
2019 Proof in gold FDC (Edition: 8) £65000
5225 One thousand pounds. (1 kilo of fine gold.) Year of the Rat. R. As 5186.
2020 — Proof in gold *FDC* (Edition: 10) £65000
5226 One thousand pounds. (1 kilo of fine gold.) Year of the Ox. R. As 5187.
2021 Proof in gold *FDC* (Edition: 10) £64000

PLATINUM

5240 Twenty five pounds. (1/4 oz of fine platinum.) Year of the Dog. R. As 5104 but
with the additional inscription '1/4 OZ FINE PLATINUM 999.5'.
2018 Unc £400

For specifications see tables on pages 187, 211 & 239.

At Her Majesty the Queen's coronation, ten symbolic sculptures named The Queen's Beasts lined her entrance to Westminster Abbey, representing centuries of royal bloodlines. This series will therefore consist of ten different designs plus a completer coin to be issued in 2021. For specification details see the tables on pages 187, 211 and 239.

The proof and bullion designs differ in the reverse arrangement so the proof issues are listed first as Collector Issues with the bullion issues following.

COLLECTOR ISSUES
CUPRO-NICKEL

Reverse and obverse design by Jody Clark

QCB1 Five pounds. (Crown.)The Lion of England. R̠. As QCA1.
  2017 — BU in presentation folder (Issued: 31,838) £13
  2018 — BU in presentation folder £13
QCB2 Five pounds. (Crown.) The Unicorn of Scotland. R̠. As QCA2.
  2017 — BU in presentation folder (Issued: 31,970) £13
QCB3 Five pounds. (Crown.) The Red Dragon of Wales. R̠. As QCA3.
  2018 — BU in presentation folder £13
QCB4 Five pounds. (Crown.) The Black Bull of Clarence. R̠. As QCA4.
  2018 — BU in presentation folder £13
QCB5 Five pounds. (Crown.) The Falcon of the Plantagenets. R̠. As QCA5
  2018 — BU in presentation folder £13
QCB6 Five pounds. (Crown.) Yale of Beaufort. R̠ As QCA6
  2019 — BU in presentation folder £13
QCB7 Five pounds. (Crown.) White Lion of Mortimer. R̠ As QCA7
  2020 — BU in presentation folder £13
QCB8 Five pounds. (Crown.) White Horse of Hanover. R̠. As QCA8.
  2020 — BU in presentation folder £13
QCB9 Five pounds. (Crown.) White Greyhound of Richmond. R̠. As QCA9.
  2021 — BU in presentation folder £13
QCB10Five pounds. (Crown.) The Griffin of Edward III. R̠. As QCA10.
  2021 — BU in presentation folder £13

SILVER

QCA1

QCA1Two pounds. (1 oz of fine silver.) The Lion of England. R̠. A lion accompanied by a shield depicting Our Royal Arms with the inscription '2017 LION OF ENGLAND.
  2017 — Proof in silver *FDC* (Issued: 8,376) £85

QCA2 QCA3

QCA2 Two pounds. (1 oz of fine silver.) The Unicorn of Scotland. R. A rearing unicorn accompanied by a shield depicting a lion rampant with the inscription 'UNICORN OF SCOTLAND' and the date of the year.
2017 — Proof in silver *FDC* (Issued: 5,952) £85

QCA3 Two pounds. (1 oz of fine silver.)The Red Dragon of Wales. R. Depiction of a rearing dragon accompanied by the Coat of Arms of Llywelyn the Great with the inscription 'RED DRAGON OF WALES' and the date of the year.
2018 — Proof in silver *FDC* (Edition: 6,000) £85

QCA4 QCA5

QCA4 Two pounds. (1 oz of fine silver.) The Black Bull of Clarence. R. A depiction of the Black Bull of Clarence supporting the arms as used by Edward IV and Richard III as well as all the Sovereigns of the Houses of Lancaster and Tudor with the inscription 'BLACK BULL OF CLARENCE' and the date of the year.
2018 — Proof in silver *FDC* (Edition: 6,000) £85

QCA5 Two pounds. (1 oz of fine silver.) The Falcon of the Plantagenets. R. A depiction of the Falcon of the Plantagenets above the personal badge of Edward IV with the inscription 'FALCON OF THE PLANTAGENETS' and the date of the year.
2019 — Proof in silver *FDC* (Edition: 5,650) £85

QCA6   QCA7

QCA6 Two pounds. (1 oz of fine silver.) Yale of Beaufort. R. A depiction of the Yale of
Beaufort supporting a shield portraying a portcullis surmounted by a royal crown
with the inscription 'YALE OF BEAUFORT' and the date of the year.
2019 — Proof in silver *FDC* (Edition: 4,360) £85

QCA7 Two pounds. (1 oz of fine silver). The White Lion of Mortimer. R. A depiction of
the White Lion of Mortimer supporting a shield portraying a white rose en soleil
with the inscription 'WHITE LION OF MORTIMER' and the date of the year.
2020 — Proof in silver FDC (Edition 4,360) £85

QCA8   QCA9

QCA8 Two pounds. (1 oz of fine silver.) White Horse of Hanover. R. A rearing white
horse above shield with royal arms of George I with the incsription 'WHTE HORSE
OF HANOVER' and the date of the year.
2020 — Proof in silver *FDC* (Edition: 4310) £85

QCA9 Two pounds. (1 oz of fine silver.) White Greyhound of Richmond. R. A reimagined
greyhound conveying its strength and power above shield depicting the symbol of
the Tudor family and inscription 'WHITE GREYHOUND OF RICHMOND'.
2021 — Proof in silver *FDC* (Edition: 3,960) £85

QCA10Two pounds. (1 oz of fine silver.) The Griffin of Edward III.
2021 — Proof in silver *FDC* £85

QCC1 Ten pounds. (5 oz of fine silver.) The Lion of England. R. As QCA1.
2017 — Proof in silver *FDC* (Issued: 674) £415

QCC2 Ten pounds. (5 oz of fine silver.) The Unicorn of Scotland. R. As QCA2.
2017 — Proof in silver *FDC* (Issued: 458) £415

QCC3 Ten pounds. (5 oz of fine silver.) The Red Dragon of Wales. R. As QCA3.
2018 — Proof in silver *FDC* (Edition: 750) £420

QCC4 Ten pounds. (5 oz of fine silver.) The Black Bull of Clarence. R.As QCA4.
2018 — Proof in silver *FDC* (Edition: 700) £420

QCC5 Ten pounds. (5 oz of fine silver.) The Falcon of the Plantagenets. ℞. As QCA5.
2018 — Proof in silver *FDC* (Edition: 550) £420
QCC6 Ten pounds. (5 oz of fine silver.) Yale of Beaufort. ℞ As QCA6
2019 — Proof in silver *FDC* (Edition: 335) £420
QCC7 Ten pounds. (5 oz of fine silver.) White Lion of Mortimer. ℞ As QCA7
2020 — Proof in silver *FDC* (Edition: 335) £420
QCC8 Ten pounds. (5 oz of fine silver.) White Horse of Hanover. ℞. As QCA8.
2020 — Proof in silver *FDC* (Edition: 315) £420
QCC9 Ten pounds. (5 oz of fine silver) White Greyhound of Richmond. ℞. As QCA9.
2021 — Proof in silver *FDC* (Edition: 370) £420
QCC10Ten pounds. (5 oz of fine silver) The Griffin of Edward III. ℞. As QCA10.
2021 — Proof in silver *FDC* £420

QCD1 Ten pounds. (10 oz of fine silver,) The Lion of England. ℞. As QCA1.
2017 — Proof in silver *FDC* (Issued: 684) £795
QCD2 Ten pounds. (10 oz of fine silver.) The Unicorn of Scotland. ℞. As QCA2.
2017 — Proof in silver *FDC* (Edition: 850) £795
QCD3 Ten pounds. (10 oz of fine silver.) The Red Dragon of Wales. ℞. As QCA3.
2018 — Proof in silver *FDC* (Edition: 700) £795
QCD4 Ten pounds. (10 oz of fine silver.) The Black Bull of Clarence. ℞.As QCA4.
2018 — Proof in silver *FDC* (Edition: 600) £795
QCD5 Ten pounds. (10 oz of fine silver.) The Falcon of the Plantagenets. ℞. As QCA5.
2018 — Proof in silver *FDC* (Edition: 400) ....£ 795
QCD6 Ten pounds. (10 oz of fine silver.) Yale of Beaufort. ℞. As QCA6.
2019 — Proof in silver *FDC* (Edition: 240) £795
QCD7 Ten pounds. (10 oz of fine silver.) White Lion of Mortimer ℞ As QCA7,
2020 — Proof in silver *FDC* (Edition: 240) £795
QCD8 Ten pounds. (10 oz of fine silver) White Horse of Hanover. ℞. As QCA8.
2020 Proof in silver *FDC* (Edition: 235) £795
QCD9 Ten pounds. (10 oz of fine silver.) White Greyhound of Richmond. ℞. As QCA9.
2021 Proof in silver *FDC* (Edition: 195) £795
QCD10Ten pounds. (10 oz of fine silver) The Griffin of Edward III. ℞. As QCA10.
2021 Proof in silver *FDC* £795

QCE1 Five hundred pounds. (1 kilo of fine silver.) The Lion of England. ℞. As QCA1.
2017 — Proof in silver *FDC* (Issued: 117) £2050
QCE2 Five hundred pounds. (1 kilo of fine silver.) The Unicorn of Scotland. ℞. As QCA2.
2017 — Proof in silver *FDC* (Edition: 225) £2050
QCE3 Five hundred pounds. (1 kilo of fine silver.) The Red Dragon of Wales. ℞. As QCA3.
2018 — Proof in silver *FDC* (Edition: 200) £2025
QCE4 Five hundred pounds. (1 kilo of fine silver). The Black Bull of Clarence. ℞. As QCA4.
2018 — Proof in silver *FDC* (Edition: 150) £2025
QCE5 Five hundred pounds. (1 kilo of fine silver.) The Falcon of the Plantagenets. ℞. As QCA5.
2018 — Proof in silver *FDC* (Edition: 125) £2025
QCE6 Five hundred pounds. (1kilo of fine silver.) Yale of Beaufort. ℞ As QCA6.
2019 — Proof in silver *FDC* (Edition: 120) £2050
QCE7 Five hundred pounds. (1 kilo of fine silver.) White Lion of Mortimer. ℞ As QCA7.
2020 — Proof in silver *FDC* (Edition: 120) £2025
QCE8 Five hundred pounds. (1 kilo of fine silver.) White Horse of Hanover. ℞. As QCA8.
2020 Proof in silver *FDC* (Edition: 115) £2050
QCE9 Five hundred pounds. (1 kilo of fine silver.) White Greyhound of Richmond. ℞. As QCA9.
2021 Proof in silver *FDC* (Edition: 80) £2050
QCE10Five hundred pounds. (1 kilo of fine silver.) The Griffin of Edward III. ℞. As QCA10.
2021 Proof in silver *FDC* £2050

GOLD

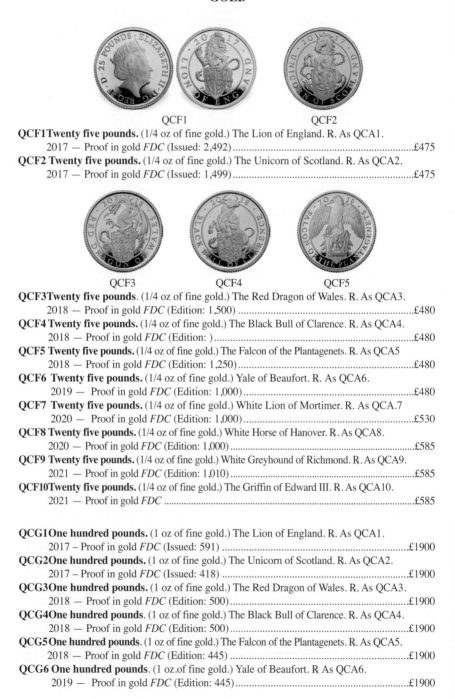

QCF1   QCF2

QCF1Twenty five pounds. (1/4 oz of fine gold.) The Lion of England. Ŗ. As QCA1.
2017 — Proof in gold *FDC* (Issued: 2,492) £475
QCF2 Twenty five pounds. (1/4 oz of fine gold.) The Unicorn of Scotland. Ŗ. As QCA2.
2017 — Proof in gold *FDC* (Issued: 1,499) £475

QCF3   QCF4   QCF5

QCF3Twenty five pounds. (1/4 oz of fine gold.) The Red Dragon of Wales. Ŗ. As QCA3.
2018 — Proof in gold *FDC* (Edition: 1,500) £480
QCF4 Twenty five pounds. (1/4 oz of fine gold.) The Black Bull of Clarence. Ŗ. As QCA4.
2018 — Proof in gold *FDC* (Edition:) £480
QCF5 Twenty five pounds. (1/4 oz of fine gold.) The Falcon of the Plantagenets. Ŗ. As QCA5
2018 — Proof in gold *FDC* (Edition: 1,250) £480
QCF6 Twenty five pounds. (1/4 oz of fine gold.) Yale of Beaufort. Ŗ. As QCA6.
2019 — Proof in gold *FDC* (Edition: 1,000) £480
QCF7 Twenty five pounds. (1/4 oz of fine gold.) White Lion of Mortimer. Ŗ. As QCA.7
2020 — Proof in gold *FDC* (Edition: 1,000) £530
QCF8 Twenty five pounds. (1/4 oz of fine gold.) White Horse of Hanover. Ŗ. As QCA8.
2020 — Proof in gold *FDC* (Edition: 1,000) £585
QCF9 Twenty five pounds. (1/4 oz of fine gold.) White Greyhound of Richmond. Ŗ. As QCA9.
2021 — Proof in gold *FDC* (Edition: 1,010) £585
QCF10Twenty five pounds. (1/4 oz of fine gold.) The Griffin of Edward III. Ŗ. As QCA10.
2021 — Proof in gold *FDC* £585

QCG1One hundred pounds. (1 oz of fine gold.) The Lion of England. Ŗ. As QCA1.
2017 – Proof in gold *FDC* (Issued: 591) £1900
QCG2One hundred pounds. (1 oz of fine gold.) The Unicorn of Scotland. Ŗ. As QCA2.
2017 – Proof in gold *FDC* (Issued: 418) £1900
QCG3One hundred pounds. (1 oz of fine gold.) The Red Dragon of Wales. Ŗ. As QCA3.
2018 — Proof in gold *FDC* (Edition: 500) £1900
QCG4One hundred pounds. (1 oz of fine gold.) The Black Bull of Clarence. Ŗ. As QCA4.
2018 — Proof in gold *FDC* (Edition: 500) £1900
QCG5One hundred pounds. (1 oz of fine gold.) The Falcon of the Plantagenets. Ŗ. As QCA5.
2018 — Proof in gold *FDC* (Edition: 445) £1900
QCG6 One hundred pounds. (1 oz.of fine gold.) Yale of Beaufort. Ŗ As QCA6.
2019 — Proof in gold *FDC* (Edition: 445) £1900

QCG7 One hundred pounds. (1 oz of fine gold.) White Lion of Mortimer. ℞ As QCA7.
2020 — Proof in gold *FDC* (Edition: 445) £2100
QCG8 One hundred pounds. (1 oz of fine gold.) White Horse of Hanover. ℞. As QCA8.
2020 — Proof in gold *FDC* (Edition: 435) £2320
QCG9 One hundred pounds. (1 oz of fine gold.) White Greyhound of Richmond. ℞. As QCA9.
2021 — Proof in gold *FDC* (Edition: 425) £2320
QCG10 One hundred pounds. (1 oz of fine gold.) The Griffin of Edward III. ℞. As QCA10.
2021 — Proof in gold *FDC* £2320

QCH1 Five hundred pounds. (5 oz of fine gold.) The Lion of England. ℞. As QCA1.
2017 — Proof in gold *FDC* (Issued: 100) £9000
QCH2 Five hundred pounds. (5 oz of fine gold.) The Unicorn of Scotland. ℞. As QCA2.
2017 — Proof in gold *FDC* (Issued: 75) £9000
QCH3 Five hundred pounds. (5 oz of fine gold.) The Red Dragon of Wales. ℞. As QCA3.
2018 — Proof in gold *FDC* (Edition: 90) £9000
QCH4 Five hundred pounds. (5 oz of fine gold.) The Black Bull of Clarence. ℞. As QCA4.
2018 — Proof in gold *FDC* (Edition: 85) £9000
QCH5 Five hundred pounds. (5 oz of fine gold.) The Falcon of the Plantagenets. ℞. As QCA5.
2018 — Proof in gold *FDC* (Edition: 85) £9000
QCH6 Five hundred pounds. (5 oz of fine gold.) Yale of Beaufort. ℞. As QCA6.
2019 — Proof in gold *FDC* (Edition: 70) £9995
QCH7 Five hundred pounds. (5 oz of fine gold.) White Lion of Mortimer. ℞. As QCA7.
2020 — Proof in gold *FDC* (Edition: 70)   £9995
QCH8 Five hundred pounds. (5 oz of fine gold.) White Horse of Hanover. ℞. As QCA8.
2020 — Proof in gold *FDC* (Edition: 65) £10600
QCH9 Five hundred pounds. (5 oz of fine gold.) White Greyhound of Richmond. ℞. As QCA9.
2021 — Proof in gold *FDC* (Edition: 69) £10600
QCH10 Five hundred pounds. (5 oz of fine gold.) The Griffin of Edward III. ℞. As QCA10.
2021 — Proof in gold *FDC* £10600

QCI1 One thousand pounds. (1 kilo of fine gold.) The Lion of England. ℞. As QCA1.
2017 — Proof in gold *FDC* (Issued: 13) £60000
QCI2 One thousand pounds. (1 kilo of fine gold.) The Unicorn of Scotland. ℞. As QCA2.
2017 — Proof in gold *FDC* (Issued: 8) £60000
QCI3 One thousand pounds. (1 kilo of fine gold.) The Red Dragon of Wales. ℞. As QCA3.
2018 — Proof in gold *FDC* (Edition: 13) £60000
QCI4 One thousand pounds. (1 kilo of fine gold.) The Black Bull of Clarence. ℞. As QCA4.
2018 — Proof in gold *FDC* (Edition: 10) £60000
QCI5 One thousand pounds. (1 kilo of fine gold.) The Falcon of the Plantagenets. ℞. As QCA5.
2018 — Proof in gold *FDC* (Edition: 13) £60000
QCI6 One thousand pounds. (1 kilo of fine gold.) Yale of Beaufort. ℞ As QCA6.
2019 — Proof in gold *FDC* (Edition: 13) £60000
QCI7 One thousand pounds. (1 kilo of fine gold.) White Lion of Mortimer. ℞ As QCA7.
2020 — Proof in gold *FDC* (Edition: 10) £60000
QCI8 One thousand pounds. (1 kilo of fine gold.) White Horse of Hanover. ℞. As QCA8.
2020 — Proof in gold *FDC* (Edition: 13) £65000
QCI9 One thousand pounds. (1kilo of fine gold.) White Greyhound of Richmond. ℞. As QCA9.
2021 — Proof in gold *FDC* (Edition: 10) £65000
QCI10 One thousand pounds. (1kilo of fine gold.) The Griffin of Edward III. ℞. As QCA10.
2021 — Proof in gold *FDC* £65000

BULLION ISSUES

SILVER

Reverse and obverse design by Jody Clark

QBA1

QBA1 Five pounds. (2 oz of fine silver.) The Lion of England. Ṛ. A lion accompanied by
a shield depicting Our Royal Arms with the inscription 'LION OF ENGLAND
2 OZ FINE SILVER 999.9 2016'.
2016 Unc...£65

QBA2   QBA3

QBA2 Five pounds. (2 oz of fine silver.) The Red Dragon of Wales. Ṛ. A depiction of a
rearing dragon accompanied by the Coat of Arms of Llywelyn the Great with
the inscription 'RED DRAGON OF WALES 2 OZ OF FINE SILVER 999.9 2017'.
2017 Unc...£65

QBA3 Five pounds. (2 oz of fine silver.) The Griffin of Edward III. Ṛ. A griffin accompanied
by a shield depicting the badge of the House of Windsor with the inscription
'GRIFFIN OF EDWARD III 2 OZ FINE SILVER 999.9 2017'.
2017 Unc...£65

QBA4

QBA4 Five pounds. (2 oz of fine silver.) The Unicorn of Scotland. ℞. A depiction of a rearing unicorn accompanied by a shield depicting a lion rampant with the inscription 'UNICORN OF SCOTLAND 2 OZ FINE SILVER 999.9 2018'.
2018 Unc £65

QBA5 Five pounds. (2 oz of fine silver.) Black Bull of Clarence. ℞. A depiction of the Black Bull of Clarence supporting the arms used by Edward IV and Richard III with the inscription 'BLACK BULL OF CLARENCE 2 OZ FINE SILVER 999.9 2018'.
2018 Unc £65

QBA6 Five pounds. (2 oz of fine silver.) Falcon of the Plantagenets. ℞. A depiction of the Falcon of the Plantagenets above the personal badge of Edward IV and the inscription 'FALCON OF THE PLANTAGENETS 2 OZ FINE SILVER 999.9 2019'.
2019 Unc £65

QBA7 Five pounds. (2 oz of fine silver.) Yale of Beaufort. ℞. A depiction of the Yale of Beaufort supporting a shield portraying a portcullis surmounted by a royal crown with the inscription 'YALE OF BEAUFORT 2 OZ FINE SILVER 999.9 2019'.
2019 Unc £65

QBA8 Five pounds. (2 oz of fine silver.) White Lion of Mortimer. ℞. A depiction of the White Lion of Mortimer supporting a shield portraying a white rose en soleil with the inscription 'WHITE LION OF MORTIMER 2OZ FINE SILVER 999.9 2020'.
2020 Unc .... £ 65

QBA9 Five pounds. (2 oz of fine silver.) White Horse of Hanover. ℞. A rearing white horse above shield with royal arms of George I and the inscription 'WHITE HORSE OF HANOVER 2 OZ FINE SILVER 999.9 2020'.
2020 Unc £65

QBA10 Five pounds. (2 oz of fine silver.) White Greyhound of Richmond. ℞. A reimagined greyhound conveying its strength and power above shield depicting the symbol of the Tudor family and inscription 'WHITE GREYHOUND OF RICHMOND 2 OZ FINE SILVER 999.9 2021'.
2021 Unc £65

QBB2

QBB1 **Ten pounds.** (10 oz of fine silver.) The Lion of England. Ꝛ. As QBA1 but with
inscription 'LION OF ENGLAND 10 OZ FINE SILVER 999.9 2017'.
2017 Unc..£320

QBB2 **Ten pounds.** (10 oz of fine silver.) The Griffin of Edward III. Ꝛ. As QBA3 but with
inscription 'GRIFFIN OF EDWARD III 10 OZ FINE SILVER 2018'.
2018 Unc..£320

QBB3 **Ten pounds.** (10 oz of fine silver.) The Red Dragon of Wales. Ꝛ. As QBA2 but with
inscription 'RED DRAGON OF WALES 10 OZ FINE SILVER 999.9 2018'
2018 Unc..£320

QBB4 **Ten pounds.** (10 oz of fine silver.) Black Bull of Clarence. Ꝛ. As QBA5 but with
inscription 'BLACK BULL OF CLARENCE 10 OZ FINE SILVER 999.9 2019'
2019 Unc..£320

QBB5 **Ten pounds.** (10 oz of fine silver.) The Unicorn of Scotland. Ꝛ. As QBA4 but with
inscription 'UNICORN OF SCOTLAND 10 OZ FINE SILVER 999.9 2019'
2019 Unc..£320

QBB6 **Ten pounds.** (10 oz of fine silver.) Falcon of the Plantagenets. Ꝛ. As QBA6 but with
inscription 'FALCON OF THE PLANTAGENETS 10 OZ FINE SILVER 999.9 2020'.
2020 Unc..£320

QBB7 **Ten pounds.** (10 oz of fine silver.) Yale of Beaufort. Ꝛ. As QBA7 but with inscription
'YALE OF BEAUFORT 10 OZ FINE SILVER 999.9 2020'.
2020 Unc..£320

QBB8 **Ten pounds.** (10 oz of fine silver.) The White Lion of Mortimer. Ꝛ. As QBA8 but
with inscription 'WHITE LION OF MORTIMER 10 OZ FINE SILVER 999.9 2021'
2021 Unc..£320

GOLD

QBC1 **Ten pounds.** (1/10th oz of fine gold.) Ꝛ. A depiction of a rearing dragon accompanied
by the Coat of Arms of Llywelyn the Great with the inscription 'RED DRAGON
OF WALES 1/10 OZ OF FINE GOLD 999.9 2017).
2017 Unc..£200

QBC2 **Ten pounds.** (1/10th oz of fine gold).Ꝛ. A griffin accompanied by a shield depicting
the badge of the House of Windsor with the inscription 'GRIFFIN OF EDWARD III
1/10th OZ FINE GOLD 999.9 2017'.
2017 Unc..£200

QBD1

QBD1 Twenty five pounds. (1/4 oz of fine gold.) The Lion of England. R. A lion
accompanied by a shield depicting Our Royal Arms with the inscription 'FINE
GOLD 999.9 2016 LION OF ENGLAND 1/4 OZ'.
2016 Unc £460

QBD2 Twenty five pounds. (1/4 oz of fine gold.) The Red Dragon of Wales.
2017 Unc £460

QBD3 Twenty five pounds. (1/4 oz of fine gold) The Griffin of Edward III.
2017 Unc £460

QBD4 Twenty five pounds. (1/4 oz of fine gold.) The Unicorn of Scotland.
Unc £460

QBD5 Twenty five pounds. (1/4 oz of fine gold.) Black Bull of Clarence.
2018 Unc £460

QBD6 Twenty five pounds. (1/4 oz of fine gold.) Yale of Beaufort.
2019 Unc £460

QBD7 Twenty five pounds. (1/4 oz of fine gold.) The Falcon of the Plantagenets.
2019 Unc £460

QBD8 Twenty five pounds. (1/4 oz of fine gold.) White Lion of Mortimer.
2020 Unc £460

QBD9 Twenty five pounds. (1/4 oz of fine gold.) White Horse of Hanover.
2020 Unc £460

QBD10 Twenty five pounds. (1/4 oz of fine gold.) White Greyhound of Richmond.
2021 Unc £460

QBE1

QBE1 One hundred pounds. (1 oz of fine gold.) The Lion of England. R. A lion
accompanied by a shield depicting Our Royal Arms with the inscription 'LION OF
ENGLAND 1 OZ FINE GOLD 999.9 2016'.
2016 Unc £1700

QBE2 One hundred pounds. (1 oz of fine gold.) The Red Dragon of Wales. R. A depiction
of a rearing dragon accompanied by the Coat of Arms of Llywelyn the Great with the
inscription 'RED DRAGON OF WALES 1 OZ OF FINE GOLD 999.9 2017'.
2017 Unc £1700

QBE3 One hundred pounds. (1 oz of fine gold.) The Griffin of Edward III. R. A griffin
accompanied by a shield depicting the badge of the House of Windsor with the
inscription 'GRIFFIN OF EDWARD III 1 OZ FINE GOLD 999.9 2017'.
2017 Unc £1700

QBE4 **One hundred pounds.** (1 oz of fine gold.) The Unicorn of Scotland. ℞. A rearing unicorn accompanied by a shield depicting a lion rampant with the inscription 'UNICORN OF SCOTLAND 1 OZ FINE GOLD 999.9 2018'.
2018 Unc £1700

QBE5 **One hundred pounds.** (1oz of fine gold.) Black Bull of Clarence. ℞. A depiction of the Black Bull of Clarence supporting the arms used by Edward IV and Richard III with the inscription 'BLACK BULL OF CLARENCE 1 OZ FINE GOLD 999.9 2018'.
2018 Unc £1700

QBE6

QBE6 **One hundred pounds.** (1oz of fine gold). Yale of Beaufort. ℞. A depiction of the Yale of Beaufort supporting a shield portraying a portcullis surmounted by a royal crown with the inscription 'YALE OF BEAUFORT 1 OZ FINE GOLD 999.9 2019'.
2019 Unc £1700

QBE7 **One hundred pounds.** (1oz of fine gold.) Falcon of the Plantagenets. ℞. A depiction of the Falcon of the Plantagenets above the personal badge of Edward IV with the inscription 'FALCON OF THE PLANTAGENETS 1 OZ FINE GOLD 999.9 2019'.
2019 Unc £1700

QBE8 **One hundred pounds.** (1 oz of fine gold.) White Lion of Mortimer. ℞. A depiction of the White Lion of Mortimer supporting a shield portraying a white rose en soleil with the inscription 'WHITE LION OF MORTIMER 1 OZ FINE GOLD 999.9 2020'.
2020 Unc ....£ 1700

QBE9   QBE10

QBE9 **One hundred pounds.** (1 oz of fine gold.) White Horse of Hanover. ℞. A rearing white horse above shield with royal arms of George I and the inscription 'WHITE HORSE OF HANOVER 1 OZ FINE GOLD 999.9 2020'.
2020 Unc ....£ 1700

QBE10 **One hundred pounds.** (1 oz of fine gold.) White Greyhound of Richmond. ℞. A reimagined greyhound conveying its strength and power above shield depicting the symbol of the Tudor family and inscription 'WHITE GREYHOUND OF RICHMOND 1 OZ FINE GOLD 999.9 2021'.
2021 Unc £1700

PLATINUM

QBF1 One hundred pounds. (1 oz of fine platinum.) The Lion of England. R. A lion
accompanied by a shield depicting Our Royal Arms with the inscription 'FINE
PLATINUM 999.9 2017 LION OF ENGLAND 1 OZ'.
2017 Unc £950
QBF2 One hundred pounds. (1 oz of fine platinum.) The Griffin of Edward III.
2017 Unc £950
QBF3 One hundred pounds. (1 oz of fine platinum.) The Red Dragon of Wales.
2018 Unc £950
QBF4 One hundred pounds. (1 oz of fine platinum.) The Unicorn of Scotland.
2019 Unc £950

QBF5

QBF5 One hundred pounds. (1 oz of fine platinum.) Black Bull of Clarence.
2019 Unc £950
QBF6 One hundred pounds. (1 oz of fine platinum.) Falcon of the Plantagenets. R. As QBE7
with inscription '1 OZ FINE PLATINUM 999.5 2020'.
2020 Unc ....£ 980
QBF7 One hundred pounds. (1 oz of fine platinum.) Yale of Beaufort. R. As QBE6 with
inscription '1 OZ FINE PLATINUM 999.5 2020'.
2020 Unc ....£ 980

COINS OF ENGLAND
& THE UNITED KINGDOM
PRE-DECIMAL ISSUES

STANDARD CATALOGUE OF BRITISH COINS
SPINK
2021

SPINK

COINS OF ENGLAND 2021
E-book available on Amazon, iBookstore,
Google, Kobo, OverDrive and across
most other platforms

For more information or enquiries please contact
Tel: +44 (0)20 7563 4119 | Email: books@spink.com
69 Southampton Row, Bloomsbury, London WC1B 4ET

WWW.SPINKBOOKS.COM

The Great Engravers series celebrates the finest artists who have worked on British coinage, beginning with William Wyon RA. The first coin in this series depicts Una and the Lion taken from the original 1839 die which casts the young Queen Victoria in the role of Una from the poem 'The Fairie Queen' while the lion she guides represents the people of Britain.

Obverse portrait by Jody Clark.

GE1 **Five pounds.** (2 oz of fine silver.) Great Engravers I – Una and the Lion.
R. William Wyon's Una & the Lion from 1839.
2019 Proof in silver *FDC* (Edition: 3,000) £350

GE2 **Two hundred pounds.** (2 oz of fine gold.) Great Engravers I – Una and the Lion.
R. William Wyon's Una & the Lion from 1839.
2019 Proof in gold *FDC* (Edition: 225).. £5000

GE3 **Five hundred pounds.** (5 oz of fine gold.) Great Engravers I – Una and the Lion.
R. William Wyon's Una & the Lion from 1839.
2019 Proof in gold *FDC* (Edition: 65).. £15000

GE4 **One thousand pounds.** (1 kilo of fine gold.) Great Engravers I – Una and the
Lion. R. William Wyon's Una & the Lion from 1839.
2019 Proof in gold *FDC* (Edition: 12).. £80000

GE5 **Two thousand pounds.** (2 kilos of fine gold.) Great Engravers I – Una and the Lion.
R. William Wyon's Una & the Lion from 1839.
2019 Proof in gold *FDC* (Edition: 4).. £150000

GE6 **Five thousand pounds.** (5 kilos of fine gold.) Great Engravers I – Una and the Lion.
R. William Wyon's Una & the Lion from 1839.
2019 Proof in gold *FDC* (Edition: 1).. £350000

A Music Legends collection celebrating innovation and success of British music was commenced in 2020 with a range of coins celebrating the legacy of one of Britain's most loved bands – Queen. A second series celebrating the work of Elton John followed and further series are planned.

QUEEN

Obverse portrait by Jody Clark.

QN1 One pounds. (1/2 oz of fine silver.) Music Legends I – Queen. R̟. As QN2.
2020 Proof in silver *FDC* (Edition: 20.000) £60

QN2   QN6

QN2 Two pounds. (1 oz of fine silver.) Music Legends I – Queen. R̟. Piano keyboard with opening notes of Bohemian Rhapsody pressed down, the group's logo and singer's signature mic stick in centre and below 'Red Special' guitar, Fender Precision Bass and Ludwig bass drum decorated with the Queen crest. Edge lettering MERCURY • MAY • TAYLOR • DEACON • on proof version. (Reverse design: Chris Facey)
2020 BU £30
— Proof in silver *FDC* with colour (Edition: 10.000) £100
QN3 Five pounds. (Crown.) Music Legends I – Queen. R̟. As QN2.
2020 BU in presentation folder £13
— BU in presentation folder with artwork from Hot Space. (Edition: 25,000) £15
— BU in presentation folder with artwork from A Kind of Magic. (Edition: 25,000) £15
— BU in presentation folder with artwork from Live. (Edition: 25,000) £15
QN4 Ten pounds. (5 oz of fine silver.) Music Legends I – Queen. R̟. As QN2.
2020 Proof in silver *FDC* (Edition: 500) £485

QN5 Twenty five pounds. (1/4 oz of fine gold.) Music Legends I – Queen. R̟. As QN6.
2020 Proof in gold *FDC* (Edition: 1350) £625

QN6 One hundred pounds. (1 oz of fine gold.) Music Legends I – Queen. R̟. Piano keyboard with opening notes of Bohemian Rhapsody pressed down, the group's logo and singer's signature mic stick in centre and below 'Red Special' guitar, Fender Precision Bass and Ludwig bass drum decorated with the Queen crest. (Reverse design: Chris Facey.)
2020 BU £1700
— Proof in gold *FDC* (Edition: 350) £2500
QN7 Five hundred pounds. (5 oz of fine gold.) Music Legends I – Queen. R. As QN6.
2020 Proof in gold *FDC* (Edition: 50) .... £ 12,000

ELTON JOHN

Obverse portrait by Jody Clark.

EJ1   **One pound.** (1/2 oz of fine silver.) Music Legends II – Elton John. ℞. As EJ2.
2020 Proof in silver *FDC* (Edition: 15.000) £60

EJ2

EJ2   **Two pounds.** (1 oz of fine silver.) Music Legends II – Elton John. ℞. Musical notes
creating an image of glasses and a straw boater's hat with inscription 'ELTON
JOHN' and below his signature bow tie against a Union flag background. With edge
lettering 'ELTON JOHN' only on this coin. (Reverse design: Bradley Morgan Johnson.)
2020 Proof in silver *FDC* with colour (Edition: 10.000) £100

EJ3   **Five pounds.** (2 oz of fine silver.) Music Legends II – Elton John. ℞. As EJ2 but with
high relief on the hat, glasses and bow tie, and with pulsating star pattern in the
lenses of the glasses.
2020 Proof in silver *FDC* (Edition: 500) £225

EJ4   **Five pounds.** (Crown.) Music Legends II – Elton John. ℞. As EJ2.
2020 BU in presentation folder with artwork from Rocket Man £13
—   BU in presentation folder with artwork from Dodgers Stadium. (Edition: 15,000) £15
—   BU in presentation folder with artwork from Illustration. (Edition: 15,000) £15
—   BU in presentation folder with artwork from The Very Best Of. (Edition: 15,000) £15

EJ5   **Ten pounds.** (5 oz of fine silver.) Music Legends II – Elton John. ℞. As EJ2 but with
high relief on the hat, glasses and bow tie, and with pulsating star pattern in the lenses
of the glasses.
2020 Proof in silver *FDC* (Edition: 425) £485

EJ6   **Twenty five pounds.** (1/4 oz fine gold.) Music Legends II – Elton John. ℞. As EJ7.
2020 Proof in gold *FDC* (Edition: 1100) £650

EJ7

EJ7 One hundred pounds. (1 oz of fine gold.) Music Legends II – Elton John.
℞. Musical notes creating an image of glasses and a straw boater's hat with inscription
'ELTON JOHN' and below his signature bow tie against a Union flag background.
(Reverse design: Bradley Morgan Johnson.)
2020 Proof in gold *FDC* (Edition: 300)...£2500

EJ8

EJ8 Two hundred pounds. (2 oz of fine gold.) Music Legends II – Elton John.
℞. As EJ7 but with high relief on the hat, glasses and bow tie, and with pulsating
star pattern in the lenses of the glasses.
2020 Proof in gold *FDC* (Edition: 50)...£5500

EJ9 Five hundred pounds. (5 oz of fine gold.) Music Legends II – Elton John.
℞. As EJ7 but with high relief on the hat, glasses and bow tie, and with pulsating
star pattern in the lenses of the glasses.
2020 Proof in gold *FDC* (Edition: 50)..£12500

EJ10 One thousand pounds. (1 kilo of fine gold.) Music Legends II – Elton John.
℞. As EJ7 but with high relief on the hat, glasses and bow tie, and with pulsating
star pattern in the lenses of the glasses. and with piano patterned edge.
(Reverse design: Bradley Morgan Johnson.)
2020 Proof in gold *FDC* (Edition: 4)..£75000

THE NEXT SERIES – DAVID BOWIE – expected late 2020.

The first group of coins in this new section launched in 2020 features James Bond, the world famous, quintessentially British spy who has been thrilling audiences for decades, ahead of the release of the 25th James Bond film 'No Time To Die'. The coins were issued in three groups:

I   Bond, James Bond – The Aston Martin DB5, the classic Bond car.
II   Pay Attention, 007 – 'Wet Nellie' the submarine car that appeared in 'The Spy who loved me'.
III   Shaken not Stirred – James Bond's iconic jacket and bow tie.

JAMES BOND

Obverse portrait by Jody Clark.

JB1   One pounds. (1/2 oz of fine silver.) TV & Film – James Bond I. Ŗ. As JB4.
2020 Proof in silver *FDC* (Edition: 15,017) £65
JB2   One pounds. (1/2 oz of fine silver.) TV & Film – James Bond II. Ŗ. As JB5.
2020 Proof in silver *FDC* (Edition: 15,017) £65
JB3   One pounds. (1/2 oz of fine silver.) TV & Film – James Bond III. Ŗ. As JB6.
2020 Proof in silver *FDC* (Edition: 15,017) £65

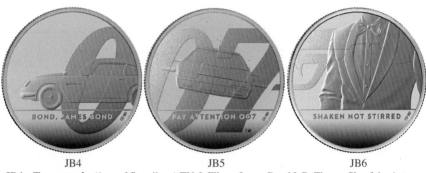

      JB4   JB5   JB6

JB4   Two pounds. (1 oz of fine silver.) TV & Film – James Bond I. Ŗ. The profile of the Aston Martin DB5, the classic Bond car. (Reverse designers: Matt Dent & Christian Davies.)
2020 Proof in silver *FDC* with colour (Edition: 8,517) £88
JB5   Two pounds. (1 oz of fine silver.) TV & Film – James Bond II. Ŗ. 'Wet Nellie' the submarine car that appeared in 'The Spy who loved me'. (Reverse designers: Matt Dent & Christian Davies.)
2020 Proof in silver *FDC* with colour (Edition: 8,517) £88
JB6   Two pounds. (1 oz of fine silver.) TV & Film – James Bond III. Ŗ. James Bond's iconic jacket and bow tie. (Reverse designers: Matt Dent & Christian Davies.)
2020 Proof in silver *FDC* with colour (Edition: 8,517) £88

JB7   Five pounds. (2 oz of fine silver.) TV & Film – James Bond I. Ŗ. As JB4.
2020 Proof in silver *FDC* (Edition: 2,017) £250
JB8   Five pounds. (2 oz of fine silver.) TV & Film – James Bond II. Ŗ. As JB5.
2020 Proof in silver *FDC* (Edition: 2,017) £250
JB9   Five pounds. (2 oz of fine silver.) TV & Film – James Bond III. Ŗ. As JB6.
2020 Proof in silver *FDC* (Edition: 2,017) £235

> *JB7-9 contain a hidden message featuring micro text of the first 24 film titles and with the help of a magnifying glass some of the letters appear bold and raised – revealing the title of the 25th James Bond film 'No Time To die'.*

JB10 Five pounds. (Crown.) TV & Film – James Bond I. R. As JB4.
2020 BU in presentation folder £13
JB11 Five pounds. (Crown.) TV & Film – James Bond II. R. As JB5.
2020 BU in presentation folder £13
JB12 Five pounds. (Crown.) TV & Film – James Bond III. R. As JB6.
2020 BU in presentation folder £13

JB13

JB13 Ten pounds. (5 oz of fine silver.) TV & Film – James Bond I. R. Aston Martin DB5,
with BMT216A number plate and gun barrel surround. (Reverse designer:
Laura Clancy.)
2020 Proof in silver *FDC* (Edition: 700)...£550

JB14 Twenty five pounds. (1/4 oz of fine gold.) TV & Film – James Bond I. R. As JB17.
2020 Proof in gold *FDC* (Edition: 1,067)..£600
JB15 Twenty five pounds. (1/4 oz of fine gold.) TV & Film – James Bond II. R. As JB18.
2020 Proof in gold *FDC* (Edition: 1,067)..£600
JB16 Twenty five pounds. (1/4 oz of fine gold.) TV & Film – James Bond III. R. As JB19.
2020 Proof in gold *FDC* (Edition: 1,067)..£600

JB17   JB18   JB19

JB17 One hundred pounds. (1 oz of fine gold.) TV & Film – James Bond I. R. The
profile of the Aston Martin DB5, the classic Bond car. (Reverse designers: Matt Dent
& Christian Davies)
2020 Proof in gold *FDC* (Edition: 360)..£2500
JB18 One hundred pounds. (1 oz of fine gold.) TV & Film – James Bond II. R. 'Wet
Nellie' the submarine car that appeared in 'The Spy who loved me'.
(Reverse designers: Matt Dent & Christian Davies)
2020 Proof in gold *FDC* (Edition: 360)..£2500
JB19 One hundred pounds. (1 oz of fine gold.) TV & Film – James Bond III. R. James
Bond's iconic jacket and bow tie. (Reverse designers: Matt Dent & Christian Davies)
2020 Proof in gold *FDC* (Edition: 360)..£2500

JB20 Two hundred pounds. (2 oz of fine gold.) TV & Film – James Bond I. Ṛ. As JB17.
2020 Proof in gold *FDC* (Edition: 260)..£5000
JB21 Two hundred pounds. (2 oz of fine gold.) TV & Film – James Bond II. Ṛ. As JB18.
2020 Proof in gold *FDC* (Edition: 260)..£5000
JB22 Two hundred pounds. (2 oz of fine gold.) TV & Film – James Bond III. Ṛ. As JB19.
2020 Proof in gold *FDC* (Edition: 260)..£5000

JB20-22 contain a hidden message featuring micro text of the first 24 film titles and with the help of a magnifying glass some of the letters appear bold and raised – revealing the title of the 25th James Bond film 'No Time To die'.

JB23 Five hundred pounds. (5 oz of fine gold.) TV & Film – James Bond I. Ṛ. As JB13.
2020 Proof in gold *FDC* (Edition: 64)..£12000

JB24 One thousand pounds. (1 kilo of fine gold.) TV & Film – James Bond I. Ṛ. As JB13.
2020 Proof in gold *FDC* (Edition: 20)..£65000

JB25 Two thousand pounds. (2 kilos of fine gold.) TV & Film – James Bond I. Ṛ. As JB13.
2020 Proof in gold *FDC* (Edition: 10)..£150000

JB26 Seven thousand pounds. (7 kilos of fine gold.) TV & Film – James Bond I. Ṛ. As JB13.
2020 Proof in gold *FDC* (Edition: 1)..£450000

For specifications see tables on pages 187 & 211.

SPINK

WHERE HISTORY IS VALUED

THE CHRISTOPHER WREN COLLECTION

THE VOIDED
LONG-CROSS
COINAGE 1247-1279
HENRY III & EDWARD I

An Illustrated Guide To
Identification
by Christopher R Wren

THE SHORT-CROSS
COINAGE 1180-1247
Henry II to Henry III

An Illustrated Guide To
Identification
by Christopher R Wren

THE ENGLISH
LONG-CROSS
PENNIES
1279-1489
Edward I to Henry VII

An Illustrated Guide To
Identification
by Christopher R. Wren

The Royal Numismatic Society Lhotka Prize-Winning Title

Contact the Book Department: Tel: +44 (0)20 7563 4119 or email books@spink.com
SPINK LONDON | 69 Southampton Row | Bloomsbury | London | WC1B 4ET
LONDON | NEW YORK | HONG KONG | SINGAPORE | LUGANO

www.spinkbooks.com

In addition to the coins listed in the previous sections, the Royal Mint has struck a number of other bullion coins based on Britannia specifications (see pages 187, 211 and 239). Many of these seem to have been supplied to bullion dealers in the USA although coins do find their way back to the UK. As this range grows an issue pattern might emerge giving rise to separate sections to be created for some of them which will result in renumbering.

SILVER

Obverse portrait by Jody Clark.

RMB1

RMB1   One pound. (1/2 oz of fine silver.) 75th Anniversary of VE Day. R. A group of people with rays echoing anti-aircraft searchlights but becoming rays of hope.
(Reverse design: Dominique Evans.)
2020 Proof in silver *FDC* (Edition: 2,000) £50

The above was issued in a set with a Canada & Netherlands coin.

RMB11 Two pounds. (1 oz of fine silver.) William Shakespeare. R. As M7.
2016 Proof in silver *FDC* matt reverse (Edition: 1,000)...£35

RMB12

RMB12 Two pounds. (1 oz of fine silver.) Elizabeth Tower or Big Ben.
2017..£30
— Proof in silver *FDC* (Edition: 800) £80
— Proof in silver *FDC* with reverse frosting (Edition: 800) £80

RMB13   RMB15

RMB13 Two pounds. (1 oz of fine silver.) Trafalgar Square.
2018 (Edition: 50,000) £30
RMB14 Two pounds. (1 oz of fine silver.) Tower Bridge. Ŗ. Similar to L36
2018 ....£30
RMB15 Two pounds. (1 oz of fine silver.) Two Dragons.
2018 ....£30
RMB16 Two pounds. (1 oz of fine silver.) Buckingham Palace. Ŗ. As Q2
2019 (Edition: 50,000) £30

RMB17   RMB18

RMB17 Two pounds. (1 oz of fine silver.) The Valiant. Ŗ. St George and the dragon with the
inscription '1 OZ FINE SILVER 999.9' and the date of the year. (Reverse design:
Etienne Millner.)
2019...£30
2020...£30
RMB18 Two pounds. (1 oz of fine silver.) The Royal Arms. Ŗ. The Lion of England and
The Unicorn of Scotland supporting the shield with the inscription '1 OZ FINE
SILVER 999' and the date of the year. (Reverse design: Timothy Noad.)
2019...£30
2020...£30
RMB19 Two pounds. (1 oz of fine silver.) 400th Anniversary of "The Mayflower" voyage to the
New World. Ŗ. "The Mayflower" bursting out of the frame as it sails through the rough
seas with inscription '1620 MAYFLOWER 2020'. (Reverse design: Chris Costello.)
2020 Proof in silver *FDC* (Edition: 5,000) £75
The above was issued in a set with a USA medal.

RMB31 Ten pounds. (10 oz of fine silver.) The Valiant. Ŗ. St George and the dragon with the
inscription '10 OZ FINE SILVER 999.9' and the date of the year. The reverse
features frosting and an incuse design. (Reverse design: Etienne Millner.)
2018...£250
2019...£250
2020...£250

GOLD

RMB41   RMB52   RMB53

RMB41 Ten pounds. (1/10 oz of fine gold.) The Royal Arms, R̟. As RMB18 with the inscription '1/10 OZ FINE GOLD 999.9'.

2020 Unc £200

RMB51 Twenty five pounds. (1/4 oz of fine gold.) 200th Anniversary of the Gold Standard. O. As RMB17 but with denomination '25'. R̟. Set of Scales with inscription '1816 2016' and '1/4 OZ FINE GOLD 999.9'. (Reverse design: Dominique Evans.)

2016 Unc £450

RMB52 Twenty five pounds. (1/4 oz fine gold.) R̟. As RMB51 but with revised reverse inscription 'THE GOLD STANDARD', date of year, '1/4 OZ FINE GOLD 999.9'. (Reverse design: Dominique Evans.)

2018 Unc £450

2019 Unc £450

2020 Unc £450

RMB53 Twenty five pounds. (1/4 oz fine gold.) 400th Anniversary of "The Mayflower" voyage to the New World. R̟. "The Mayflower" bursting out of the frame as it sails through the rough seas with inscription "1620 MAYFLOWER 2020". (Reverse design: Chris Costello.)

2020 Proof in gold *FDC* (Edition: 500) £550

The above was issued in a set with a USA coin.

RMB71

RMB71 One hundred pounds. (1 oz of fine gold.) Two Dragons.

2018 BU ....£ 1700

RMB72 One hundred pounds. (1 oz of fine gold.) The Royal Arms. R̟. As RMB18 with the inscription "1OZ FINE GOLD 999.9".

2019 BU £1700

2020 BU £1700

PLATINUM

RMB81 One hundred pounds. (1 oz platinum.) The Royal Arms. R̟. As RMB18 with the inscription '1 OZ PLATINUM 999.5'.

2020 BU £750

CONSIGN NOW

THE GLOBAL COLLECTABLES AUCTION HOUSE

LONDON | NEW YORK | HONG KONG | SINGAPORE | SWITZERLAND

WHERE HISTORY IS VALUED

WWW.SPINK.COM

SPINK

Where History is Valued

LONDON | NEW YORK | HONG KONG | SINGAPORE | SWITZERLAND

THE AUCTION SPECIALISTS

providing

OUTSTANDING SERVICE

for Collectors and Numismatists

For more information or to consign please contact:
Tel.: +44 (0)20 7563 4007 | Email: coins@spink.com
SPINK LONDON | 69 Southampton Row | Bloomsbury | WC1B 4ET

WWW.SPINK.COM *Follow us on social media* #SPINK_AUCTIONS

NOTES

NOTES

NOTES

NOTES